GIFTED AND TALENTED TEST PREP

for children in preschool and kindergarten

Gateway Gifted Resources™
www.GatewayGifted.com

Thank you for selecting this book. We are a family-owned publishing company - a consortium of educators, book designers, illustrators, parents, and kid-testers.

We would be thrilled if you left us a quick review on the website where you purchased this book!

The Gateway Gifted Resources™ Team
www.GatewayGifted.com

TABLE OF CONTENTS

INTRODUCTION

ABOUT THIS BOOK

This book introduces reasoning exercises, problem-solving tasks, and cognitive skill-building activities to young children through kid-friendly subjects, all in a format designed to help prepare them for taking the NNAT2® and NNAT3®.

THIS BOOK HAS 5 PARTS:

1. Introduction (p. 4-9):

- About This Book
- About The Test
- Test-Taking Tips
- The "Gifted Detective Agency"

2. Gifted Workbook (p. 10-69)

- Pages 10-36 are designed as skill-building activities, while pages 37-69 are designed to be similar to the content tested in the test's two test sections. (See page 7 for more on these two sections.)
- This workbook offers fun, kid-friendly themes to engage children and introduce them to standardized gifted test format.
- The exercises are meant to be done together with no time limit.
- Some sections include additional explanations and tips. Be sure to read these.

The "Gifted Detective Agency"

To increase child engagement and to add an incentive to complete book exercises, a detective theme accompanies this book. Read page 9 ("Gifted Detective Agency") together with your child. The book's characters belong to a detective agency. They want your child to help them solve "puzzles" (the exercises in the book) so that your child can join the detective agency, too! As your child completes the book, allow him/her to "check" the boxes at the bottom of the page. If your child "checks all the boxes," (s)he will "join" the Gifted Detective Agency. We have included boxes at the bottom of every page of the book that features exercises. However, feel free to modify as you see fit the number of pages/exercises your child must complete in order to receive his/her certificate. (The certificate for you to complete with your child's name is on page 101.)

3. Practice Question Set (p. 70-93)

The Practice Question Set provides:

- an introduction for children to test-taking in a relaxed manner, where parents can provide guidance if needed (without telling the answers!)
- an opportunity for children to practice focusing on a group of questions for a longer time period (something to which most children are not accustomed)
- a way for parents to identify points of strength and weakness in the two types of test questions

The Practice Question Set is meant to help children develop critical thinking and test-taking skills. A "score" (a percentile rank) cannot be obtained from the Practice Question Set. (See page 6 for more on gifted test scoring.)

4. Directions and Answer Keys (p. 95-99)

(Please use a pair of scissors to cut out pages 95-99.)

These pages provide answer keys for both the Workbook and the Practice Question Set. They also include the directions to read to your child for the Practice Question Set. (To mimic actual tests, the directions are separate from the child's pages in the Practice Question Set.)

5. Afterword (p. 100)

Information on additional books, free 40+ practice questions, and your child's certificate

A NOTE ON FILLING IN "BUBBLES"

Your child may or may not have to fill in "bubbles" (the circles) to indicate answer choices. When taking a standardized gifted test, if your child is at the Pre-K level, (s)he will most likely only have to point to the answer choice. If your child is at the Kindergarten level, (s)he may have to fill in bubbles. Check with your testing site regarding its "bubble" use. We have included "bubbles" in this publication to distinguish the answer choices.

If your child is at the Kindergarten level, show him/her the "bubbles" under the answer choices. Show your child how to fill in the bubble to indicate his/her answer choice. If your child needs to change his/her answer, (s)he should erase the original mark and fill in the new choice.

A NOTE ON THE QUESTIONS

Because each child has different cognitive abilities, the questions in this book are at varied skill levels. The exercises may or may not require a great deal of parental guidance to complete, depending on your child's ability.

You will notice that most sections of the Workbook begin with a relatively easy question. We suggest always completing at least the first question (which will most likely be an easy one) with him/her. Make sure there is not any confusion about what the question asks or with the directions.

WHAT YOU NEED

- *Gifted Games* book
- Pencil and eraser for your child
- Answer Keys/Directions (pages 95-99) cut out and by your side

ABOUT GIFTED TESTS

Gifted tests, like the NNAT2® and NNAT3®, assess a child's cognitive abilities, reasoning skills, and problem-solving aptitude.

Testing procedures vary by school and/or program. These tests may be given individually or in a group environment, by a teacher or other testing examiner. These tests may be used as the single determinant for admission to a selective kindergarten or to a school's gifted program. However, some schools/programs use these tests in combination with individual IQ tests administered by psychologists or as part of a student "portfolio." Other schools use them together with tests like Iowa Assessments™ to measure academic achievement. In other instances, schools/programs may use only certain sections of the tests to screen. (See the next page for more information on test sections.) **Check with your testing site to determine its specific testing procedures.**

Here is a general summary of the scoring process for multiple-choice standardized gifted tests. **Please check with your school/program for its specific scoring and admissions requirements.** First, your child's raw score is established. The raw score equals the number of questions your daughter/son correctly answered. Points are not deducted for questions answered incorrectly. Next, this score is compared to other test-takers of his/her same age group using various indices to then calculate your child's percentile rank. If your child achieved the percentile rank of 98%, then (s)he scored as well as or better than 98% of test-takers in his/her age group. In general, most gifted programs only accept top performers of *at least* 98% or *higher*. (Please note that a percentile rank "score" cannot be obtained from our practice material. This material has not been given to a large enough sample of test-takers to develop any kind of base score necessary for percentile rank calculations.)

NNAT2® LEVEL A & NNAT3® LEVEL A (NAGLIERI NONVERBAL ABILITY TEST®)

- The NNAT2® and NNAT3® are very similar tests.
- The NNAT2® Level A and NNAT3® Level A are for Kindergarten.
- Both tests have 48 questions and last approximately 30 minutes.
- Both tests' questions consist of shapes, patterns, and figures.
- As "non-verbal" tests, they do not require test-takers to listen to multiple question prompts, nor do they assess verbal comprehension or verbal skills.
- Please check with your school/program if you are unsure whether your child will be given the NNAT2® Level A or the NNAT3® Level A.

There are two sections: Pattern Completion and Reasoning by Analogy.

Here are examples of the two question types.

Pattern Completion (the child selects the answer to go in place of the question mark to complete the "puzzle")

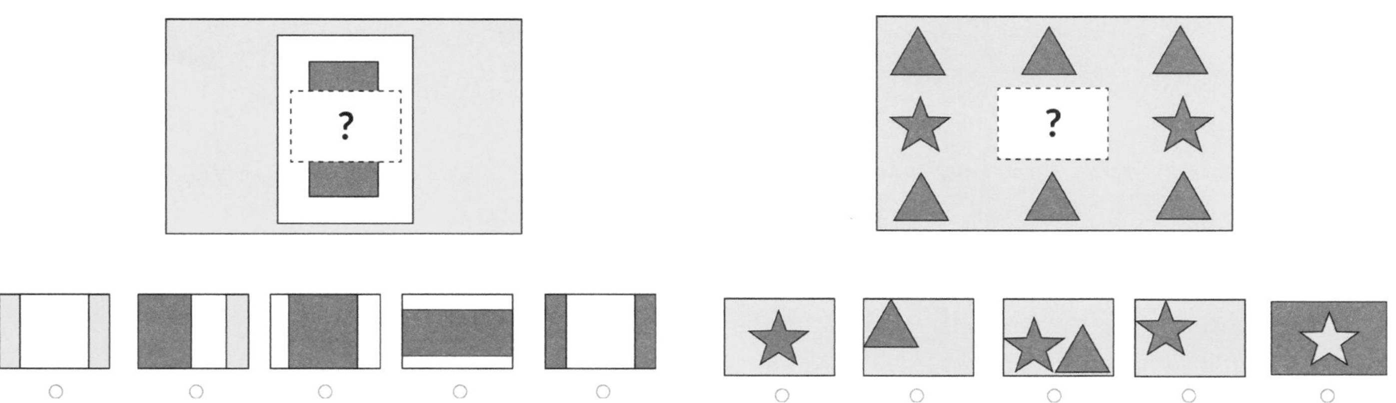

Reasoning by Analogy (the child selects the answer to go in place of the question mark to complete the analogy)

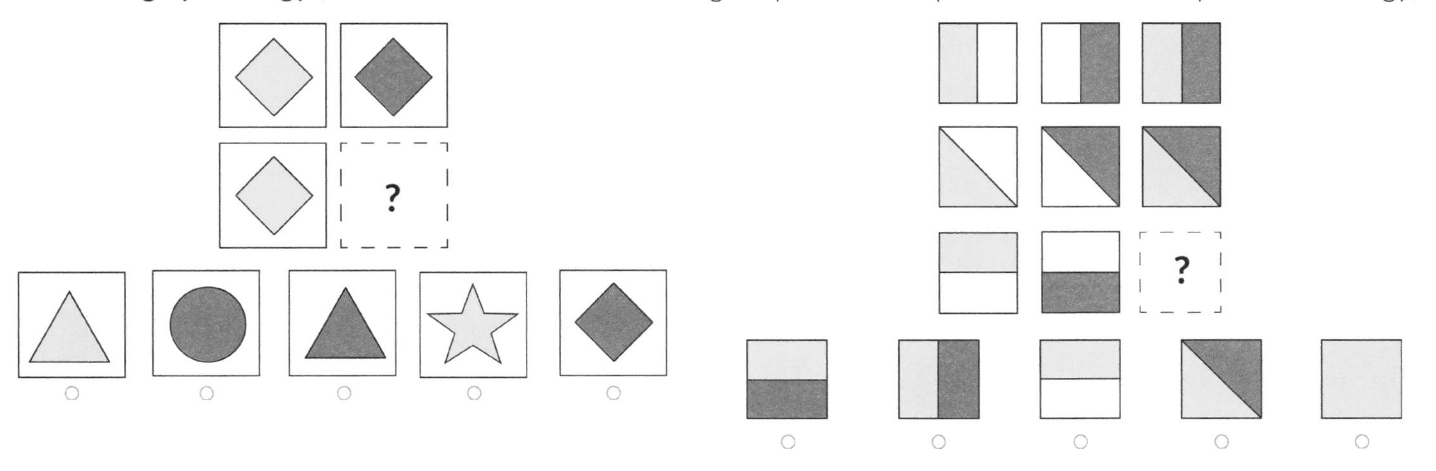

Pages 37-69 of the Workbook, as well as the Practice Question Set (pages 70-93), are organized by question type. We suggest referencing question type labels listed at the top of pages 37-69 of the Workbook, as well as on page 99 in the Answer Key, in order to gain a better understanding of the material in each question type. After your child completes the Practice Question Set, you can use the Answer Key to evaluate your child's strengths/weaknesses by question type.

TEST-TAKING TIPS

Work Through The Exercise: In the Workbook section of this book, go through the exercises together by talking about them: what the exercise is asking the child to do and what makes the answer choices correct/incorrect. This will not only familiarize your child with working through exercises, it will also help him/her develop a process of elimination (getting rid of any answer choices that are incorrect).

Answer Choices: Make sure your child looks at **each** answer choice. You may wish to point to each answer choice if you notice your child not looking at each one.

Guessing: For the test outlined in this book, test-takers receive points for the number of correct answers. It is advantageous to at least guess instead of leaving a question unanswered. If your child says that (s)he does not know the answer, (s)he should first eliminate any answers that are obviously not correct. Then, (s)he can guess from those remaining.

Choose ONE Answer: Remind your child to choose only ONE answer. If your child has a test with "answer bubbles," remind him/her that he/she must fill in only ONE bubble per question. If your child must instead point to an answer, remind him/her to point to only one answer per question.

Common Sense Tips: Children are like adults when it comes to common sense exam-readiness for test day. Make sure your child:

- is familiar with the test site (If the exam will be at a location that is new to your child, go to the testing site together before test day. Simply driving by or walking by the outside of the building not only ensures you know how to reach the site; it also will give your child a sense of familiarity, come test day.)
- is well-rested
- has eaten a breakfast for sustained energy and concentration (complex carbohydrates and protein; avoid foods/drinks high in sugar)
- has a chance to use the restroom prior to the test (The administrator may not allow a break during the test.)

Try not to get overly-stressed about the gifted testing process (as difficult as that may be). It is surprising how much children can sense from adults, and children learn best through play. So, the more fun that you can make test prep (by using something like a detective theme!), the better.

THE GIFTED DETECTIVE AGENCY *(Read this page with your child.)*

We're the Gifted Detective Agency. We need another member, someone else to join us. We think YOU have what it takes!

"What does a detective do?" you may ask. Well, a detective figures out puzzles, solves problems, and finds answers to questions.

To prove you're ready to join the Gifted Detective Agency, you'll put your skills to the test in this book. Together with your mom, dad, or other adult, you need to solve puzzles. The adult helping you will explain what to do, so listen carefully!

A good detective:

- Pays attention and listens closely
- Looks carefully at all choices before answering a question
- Keeps trying even if some questions are hard

After you finish the questions on each page, mark the box at the bottom. Like this:

Your parent (or other adult) will tell you which pages to do. After finishing them all, you will become a member of the Gifted Detective Agency! (Remember, it's more important to answer the questions the right way than to try to finish them really fast.) After you're done, you'll get your very own Gifted Detective Agency certificate.

When you're ready to start the puzzles, write your name here: ____________________

WILL YOU HELP ALEX ANSWER THESE QUESTIONS?

Directions: Look at the picture in the first box. Then, look at the group of pictures in the next box. Find the picture or pictures that are exactly the same as the picture in the first box. There could be more than one picture that is exactly the same, so look carefully.

1.

2.

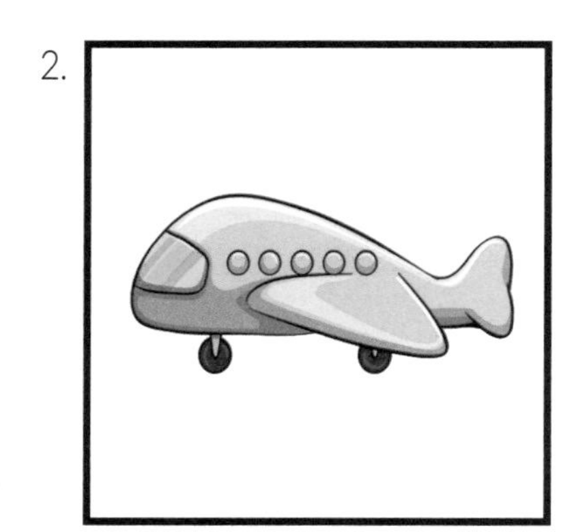

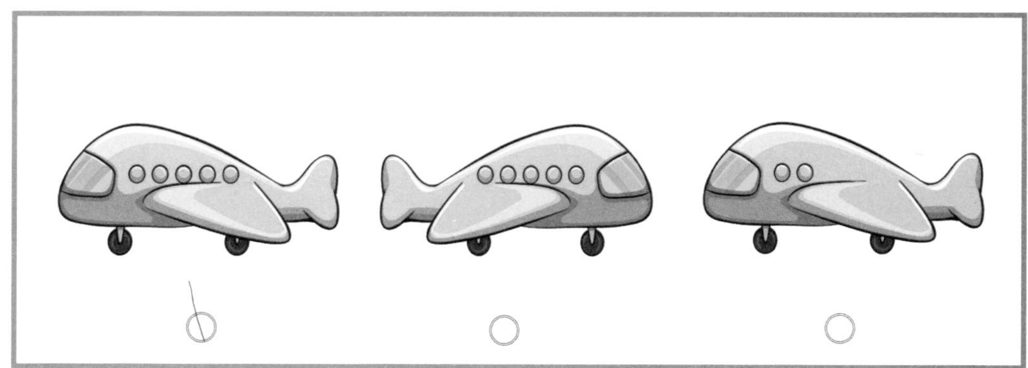

3.

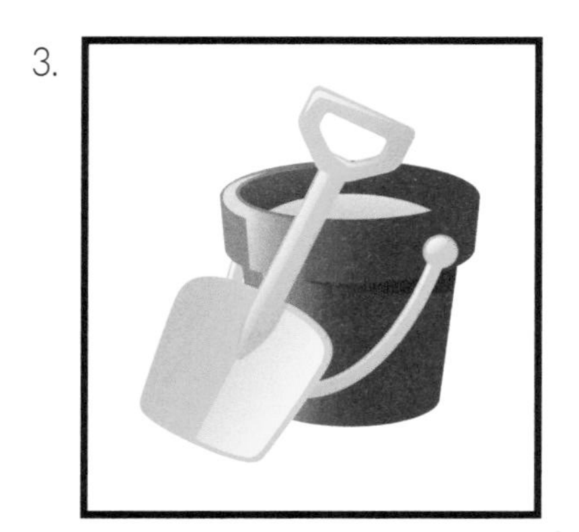

4.

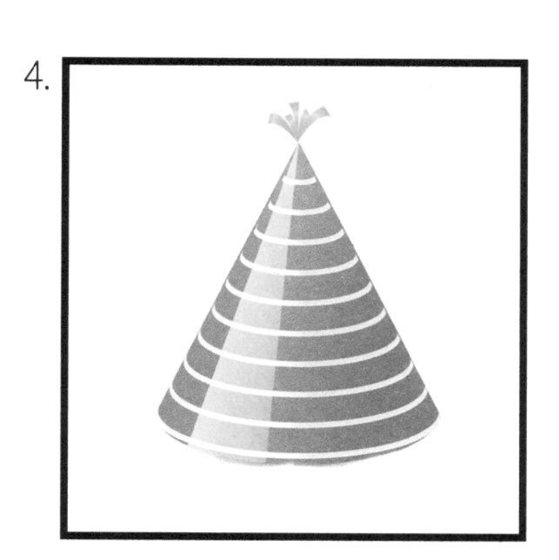

5.

6.

7.

8.
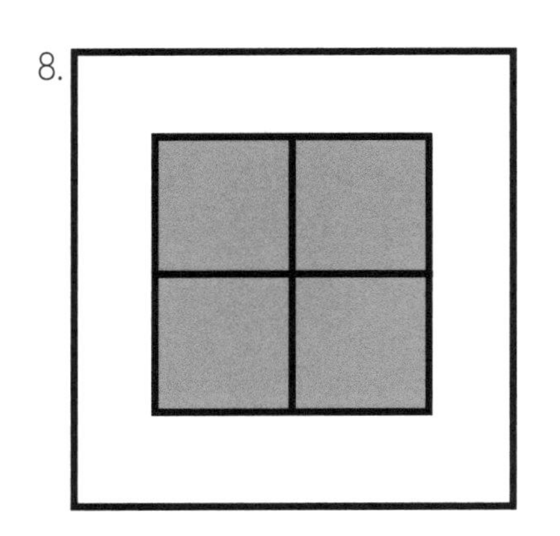
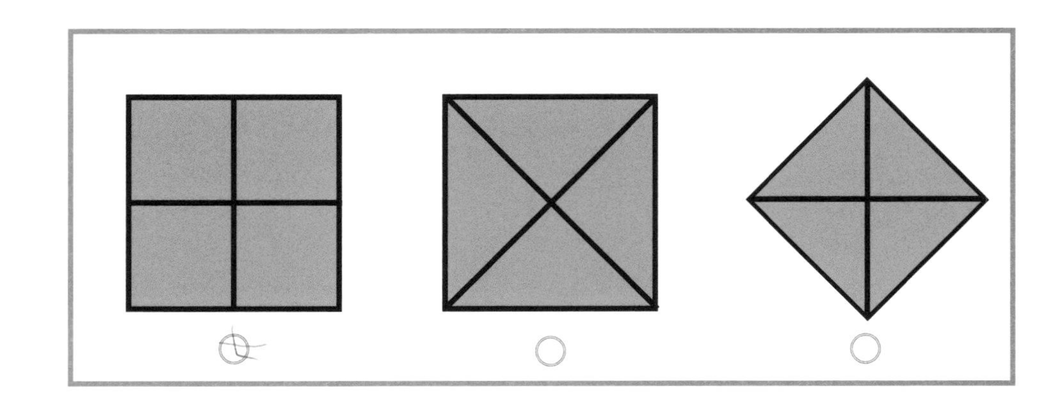

9.
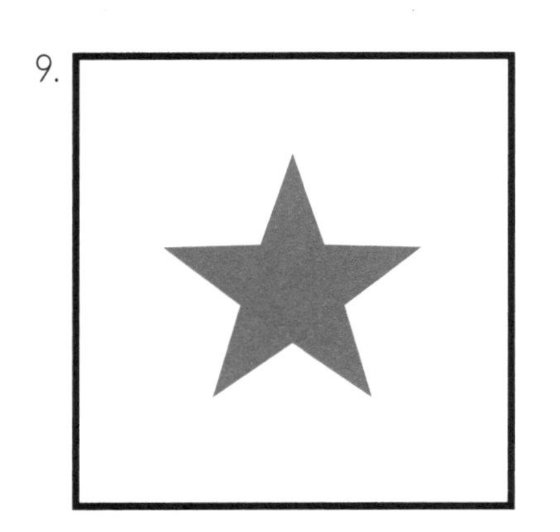
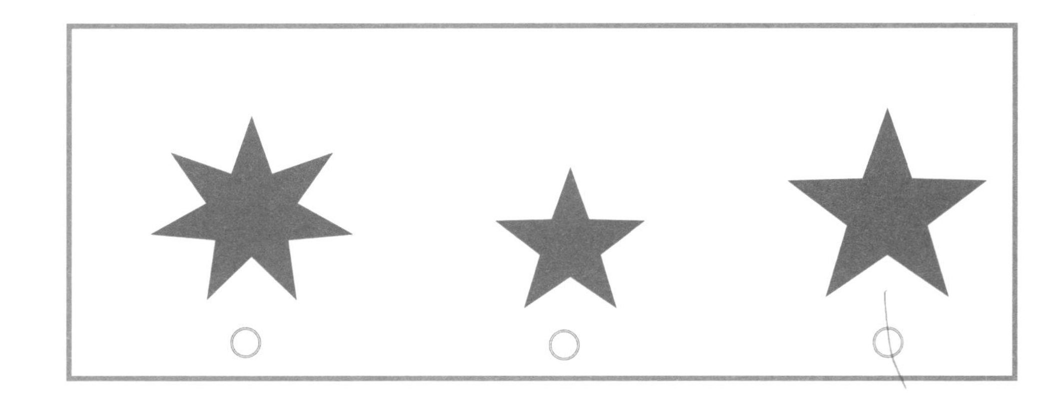

10.
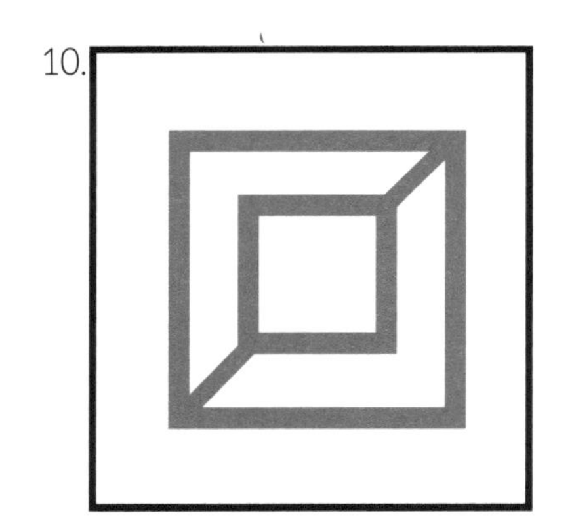
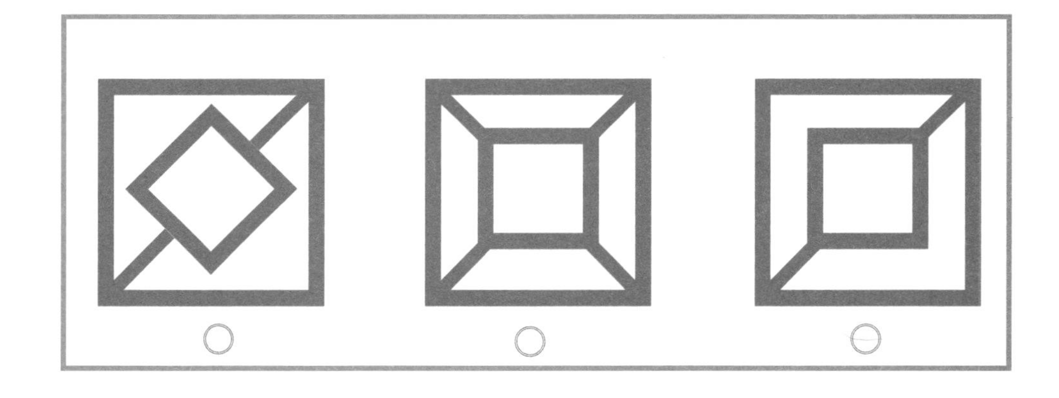

11.
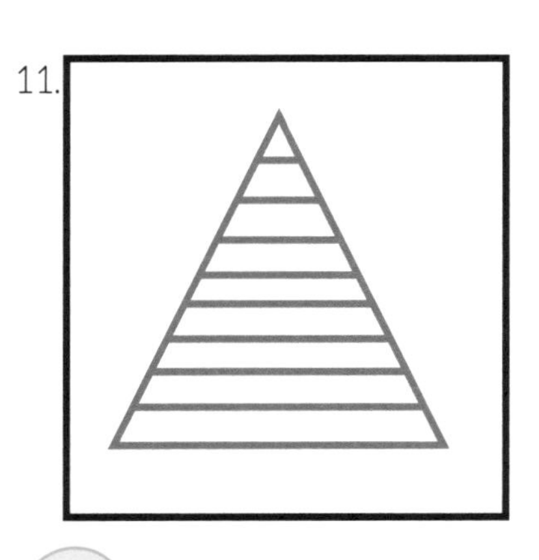
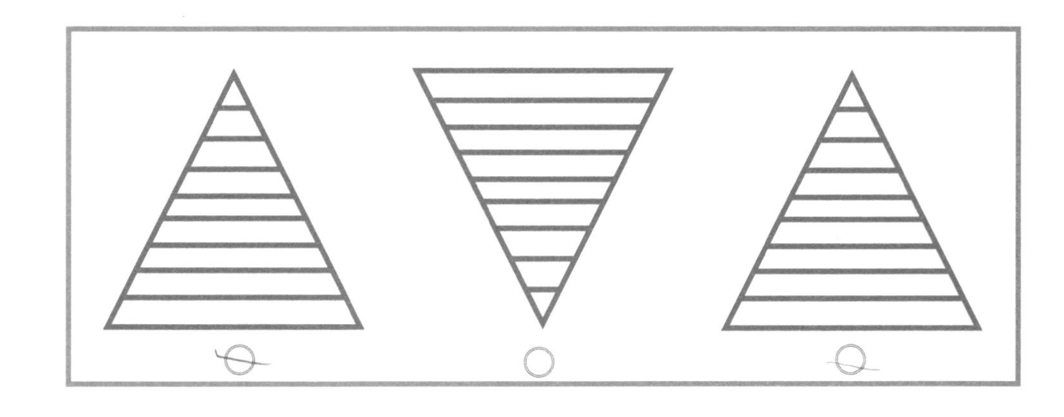

12.

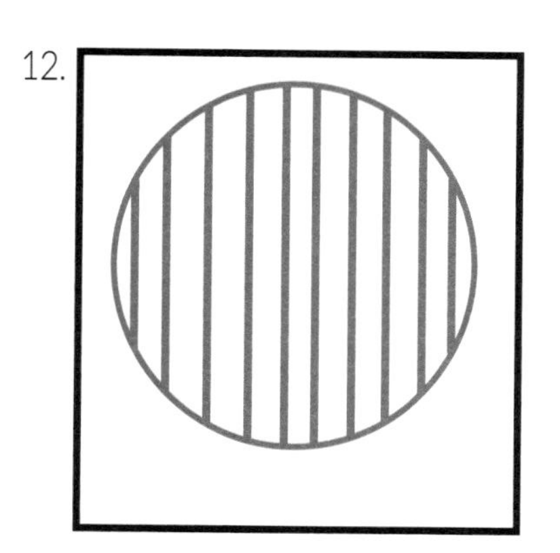

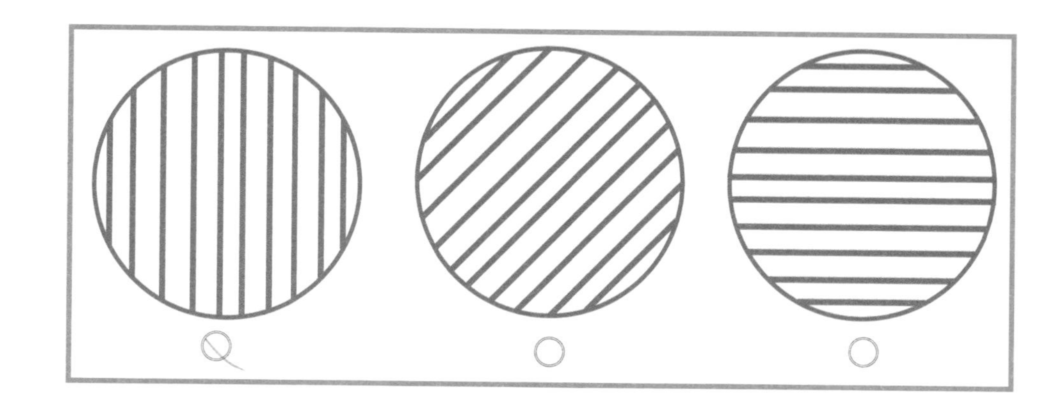

13.

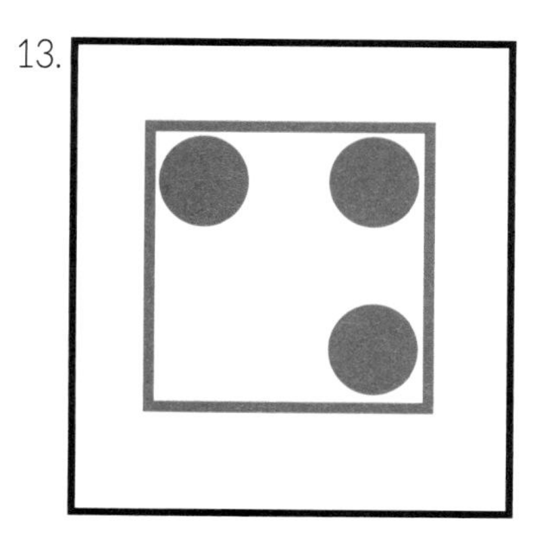

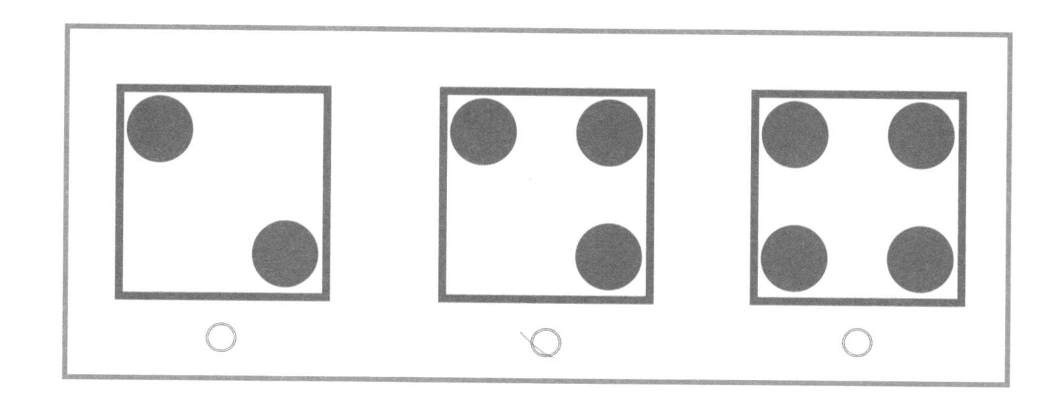

14.

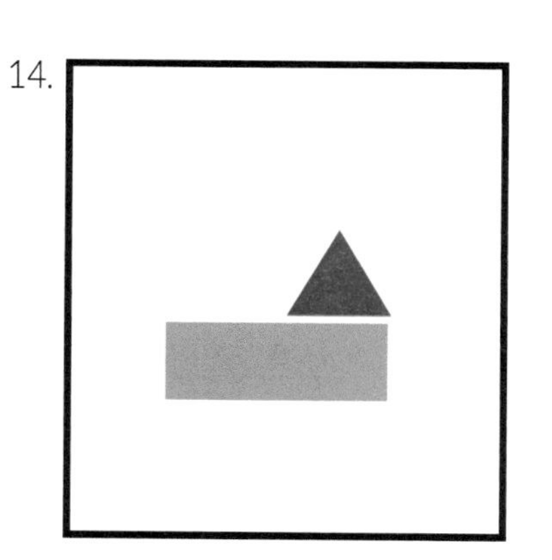

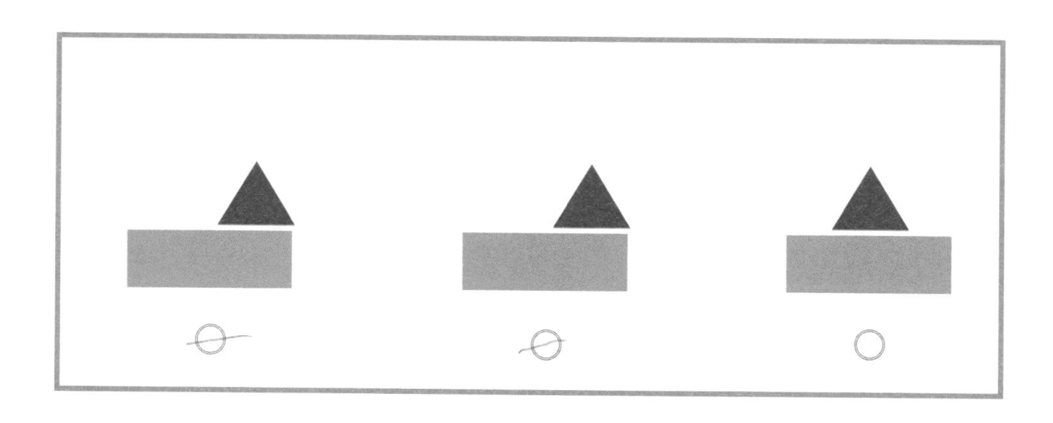

15.

SOPHIE NEEDS YOUR HELP TO MATCH PICTURES.

Directions: Look at the pictures on the top row. Then, find the picture on the bottom row that looks exactly the same. Point to your answer.

1.

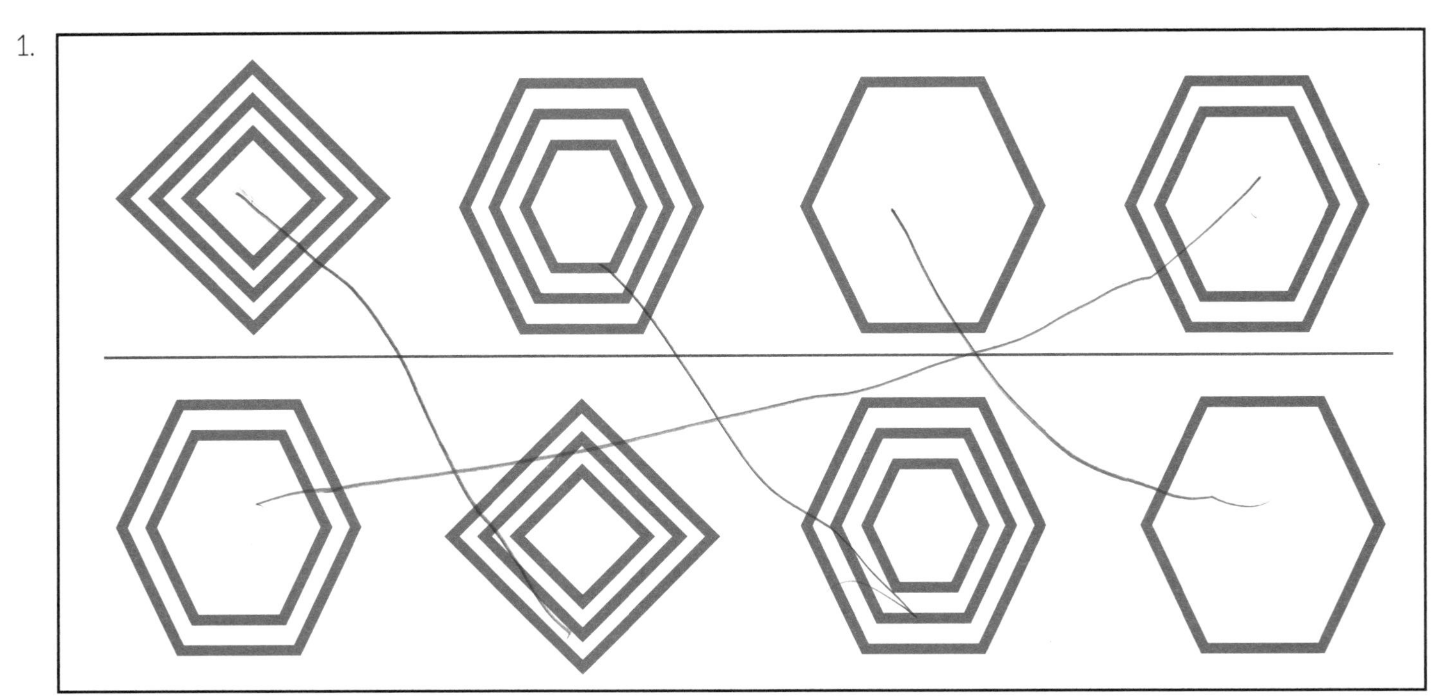

2.

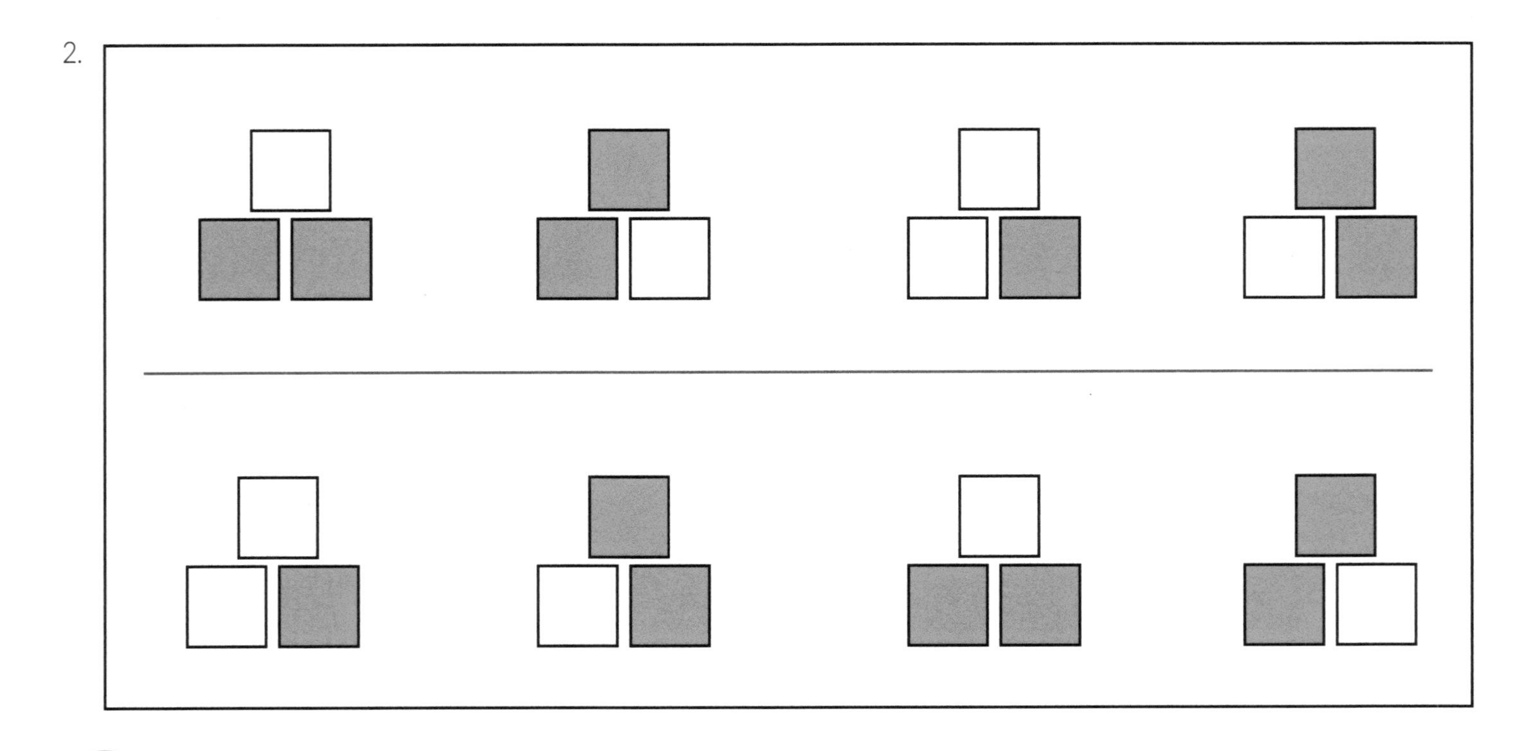

3.

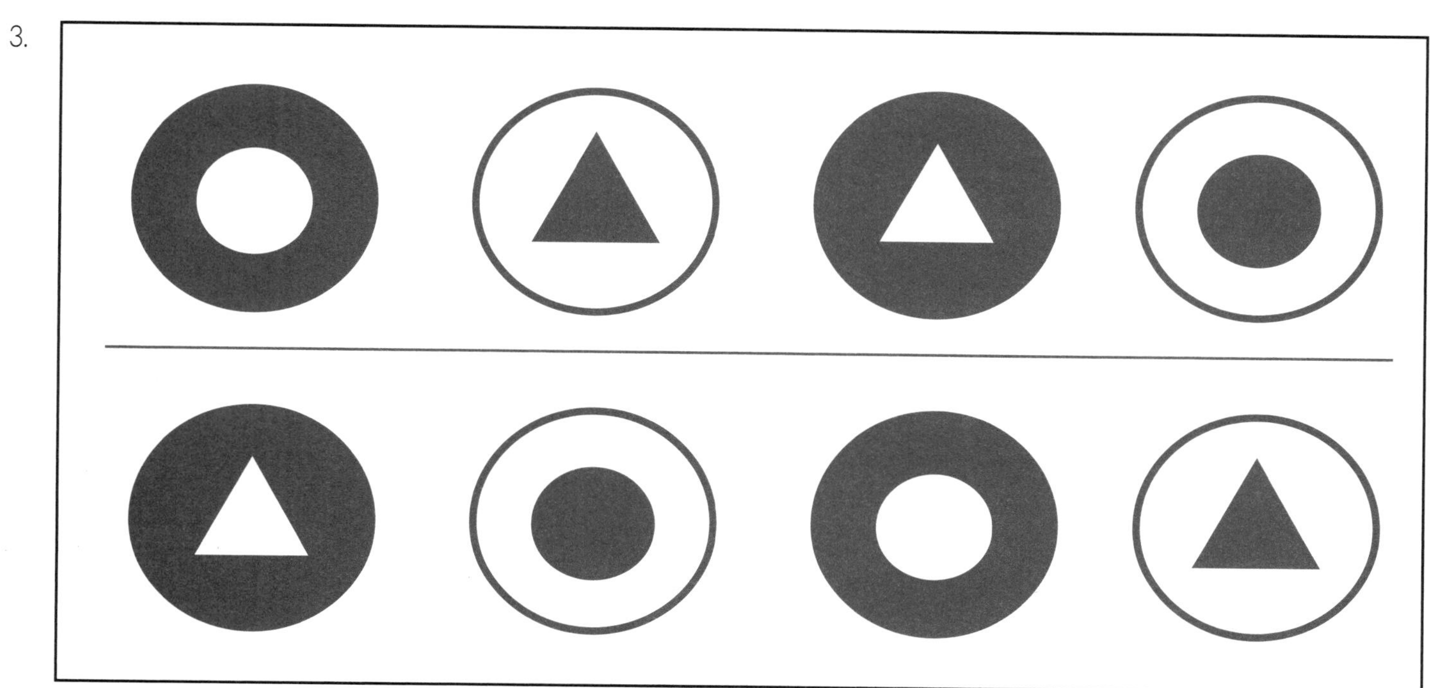

4.

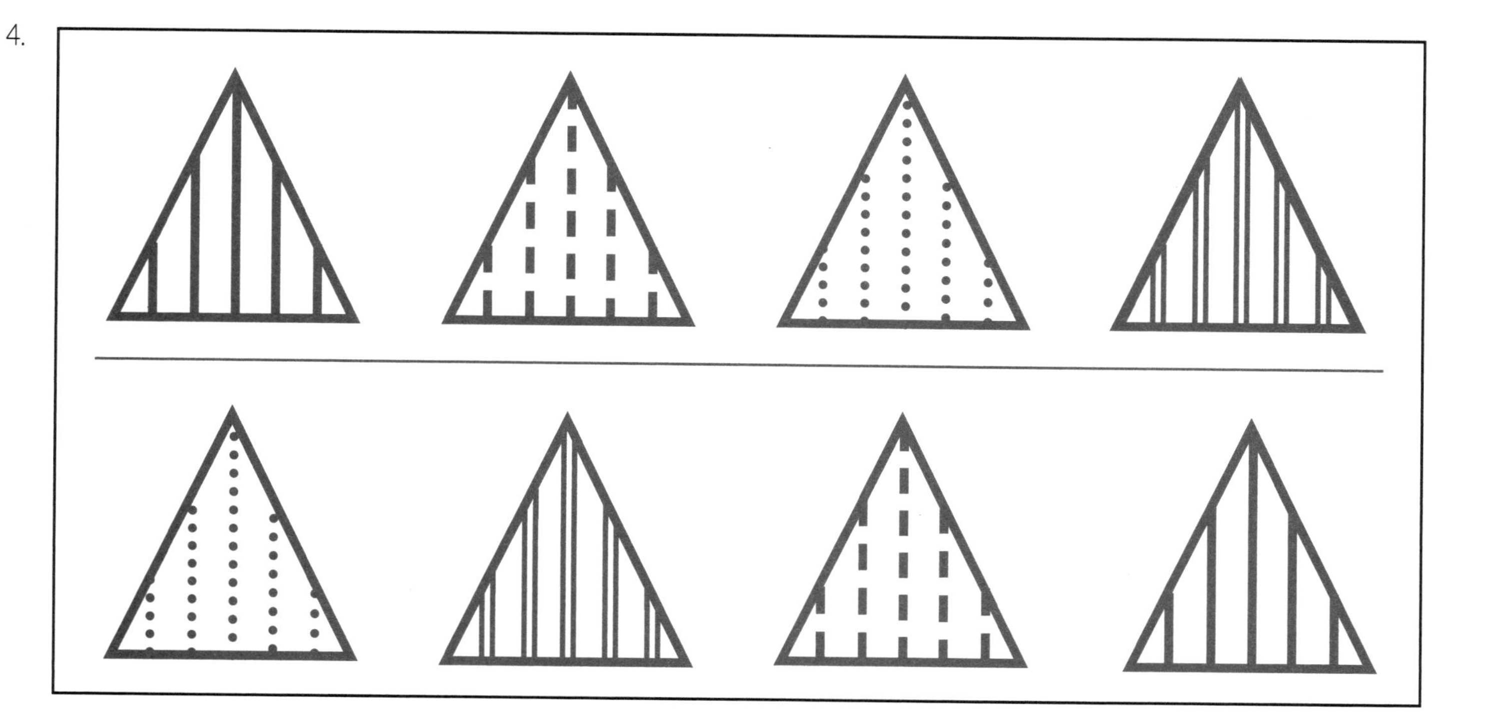

5.

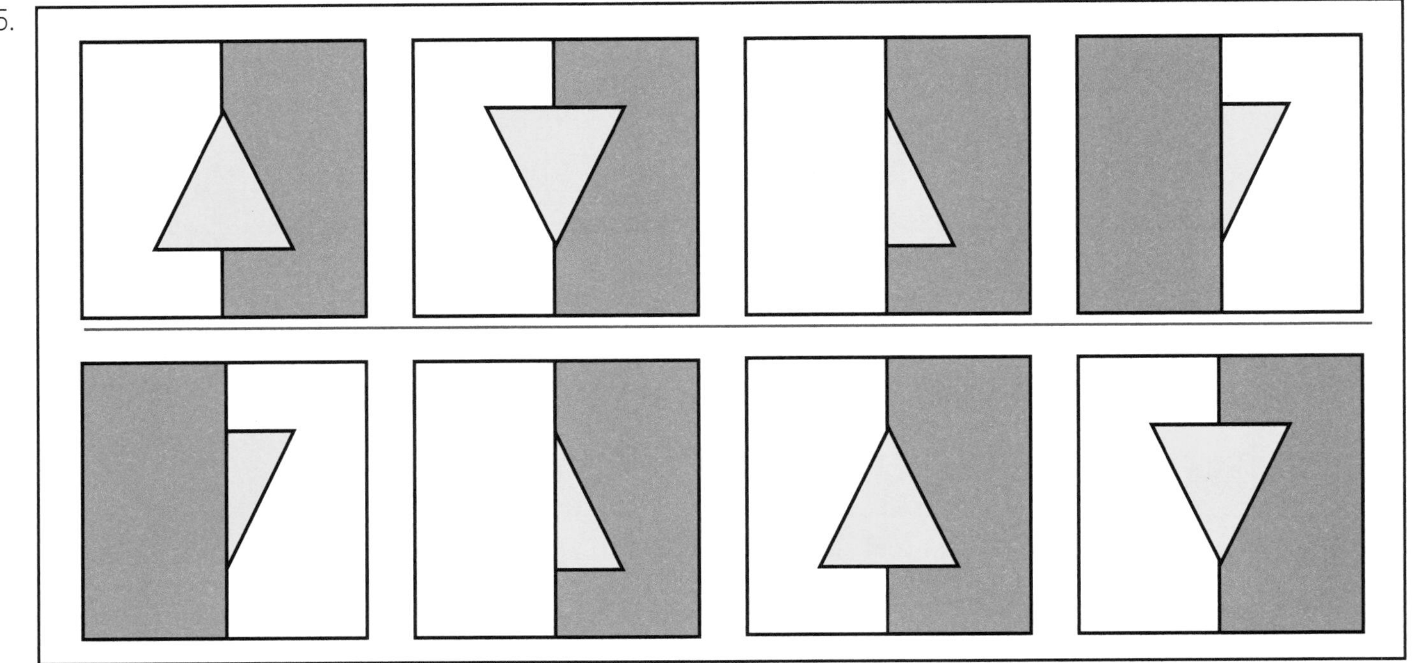

6.

7.

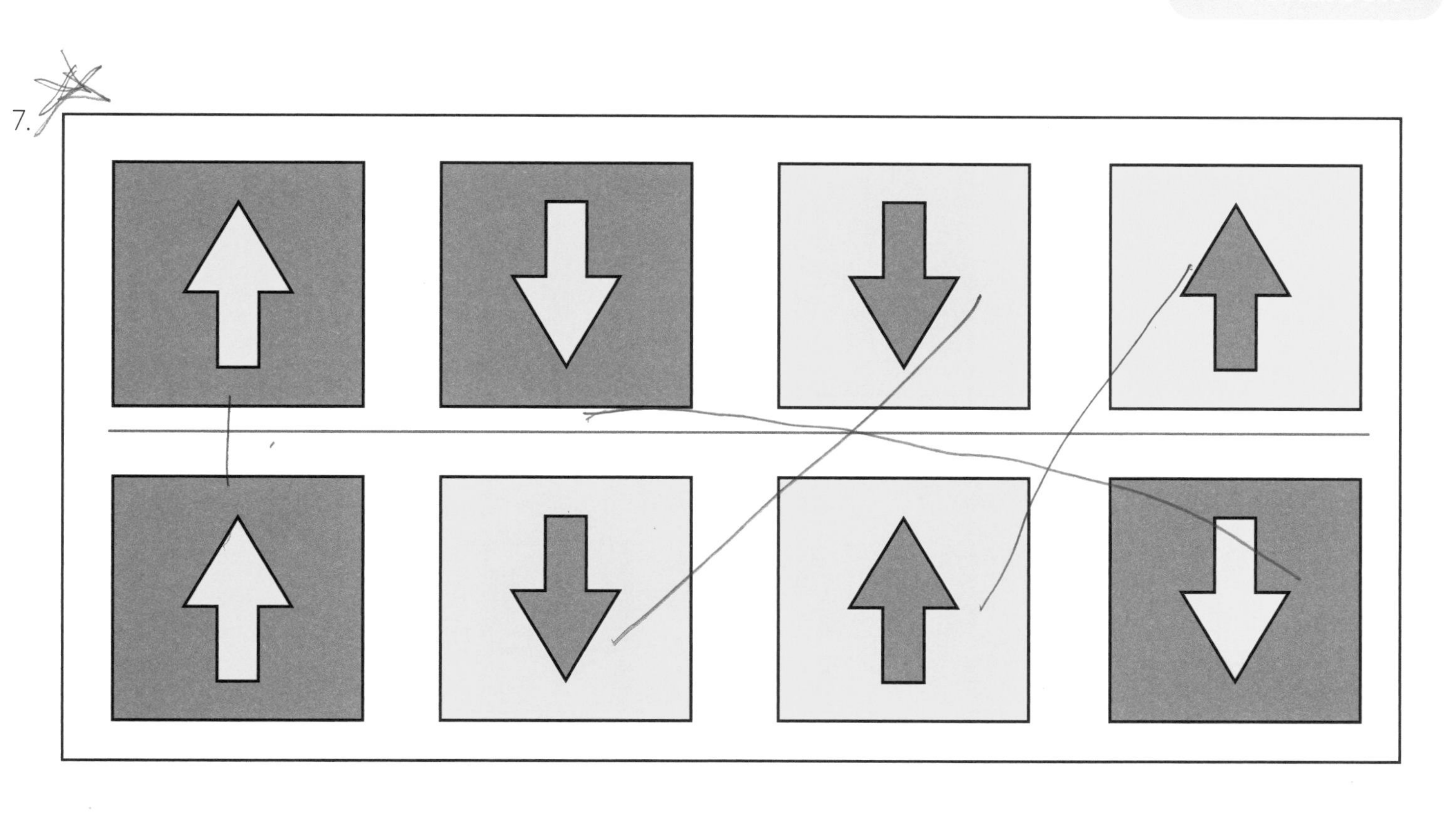

8.

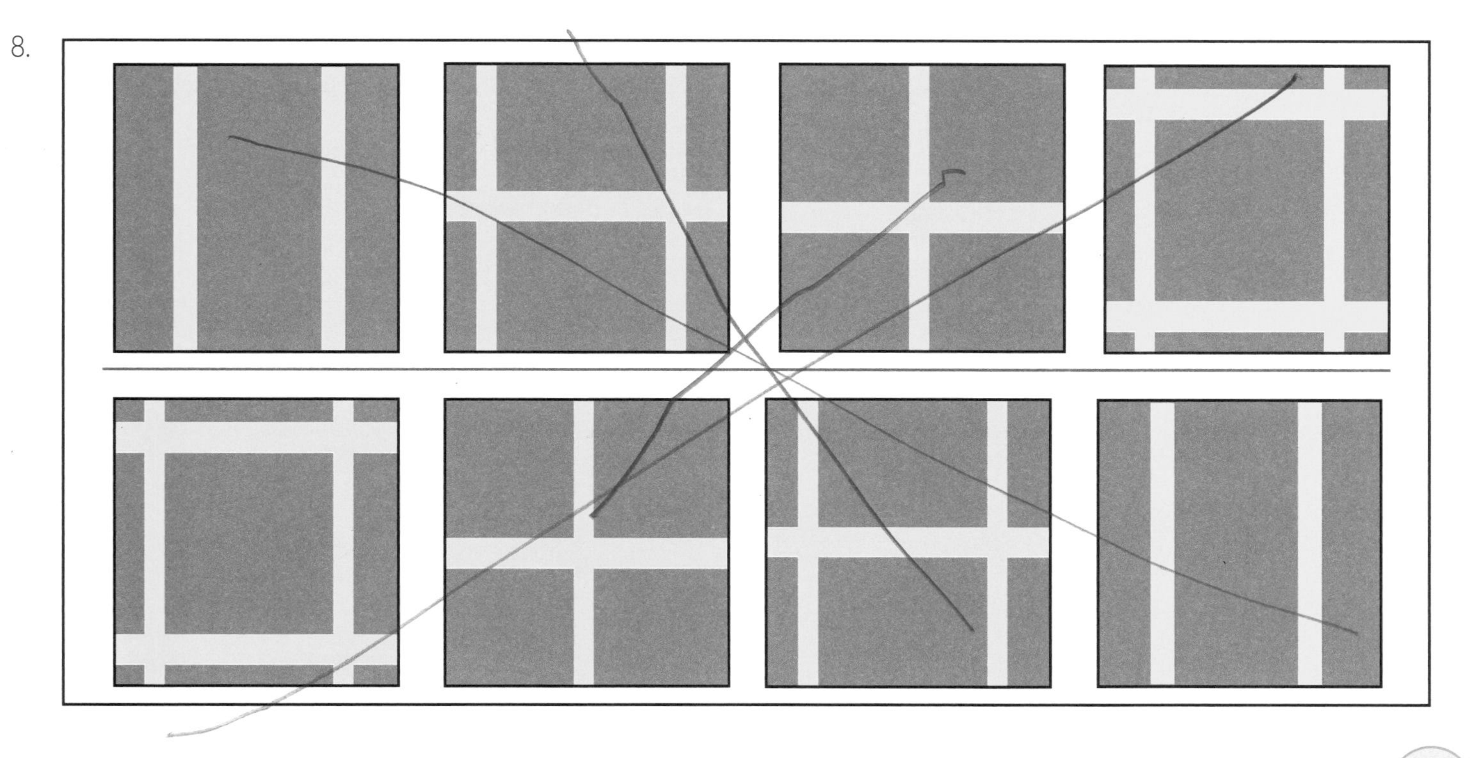

9.

10.

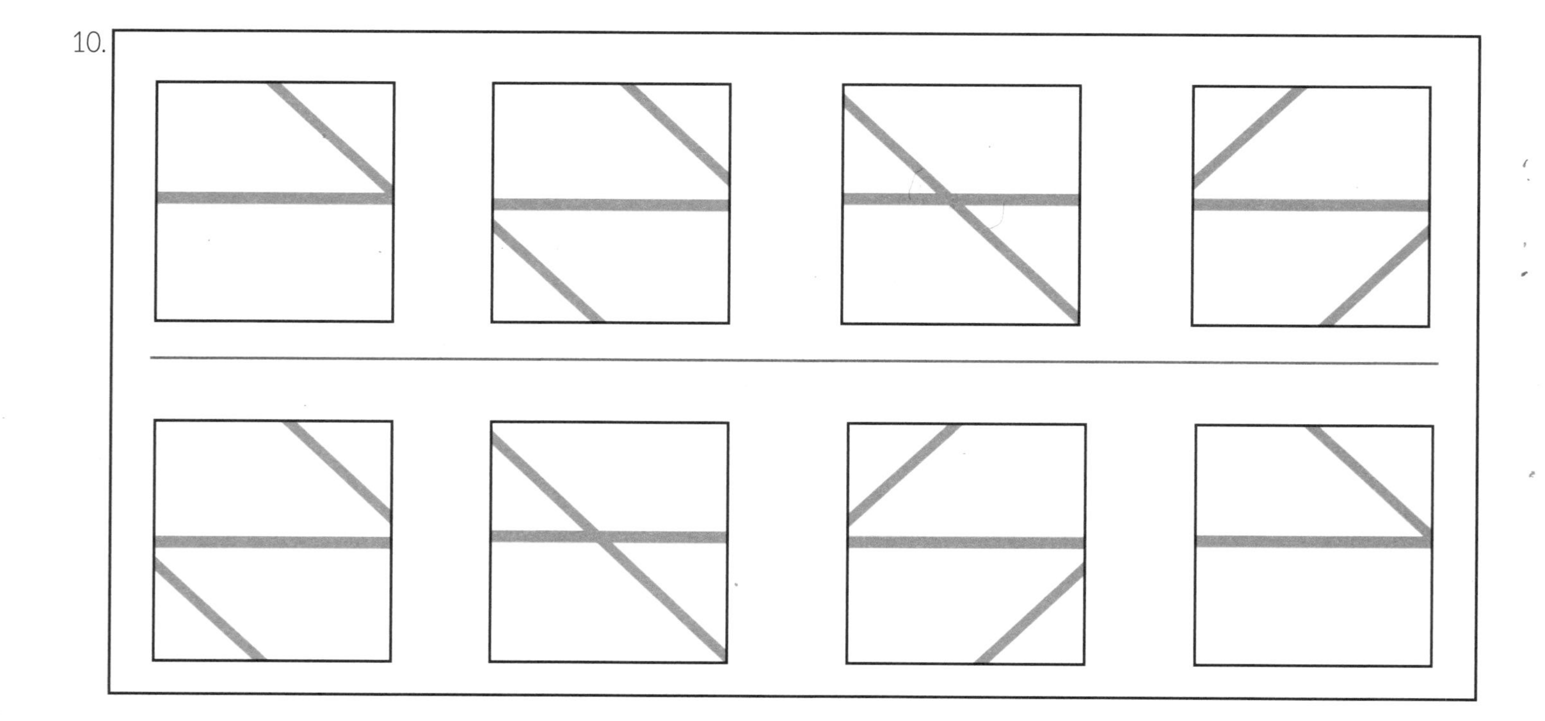

11.

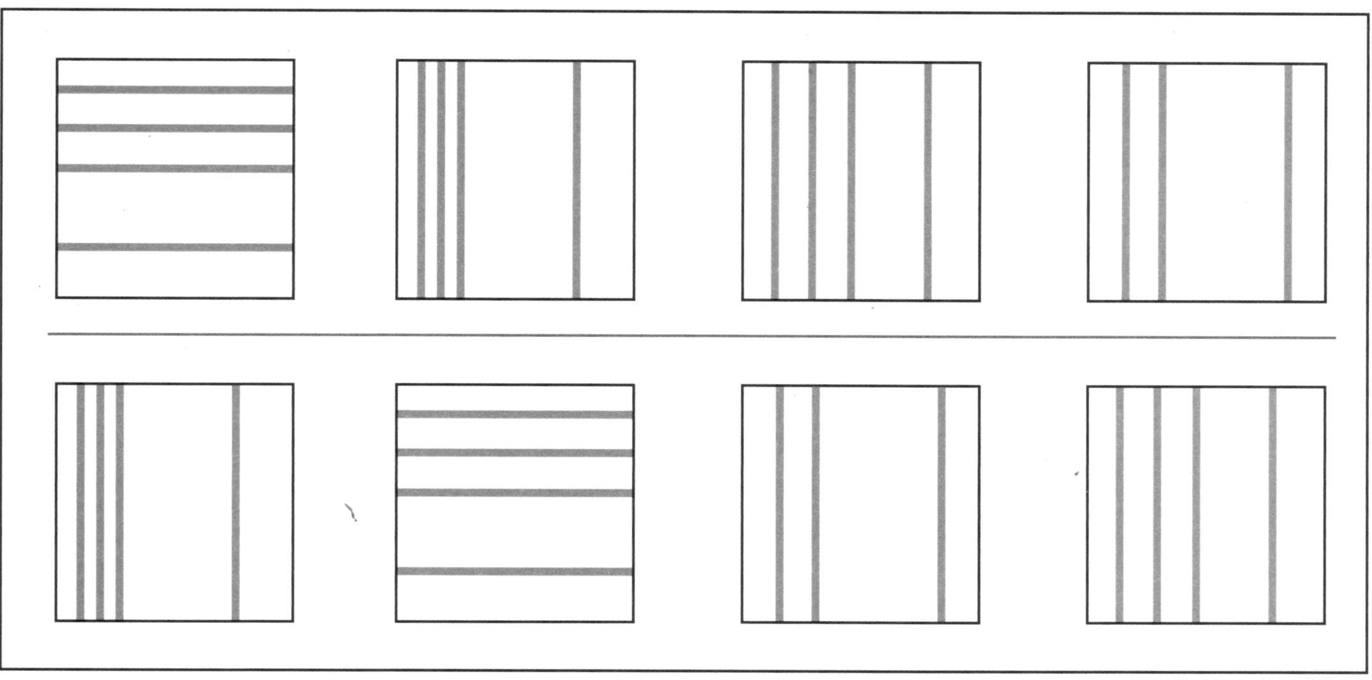

12.

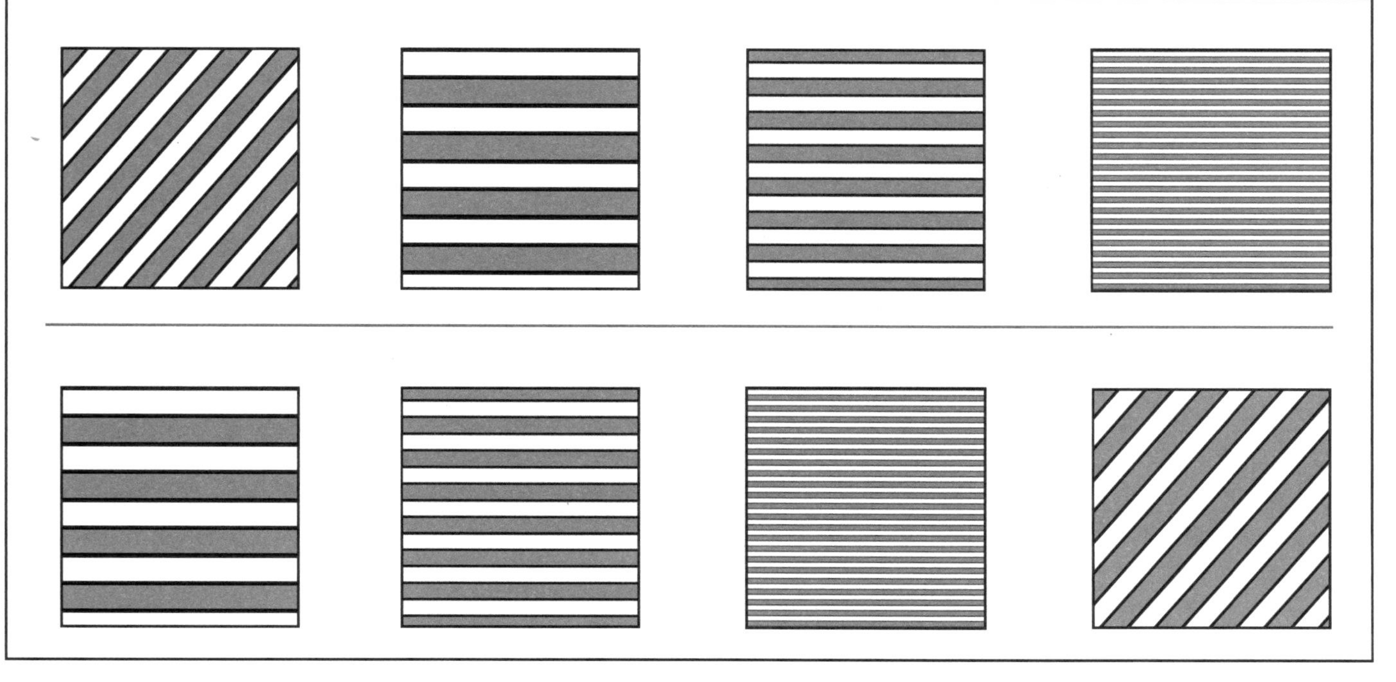

LET'S GIVE MAY A HAND AND FINISH THE PUZZLES.

Directions: Here is a puzzle where a piece is missing. (Point to the box that has the question mark.) Which one of the boxes (point to the row of answer choices) would go here? (Point to the box that has the question mark again.)

Parent note: Help your child complete these by asking him/her to look closely at the colors and lines (and in some cases, shapes) of the puzzle. Then, (s)he should do the same with the area around the white box. How do the colors/lines/shapes look next to the white box?

Ask your child what (s)he thinks the puzzle would look like below the white box, if (s)he could pick it up.

1.

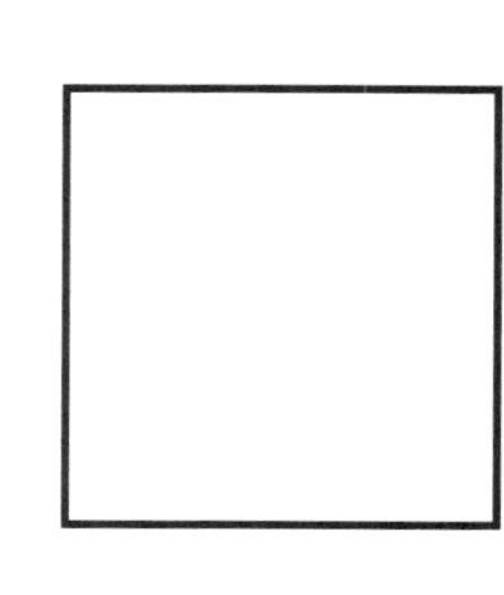

2.

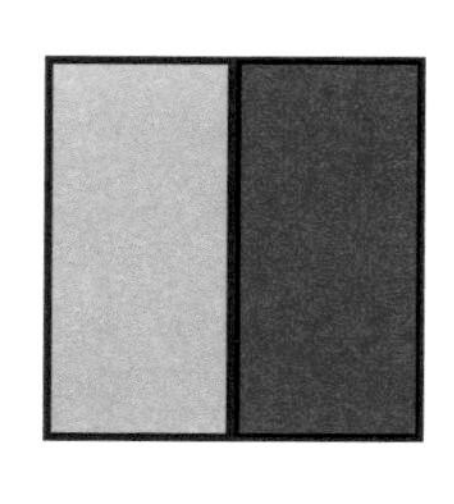
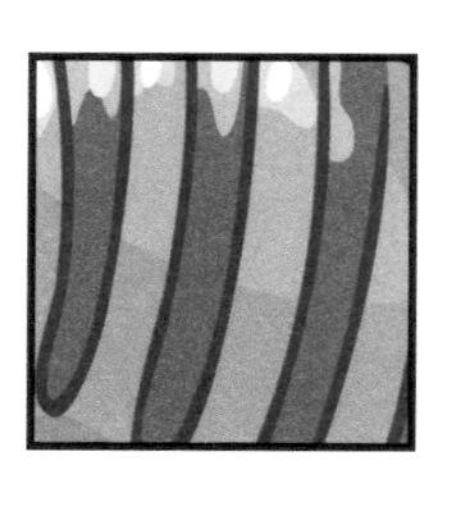

3.

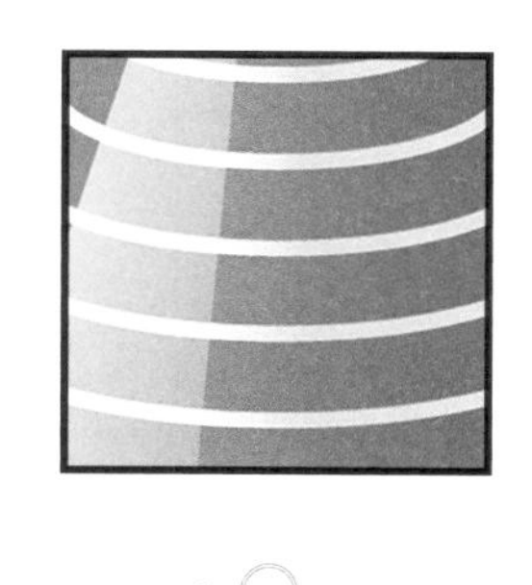

4.

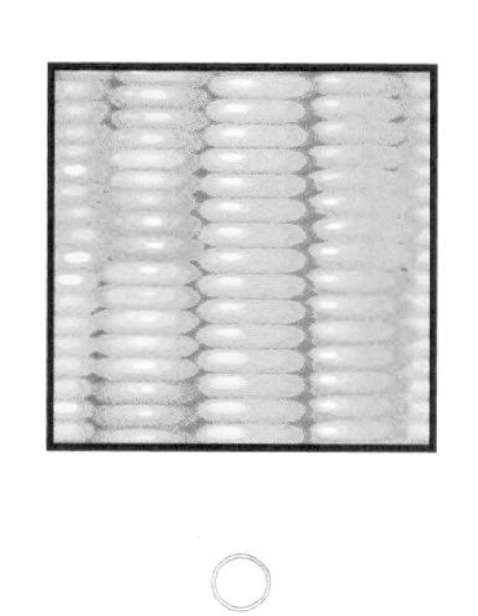

5.

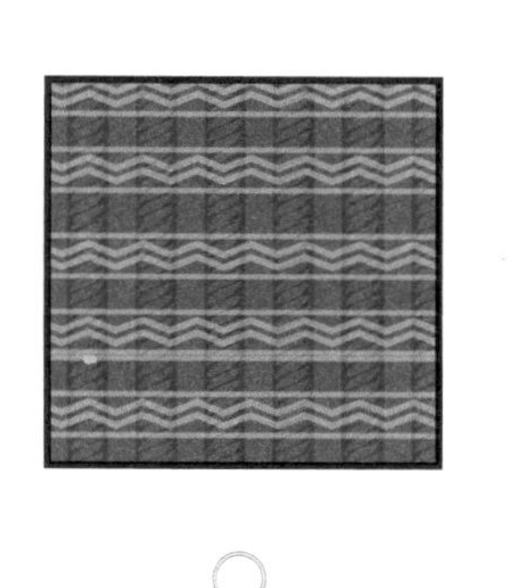
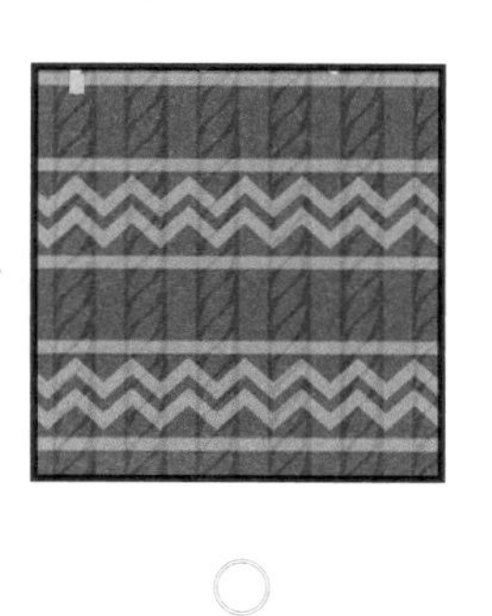

6.

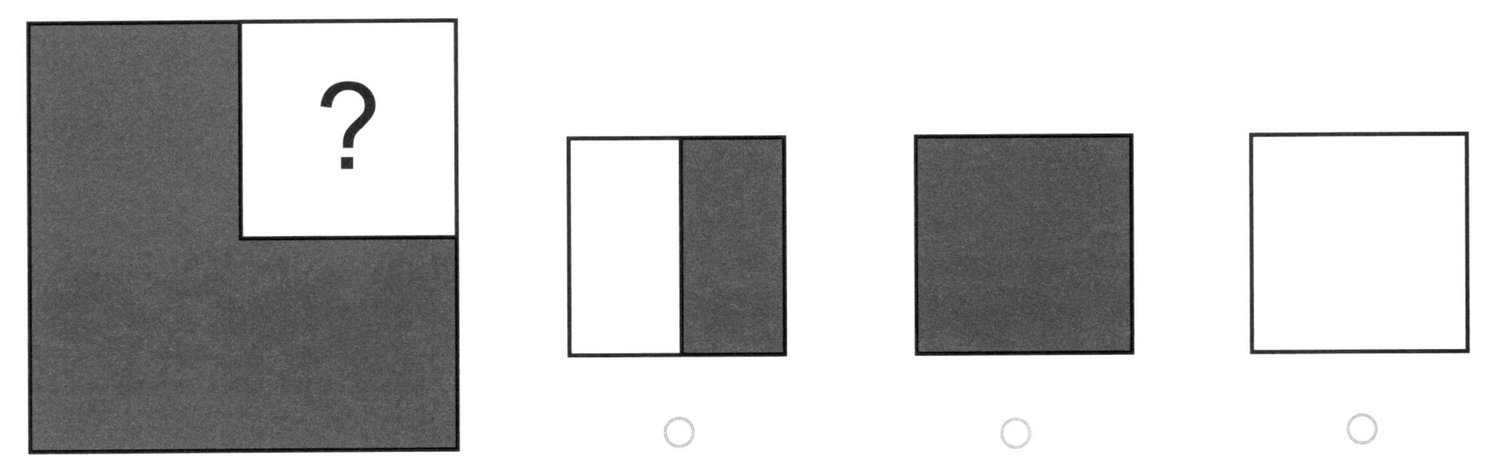

7.

?

8.

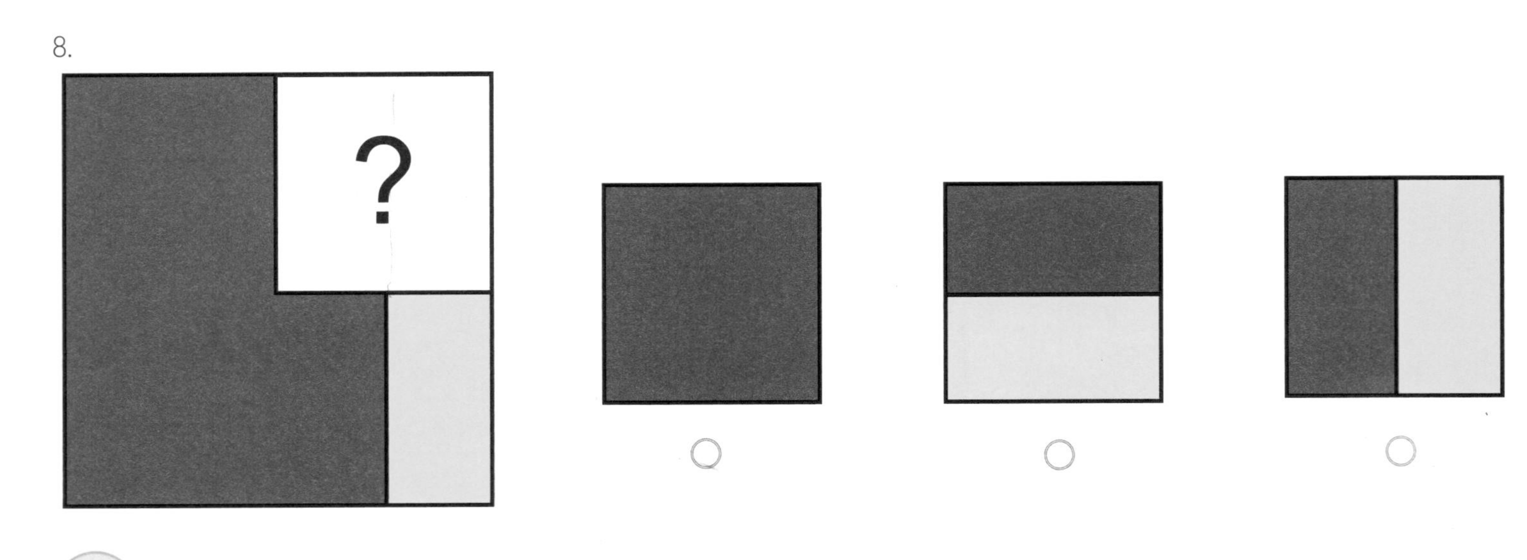

9.

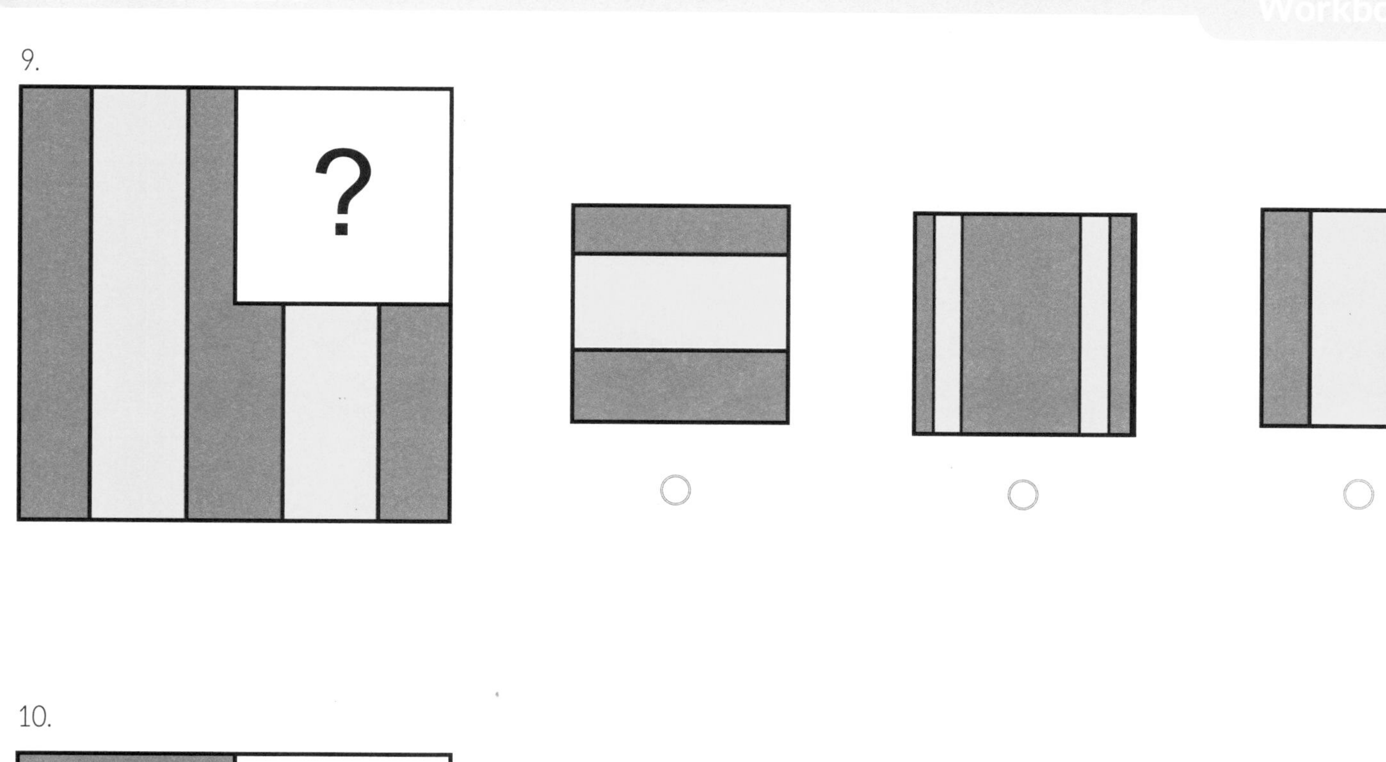

10.

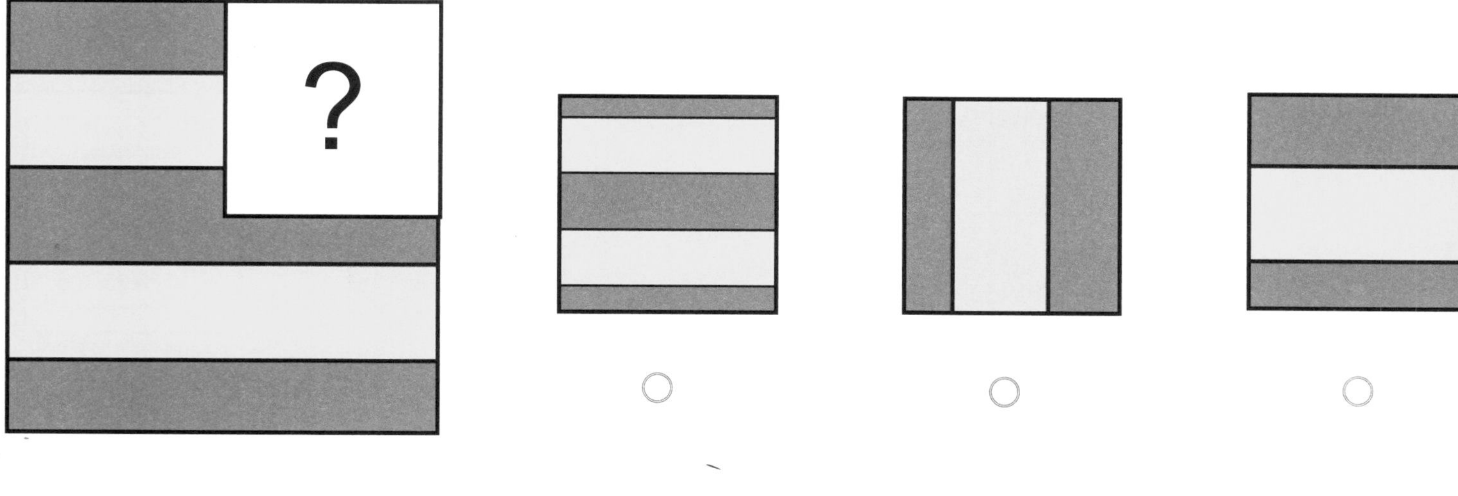

11.

12.

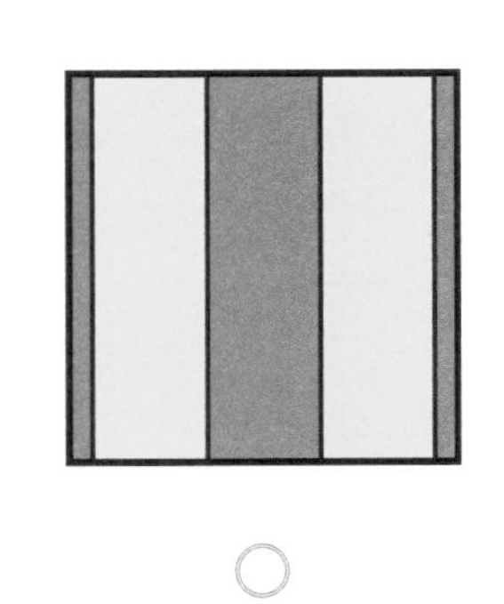

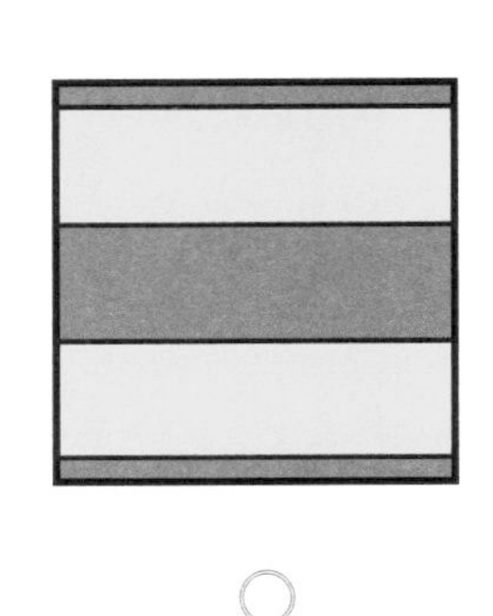

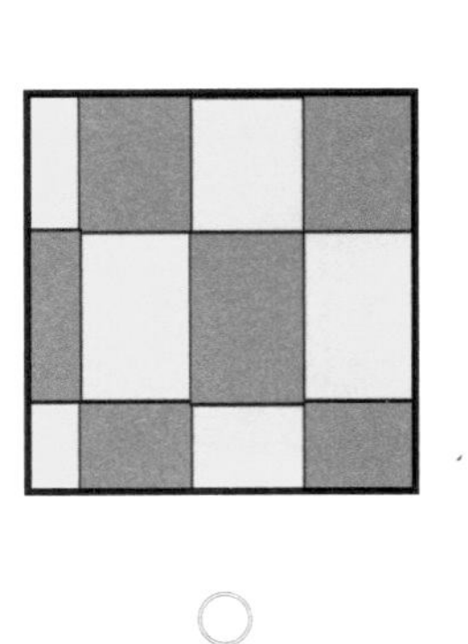

13.

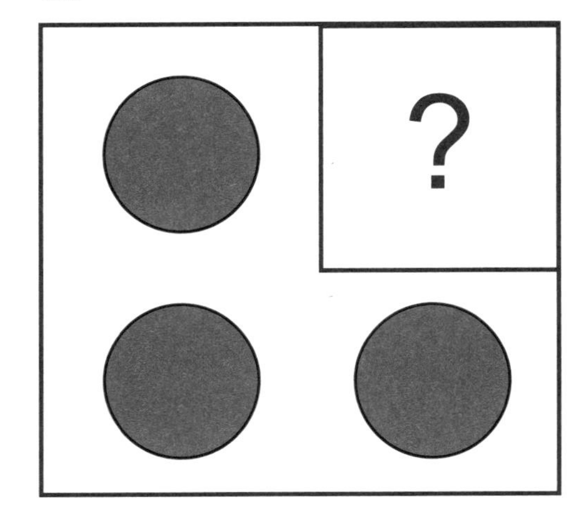

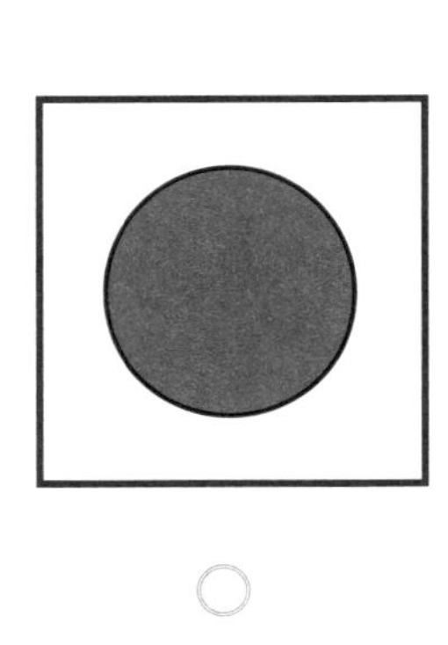

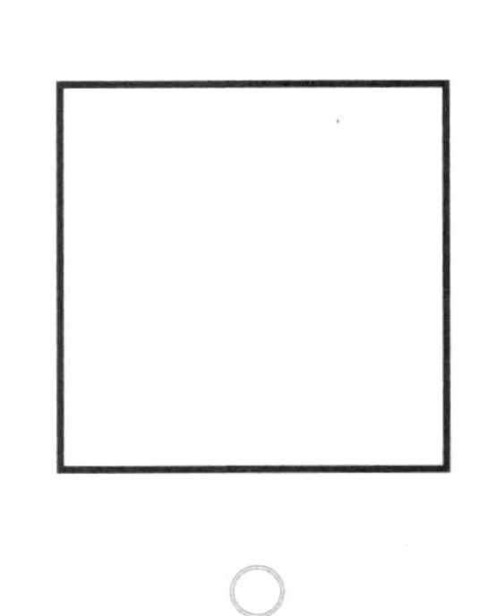

14.

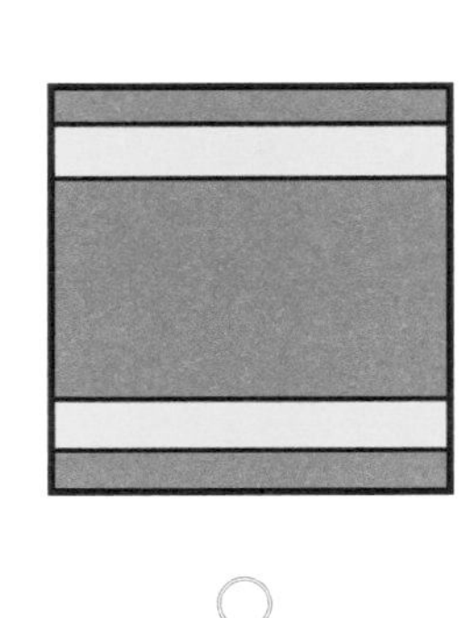

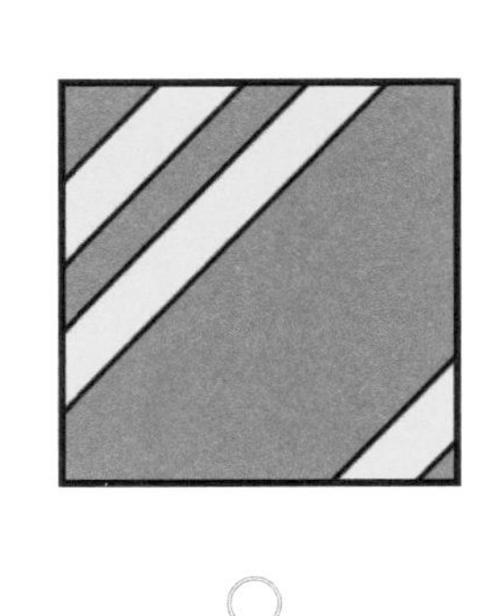

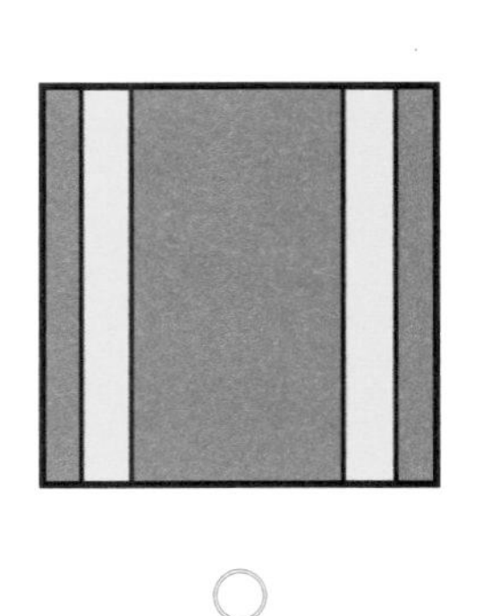

15.

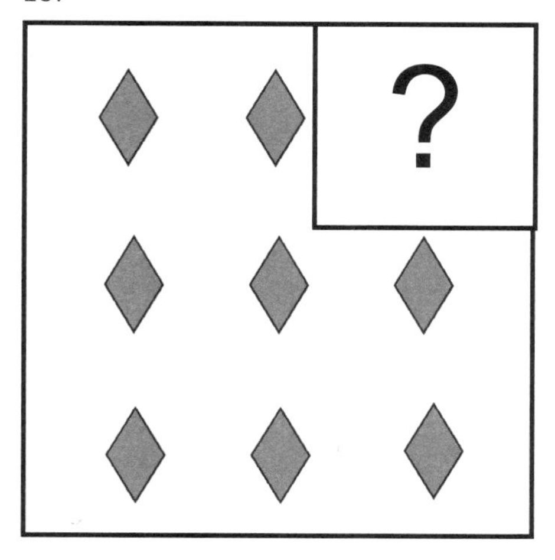

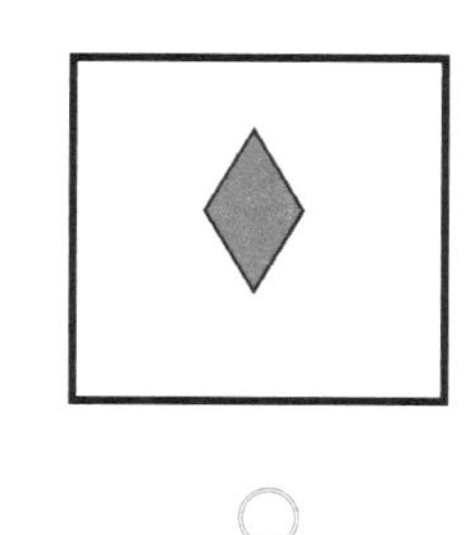

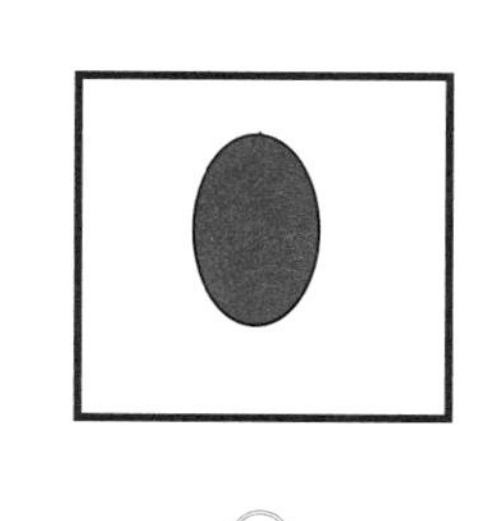

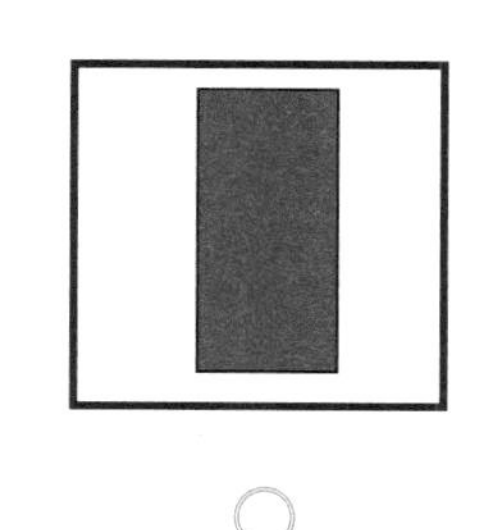

16

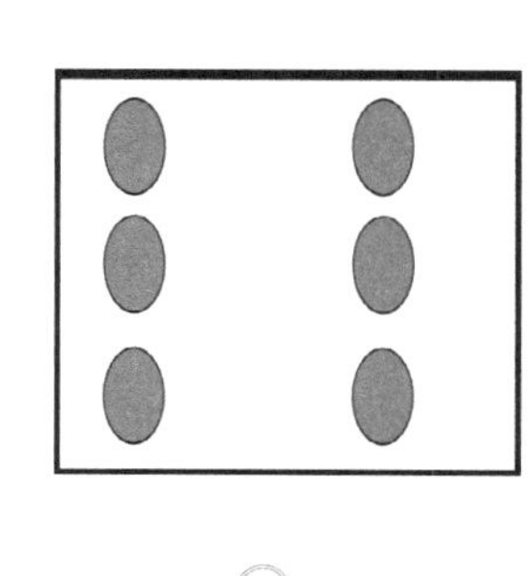

17.

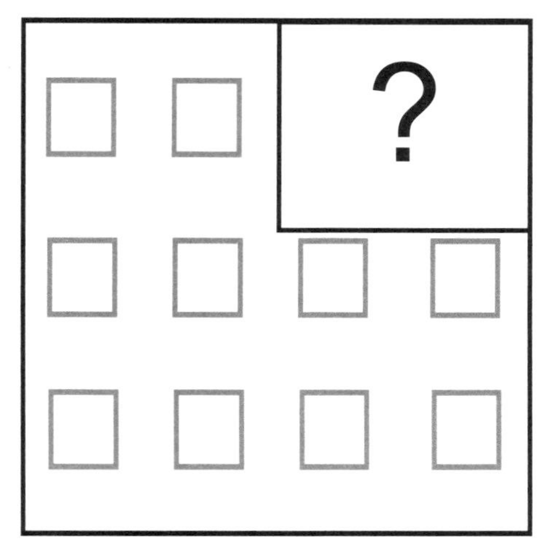

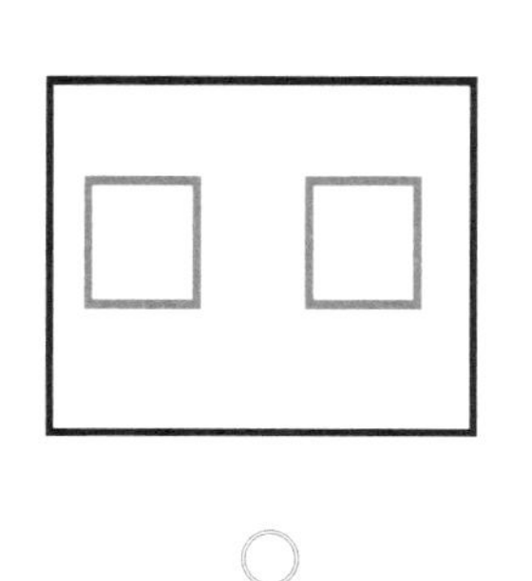

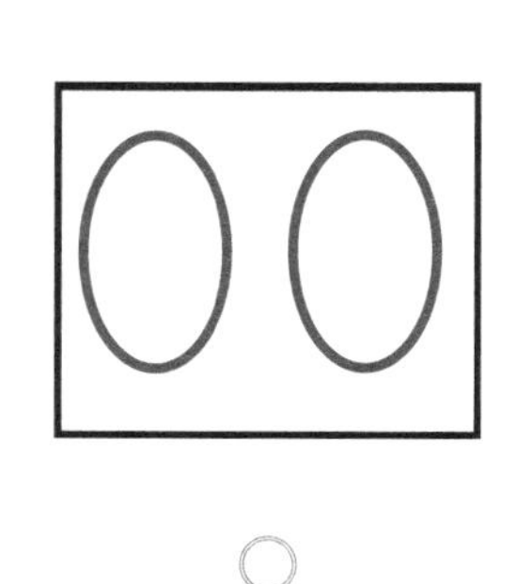

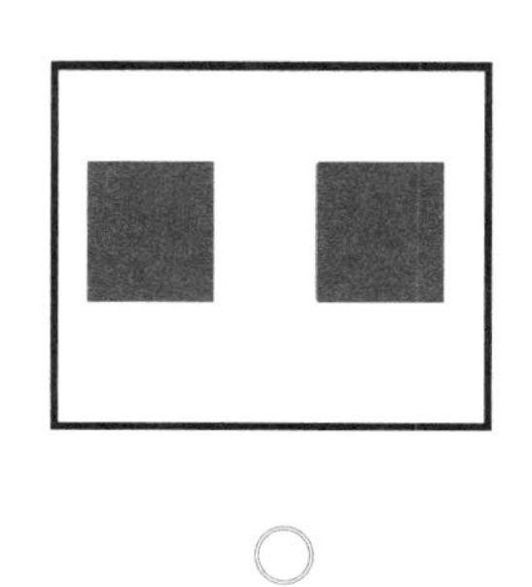

WILL YOU HELP MAX PUT TOGETHER THE SHAPES?

Directions: Look at the two shapes in the first box. Imagine how these two shapes would look if they were put together. Then, look at the answer choices in the next box. Which answer choice shows how the shapes in the first box would look if they were put together?

1.

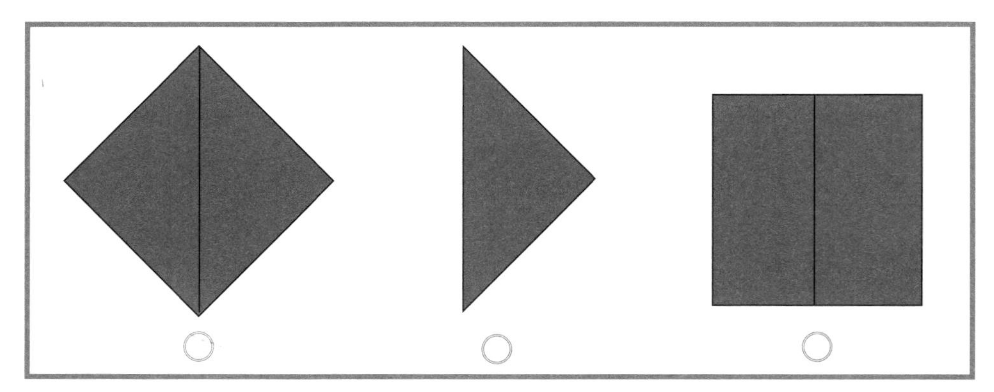

2.
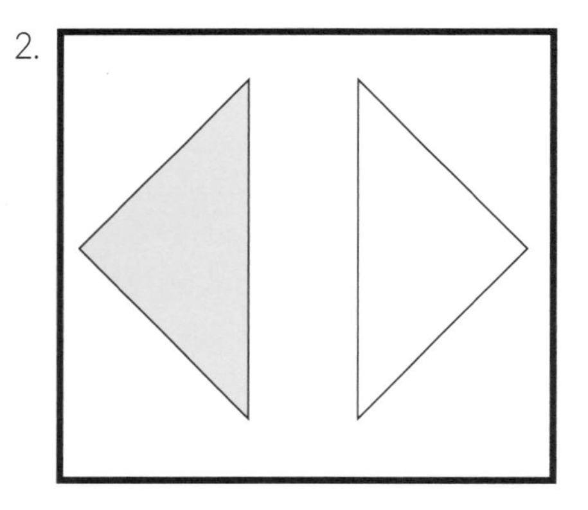
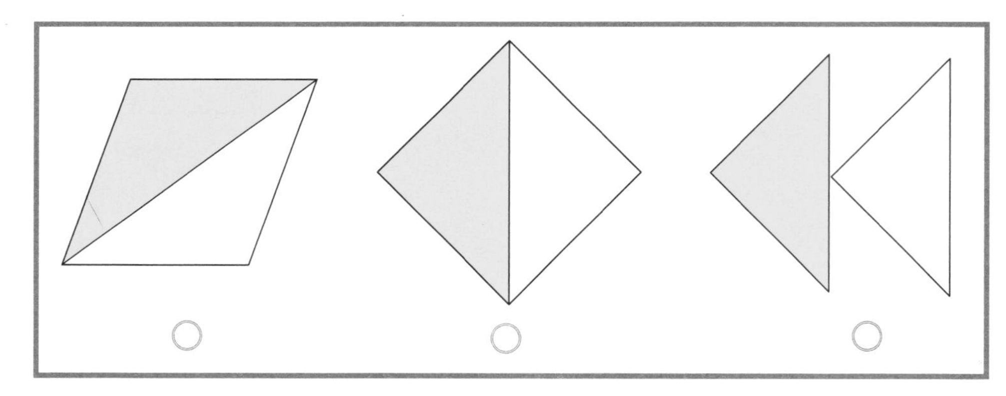

3.
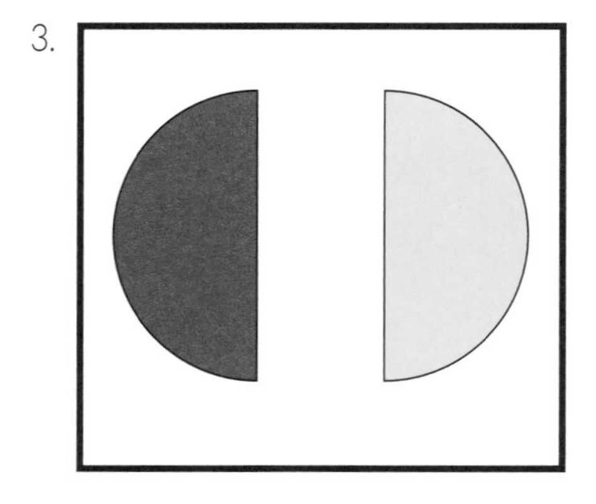
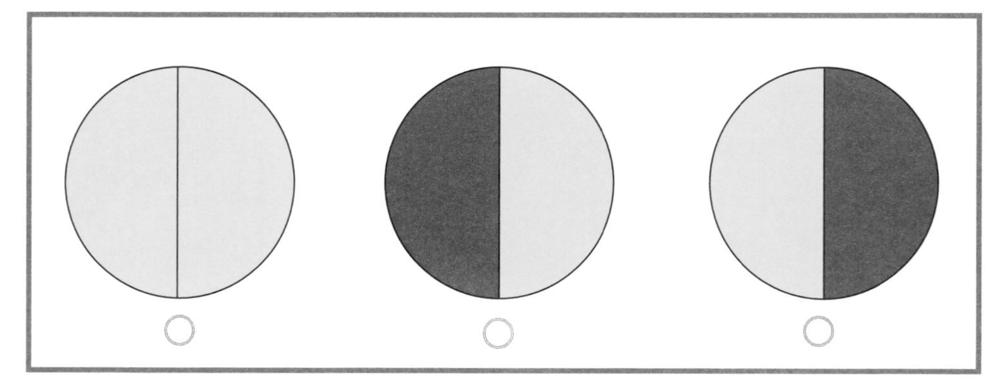

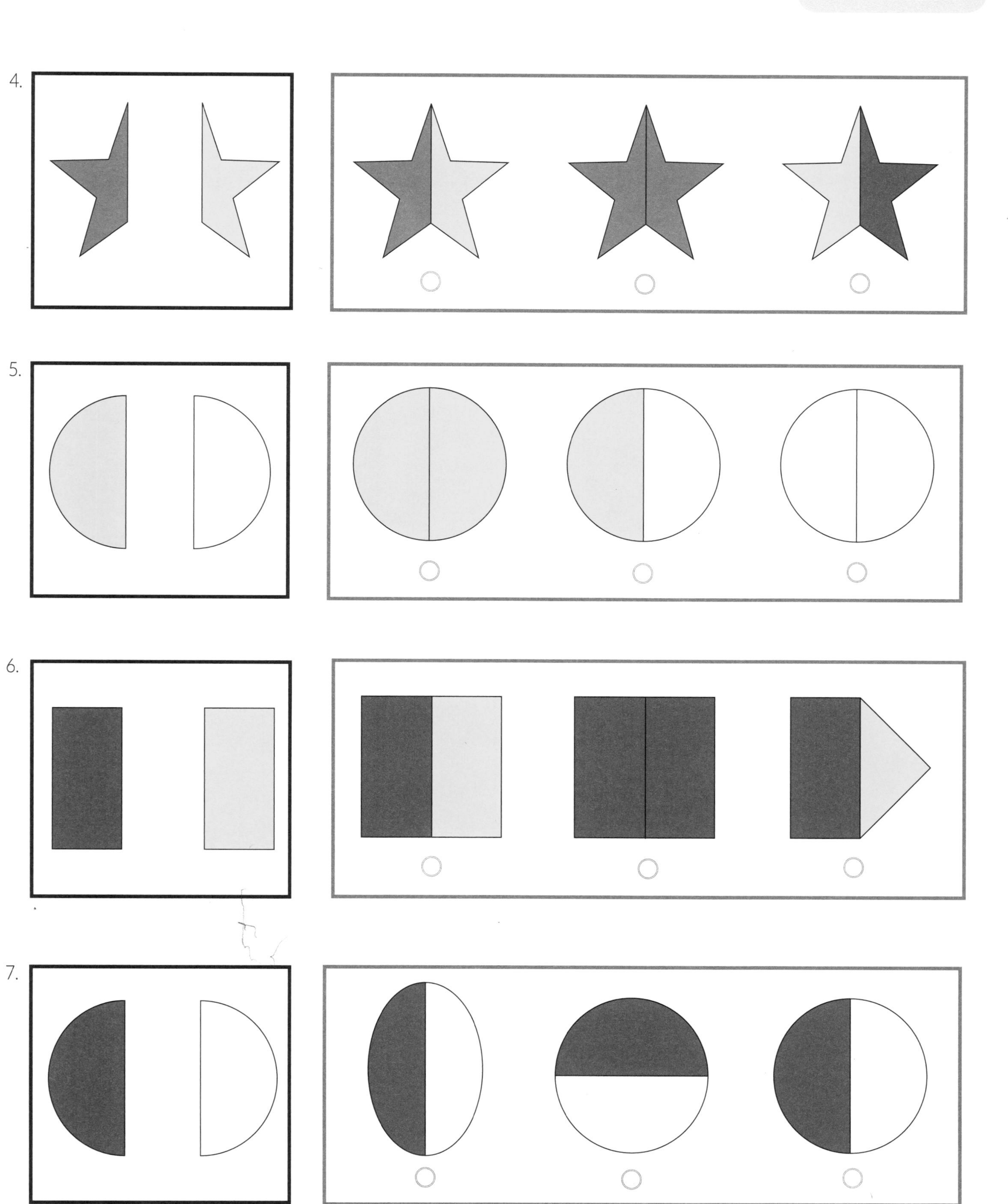
4.
5.
6.
7.

ANYA NEEDS YOUR HELP TO FIGURE OUT WHICH PICTURE DOESN'T BELONG!

Directions: Look at this row of pictures. One of these pictures in the row does not belong. This picture is not like the others in the row. Which picture does not belong?

1.

2.

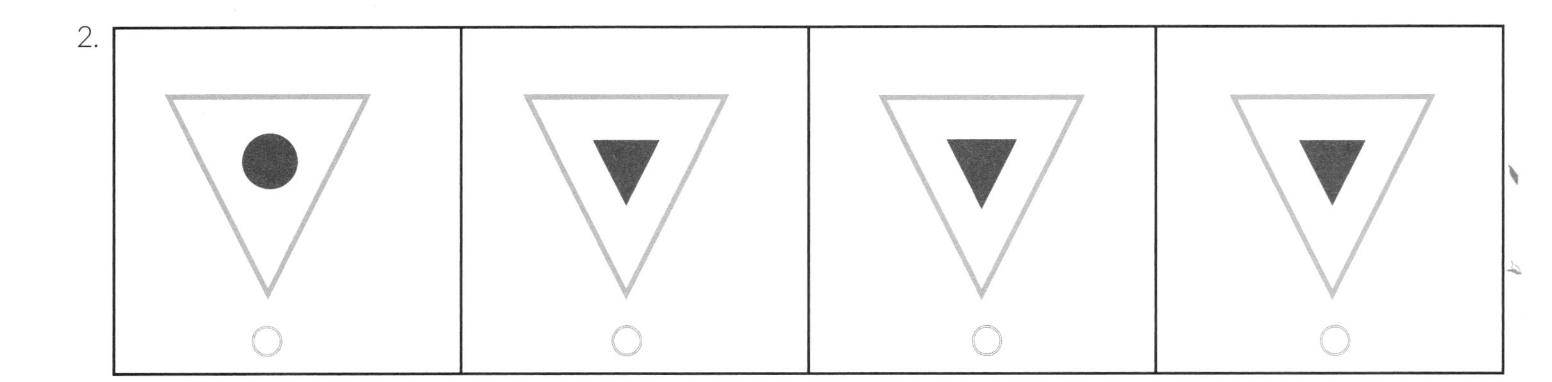

3.

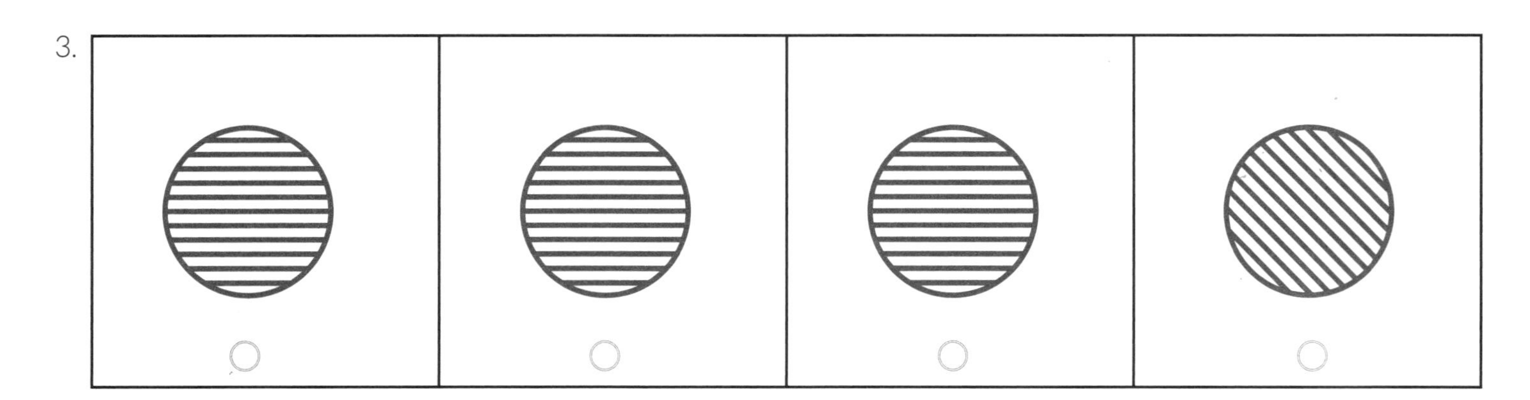

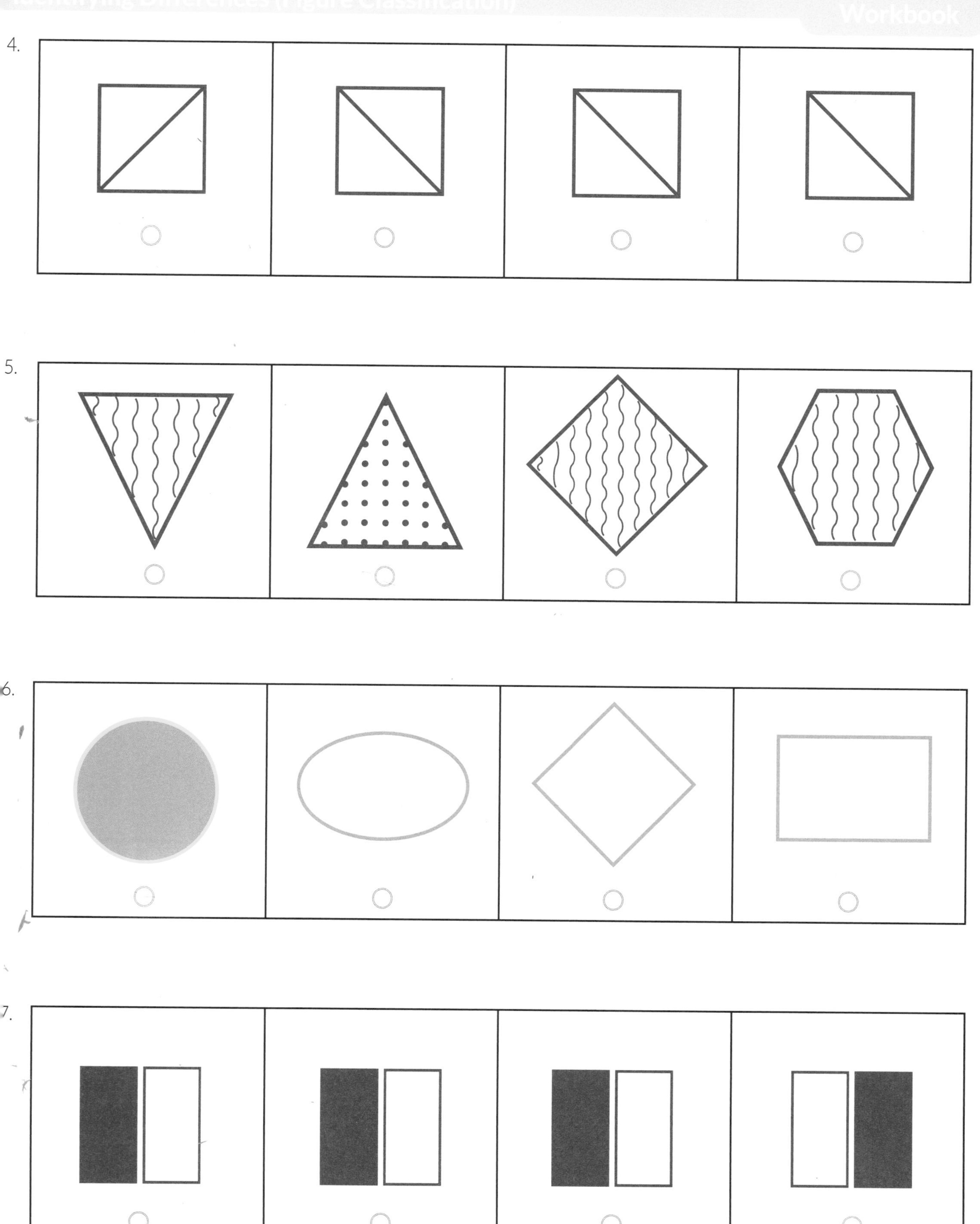
4.
5.
6.
7.

8.

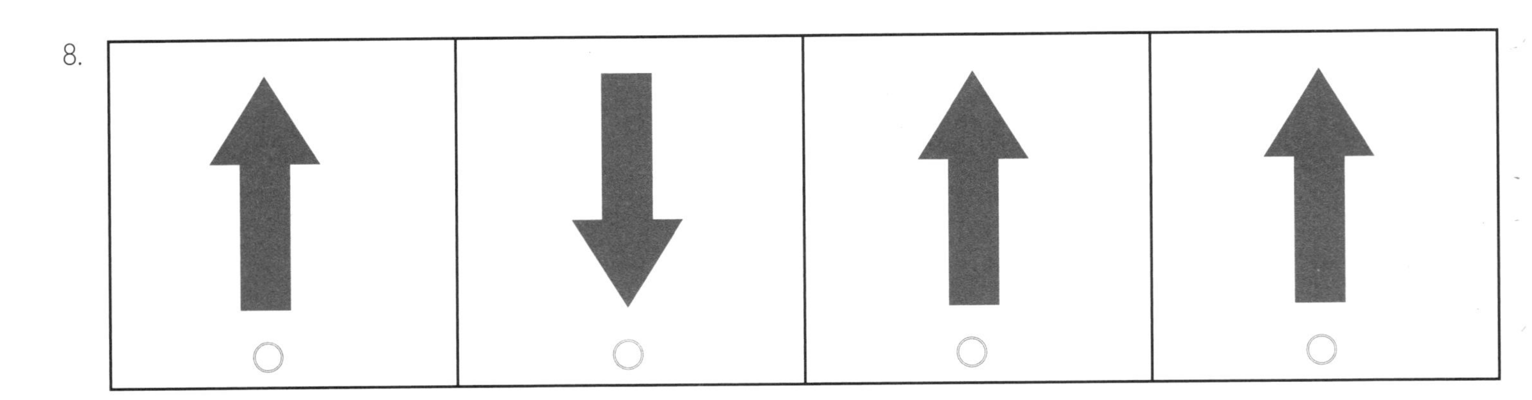

9.

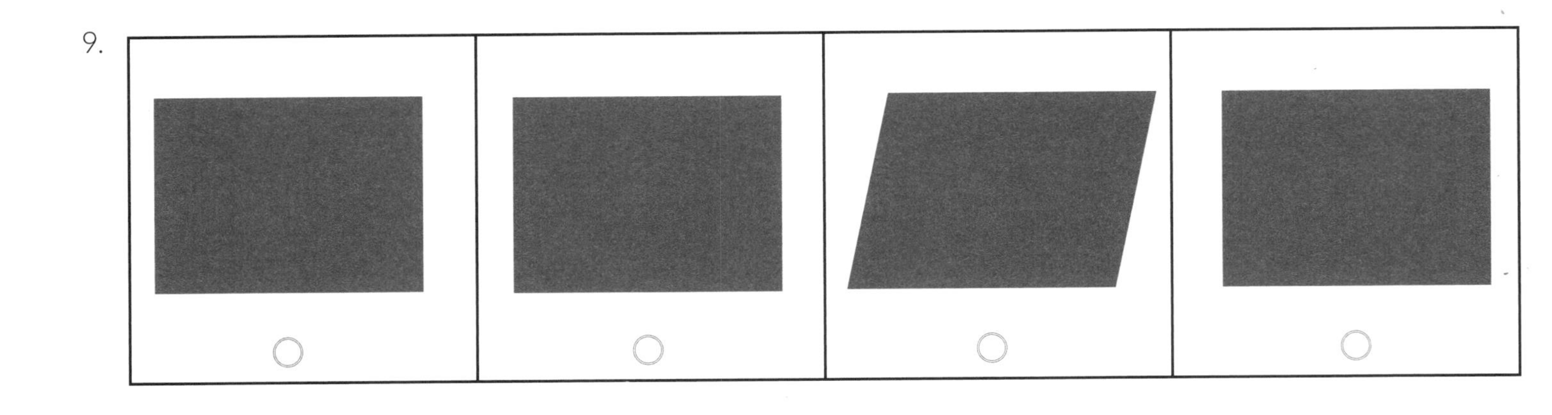

10.

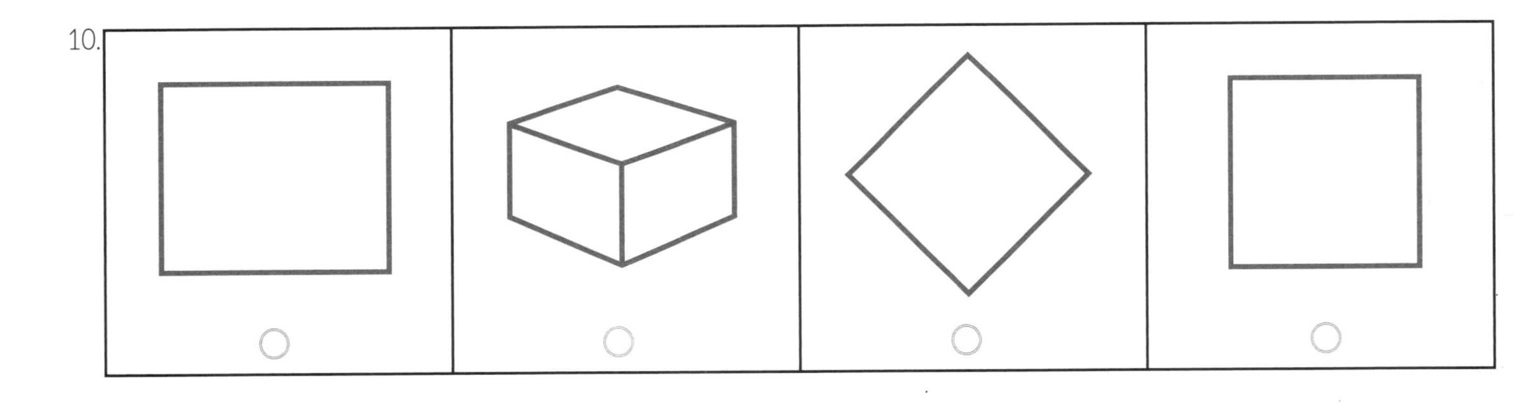

11.

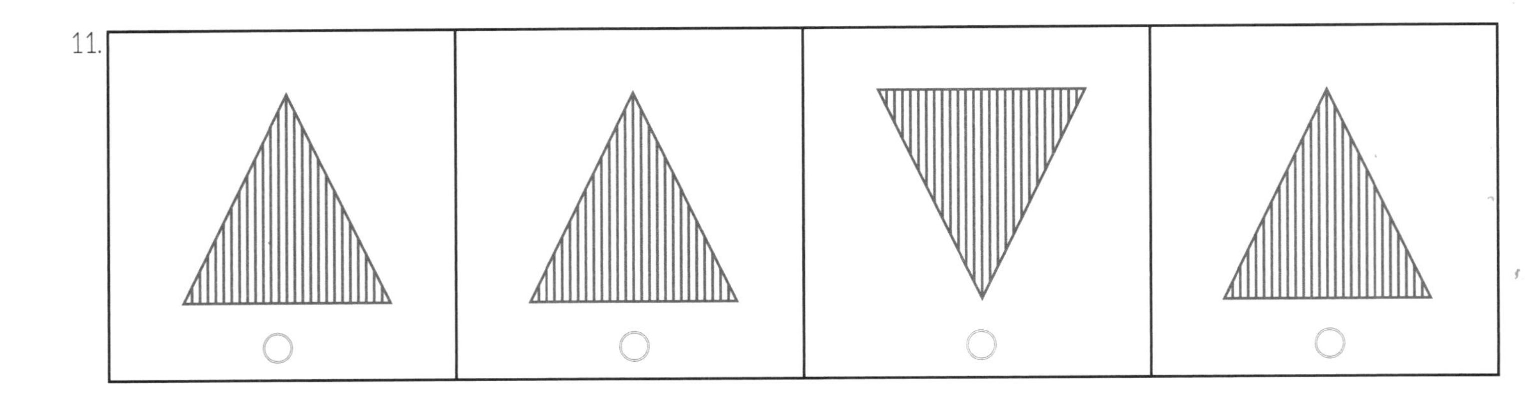

12.

13.

14.

15.

16.

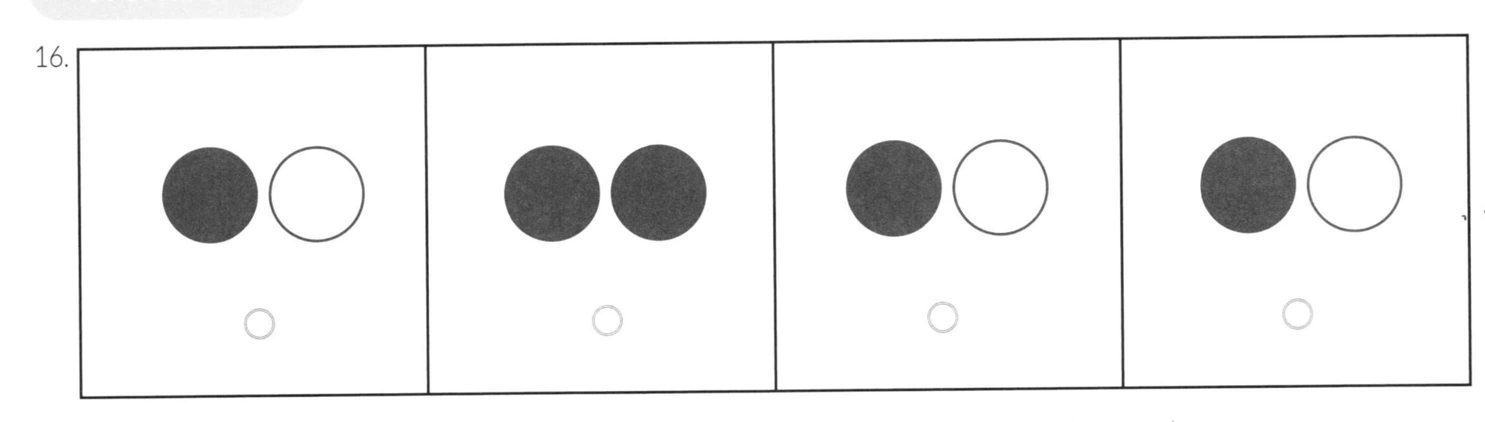

17.

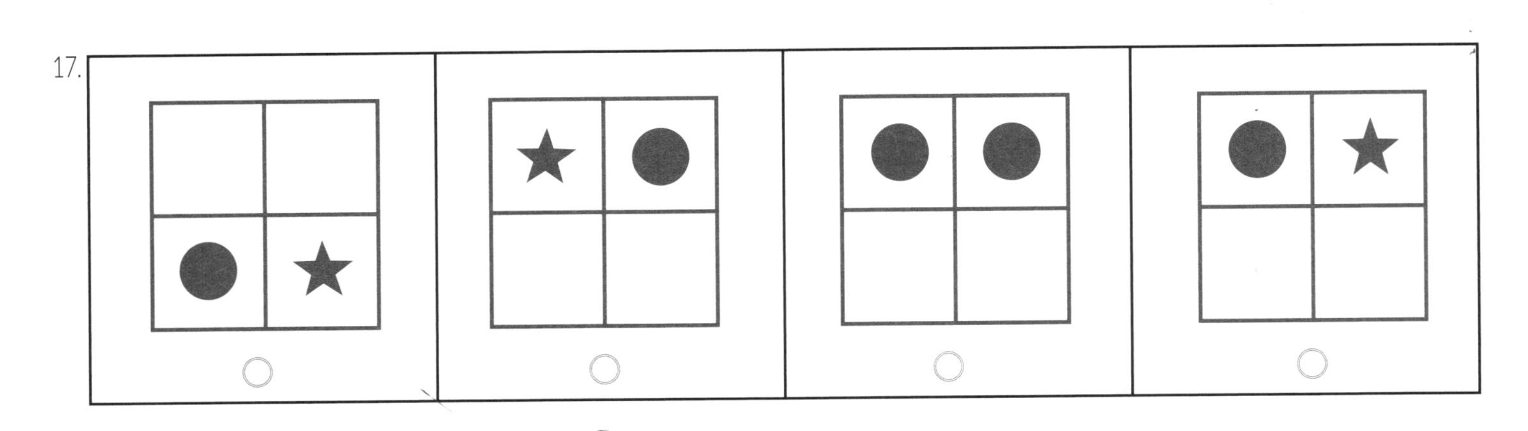

18.

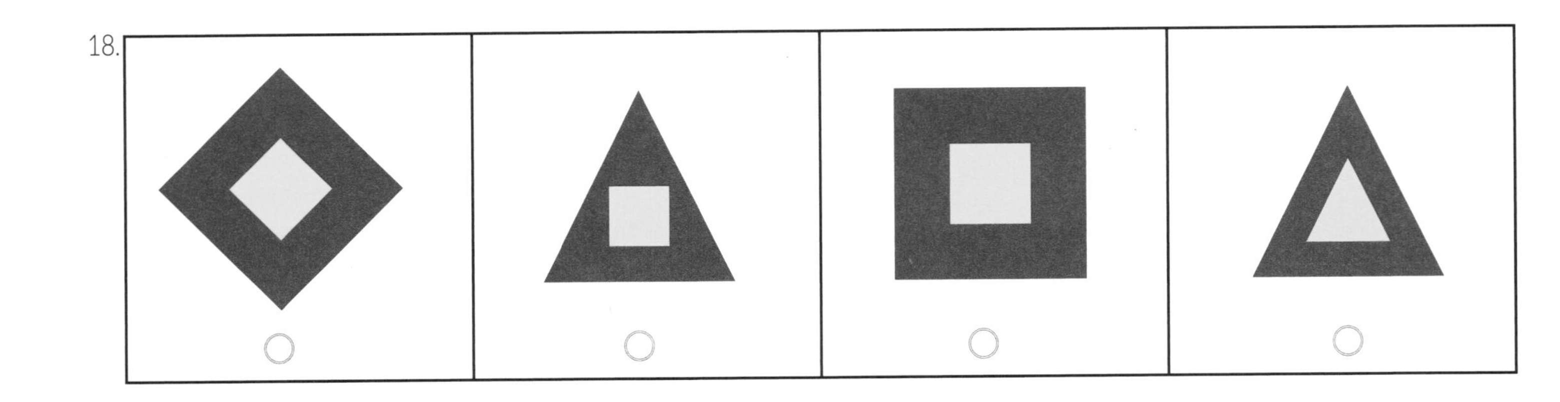

19.

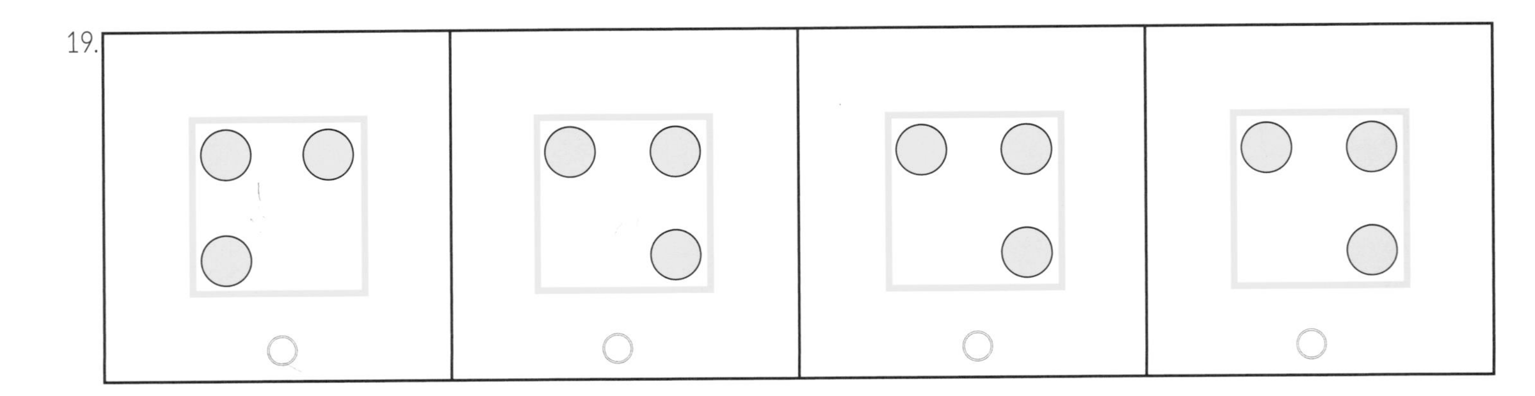

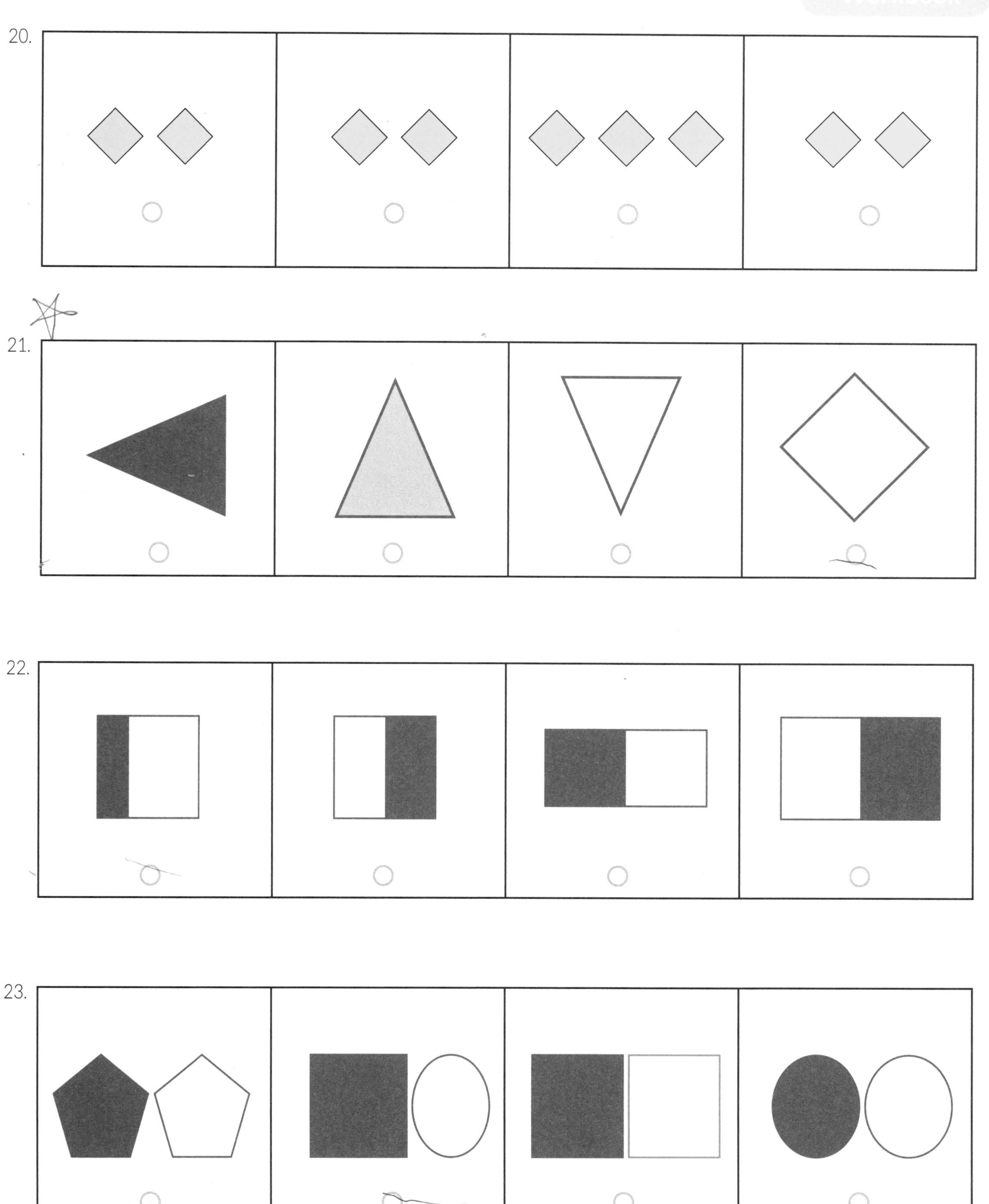
20.
21.
22.
23.

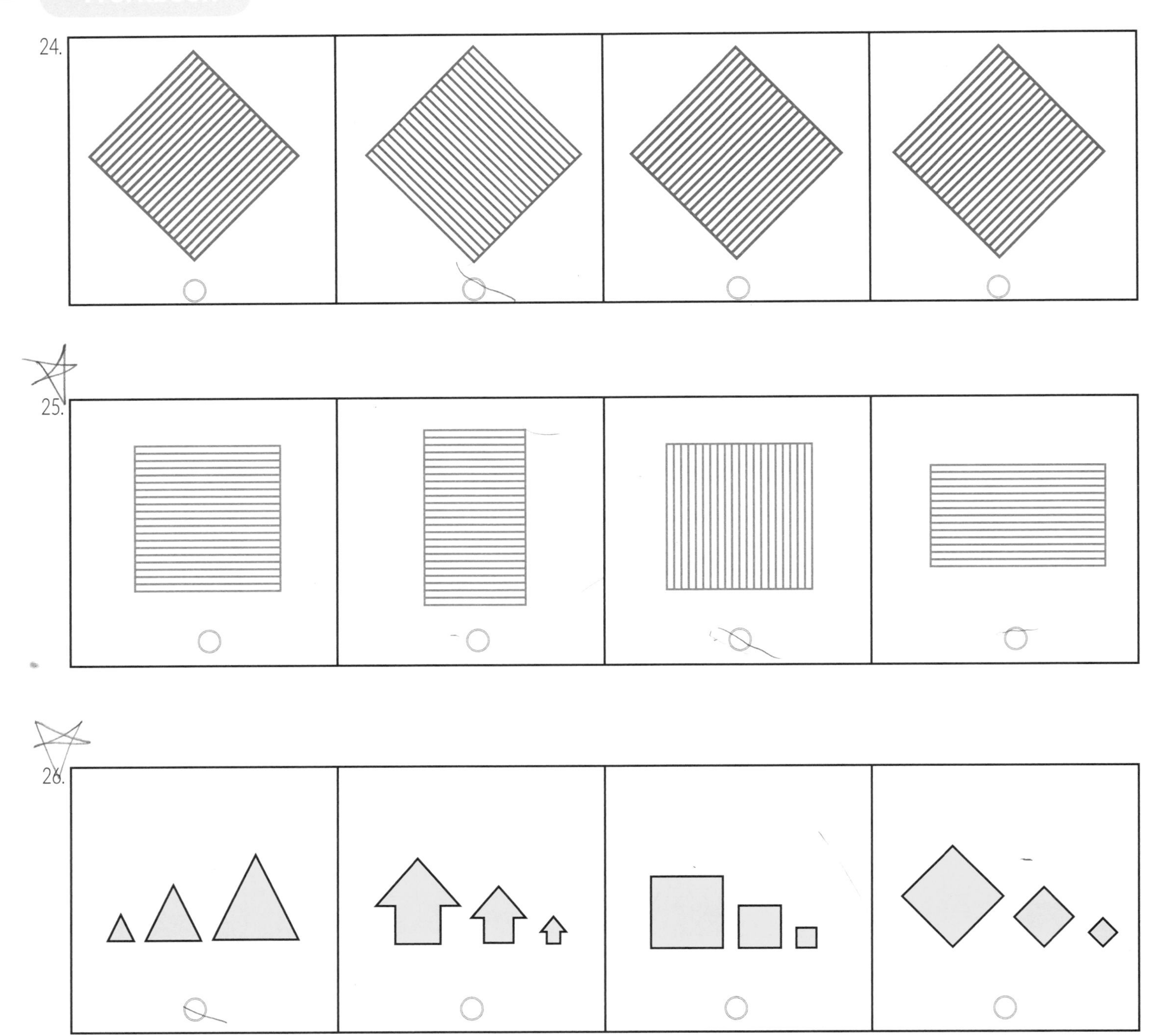

ANYA SAYS, "GREAT WORK, YOU'RE GOING TO BE A TERRIFIC DETECTIVE!"

MAX NEEDS YOUR HELP WITH PATTERNS.

Directions: Look at this row of boxes. The pictures that are inside belong together in some way. Another picture should go inside the empty box. Under the boxes is a row of pictures. Which one should go in this empty box?

Example (read this to your child): In the first box there is a square. In the next box, there is a circle. Then, there is another square. Then, there is another circle. The pattern is: square, circle, square, circle. What goes in the empty box? What comes next? Let's look at the answer choices. If the pattern is square, circle, square, circle, then a square comes after the circle. The square is the answer.

1.

2.

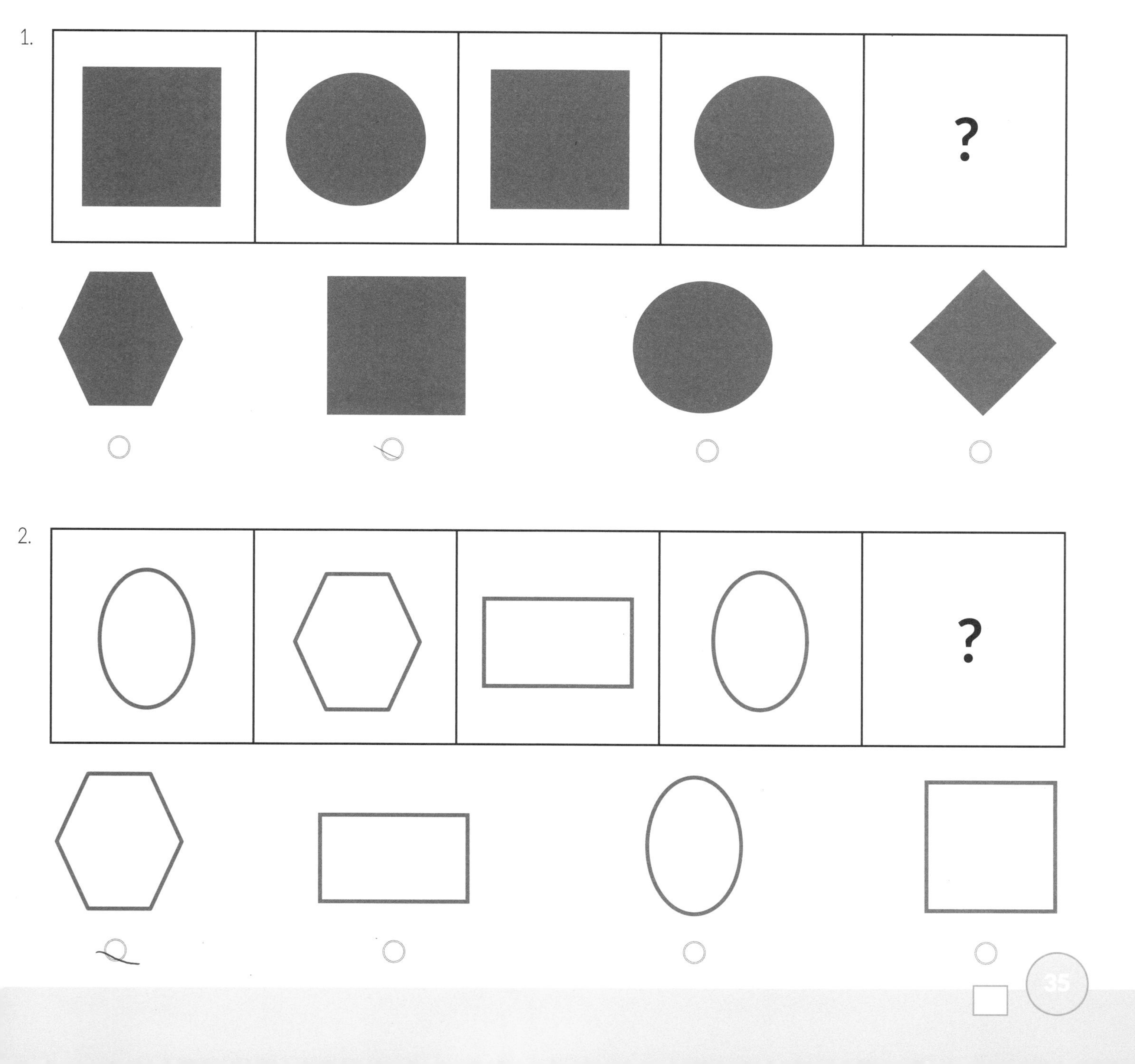

3.

				?

4.

				?

5.

				?

LET'S HELP ALEX FINISH SOME PUZZLES.

Directions: Here is a puzzle where a piece is missing. (Point to the box that has the question mark.) Which one of the answer choices (point to the row of answer choices) would go here? (Point to the box that has the question mark again.)

Parent note: Help your child complete these by asking him/her to look closely at the colors and lines (and in some cases, shapes) of the puzzle. Then, (s)he should do the same with the area around the white box. How do the colors/ lines/shapes look next to the white box?

Ask your child what (s)he thinks the puzzle would look like below the white box, if (s)he could pick it up.

1

2

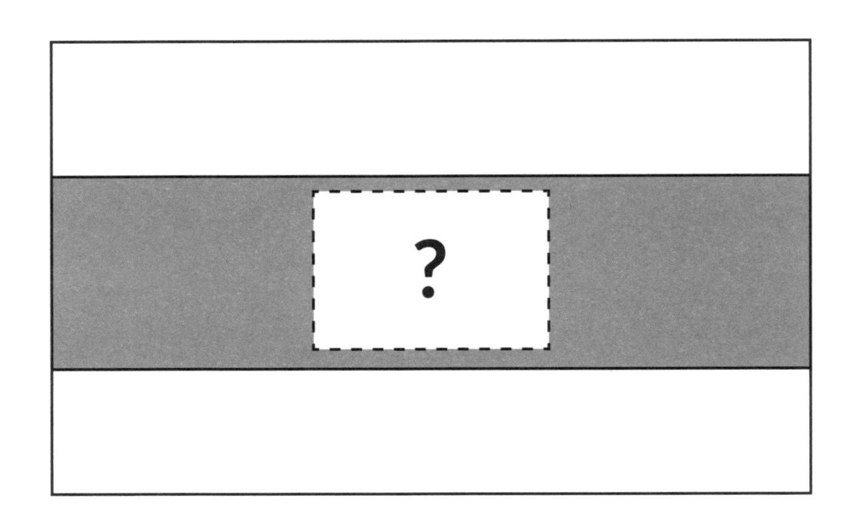

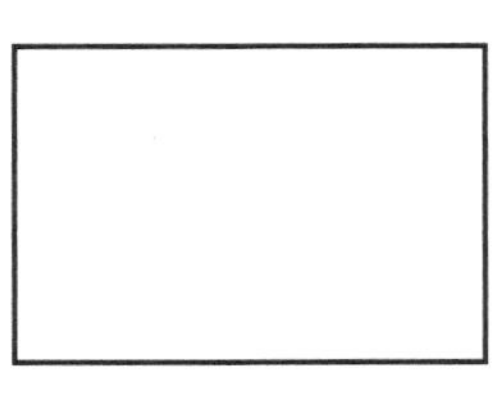
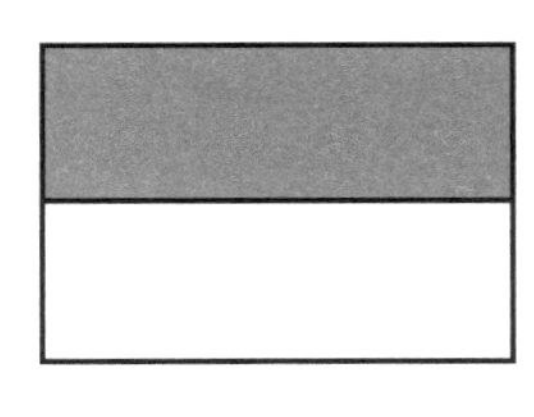
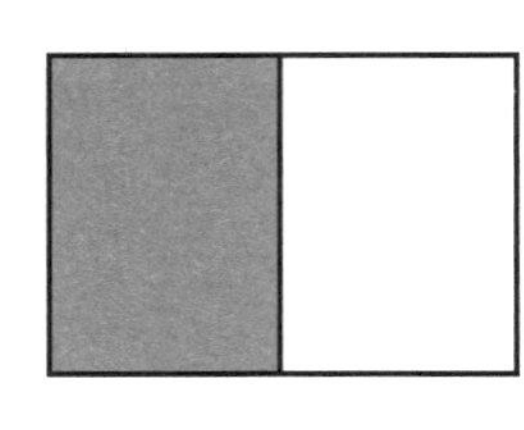

3

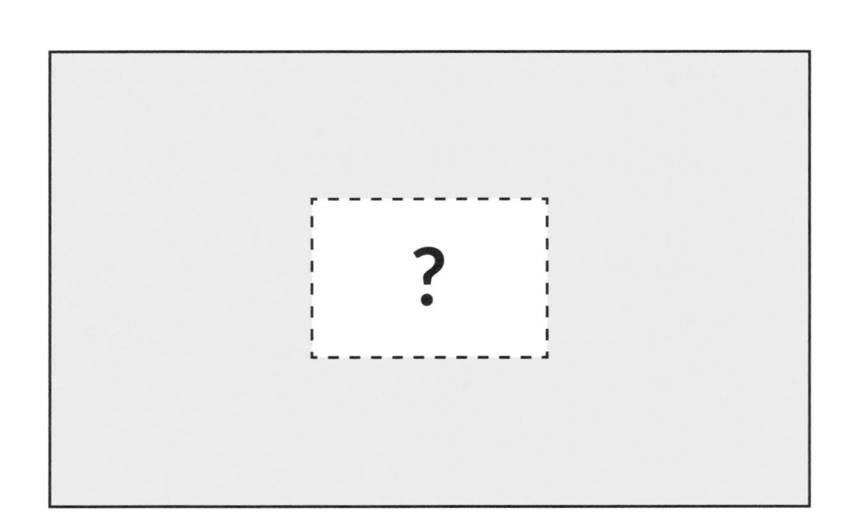

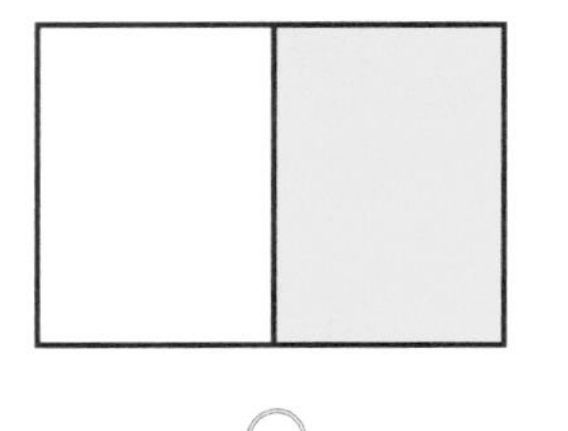
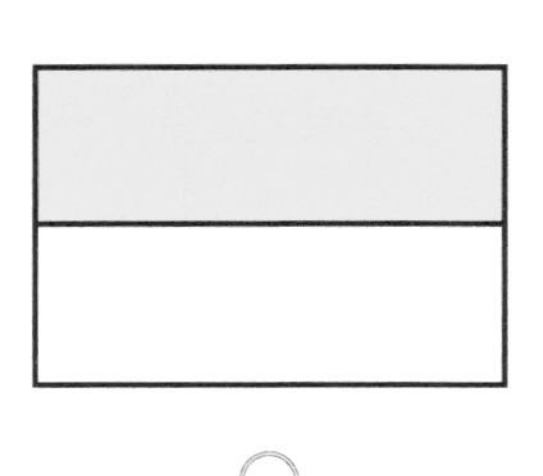

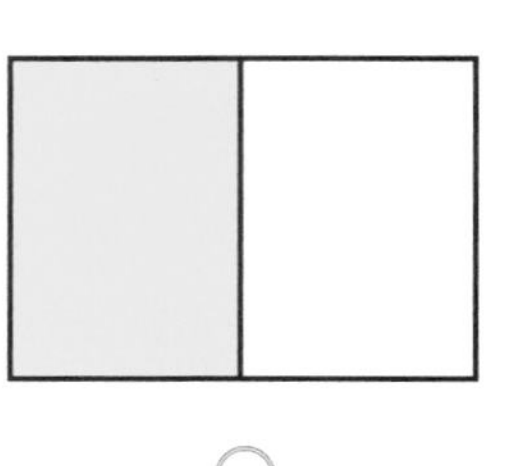

4

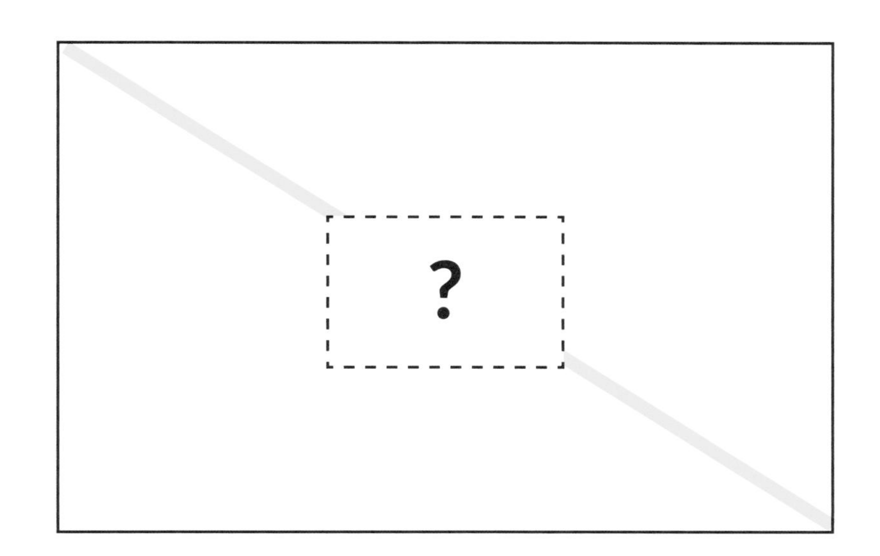

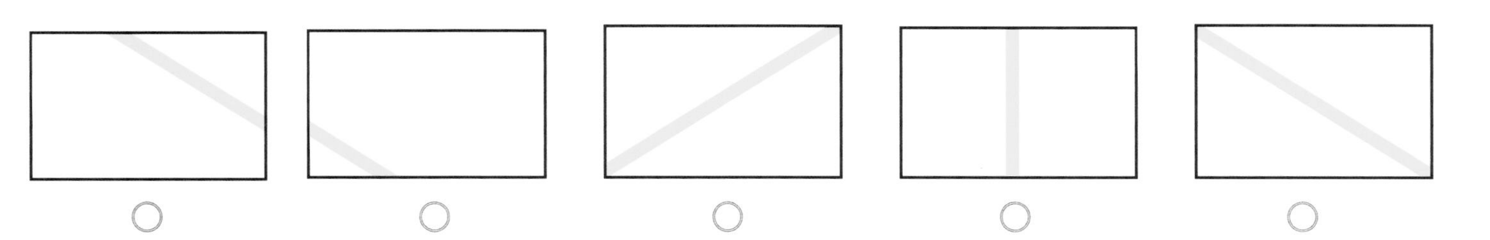

5

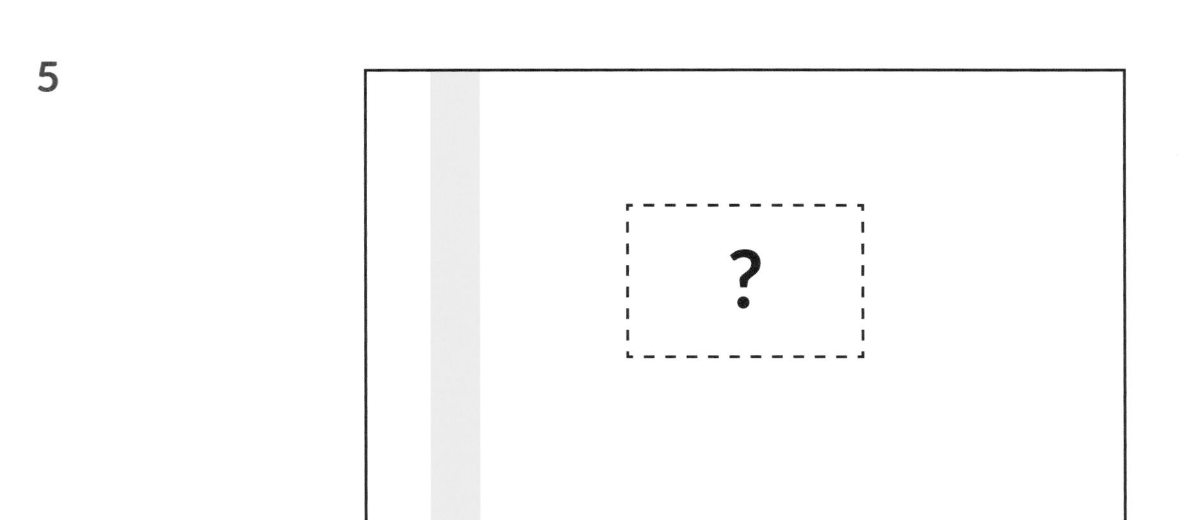

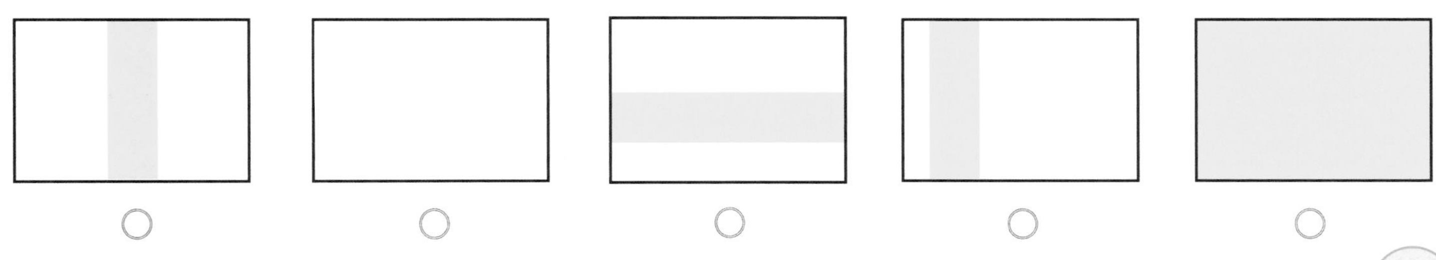

6

?

7

?

8

?

9

?

10

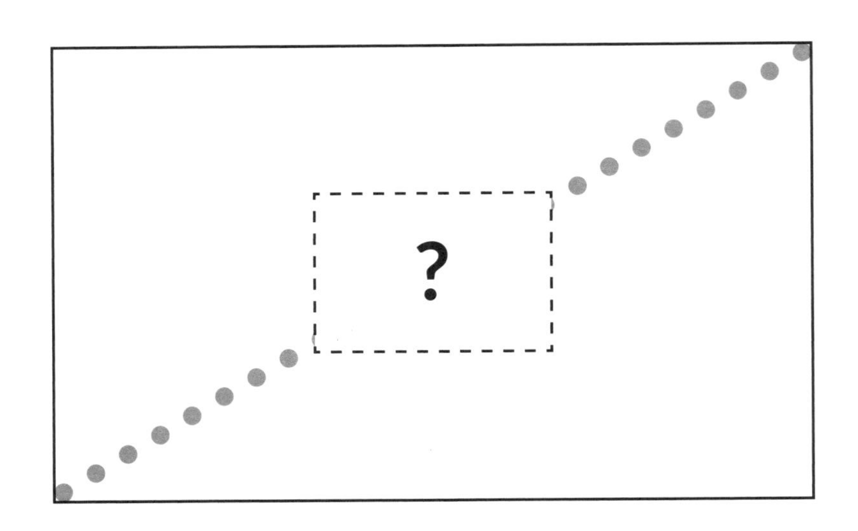

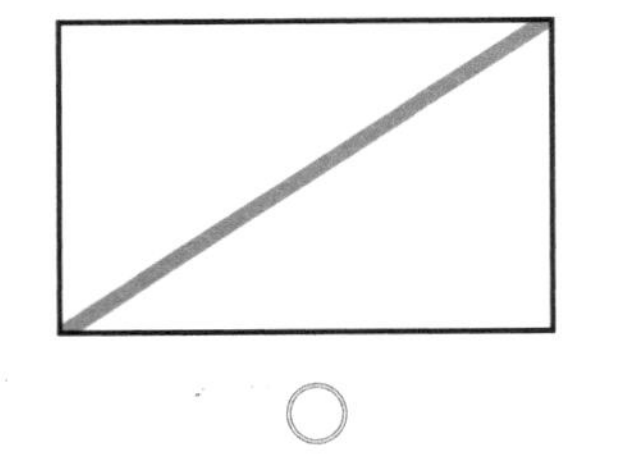

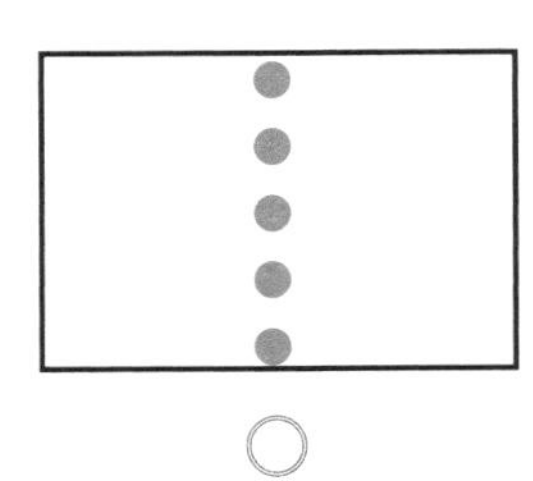
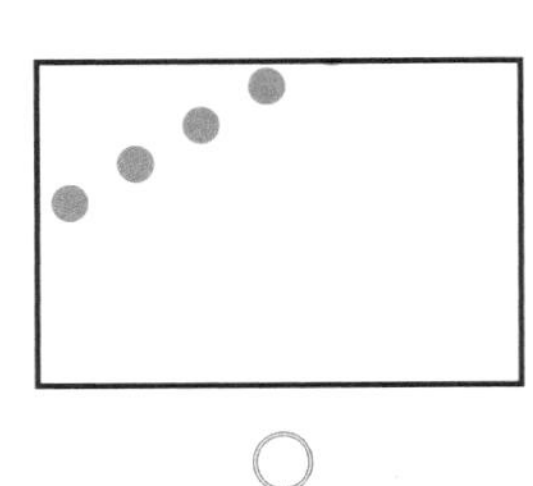
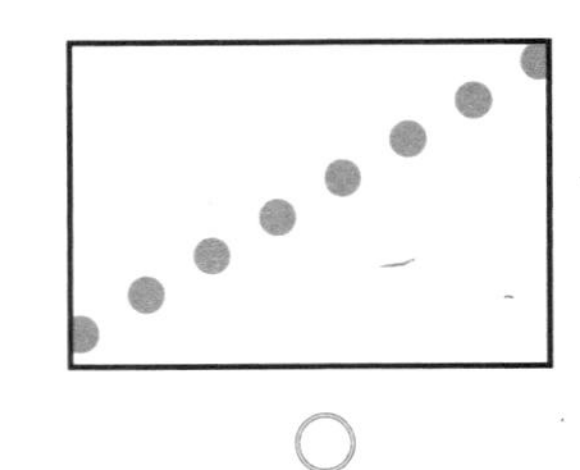

11

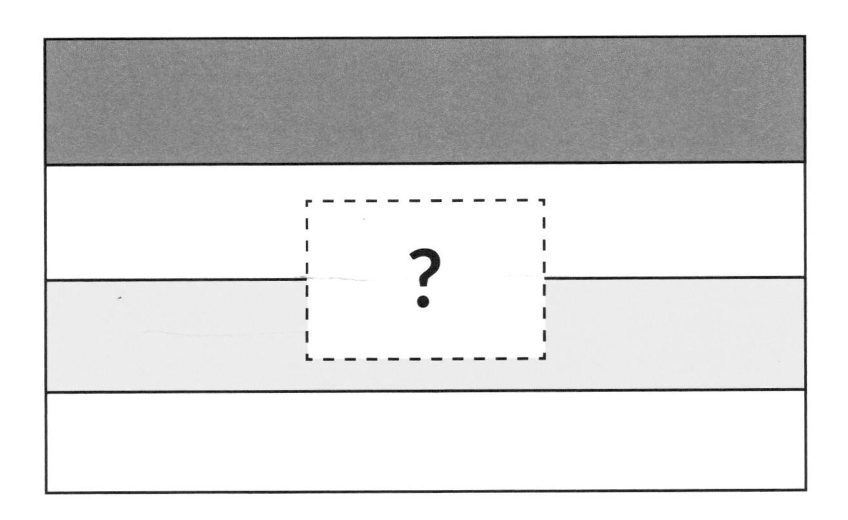

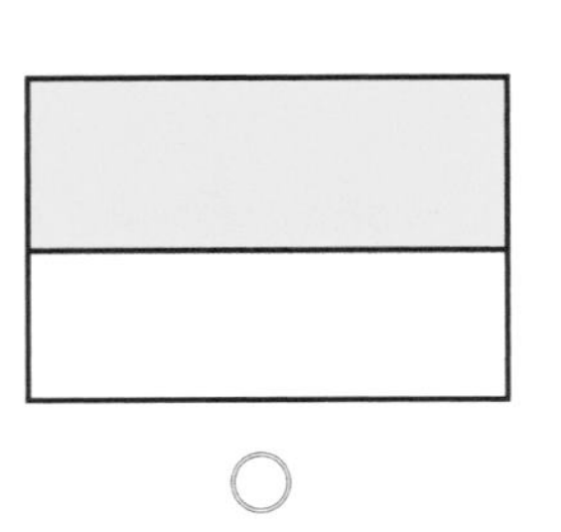
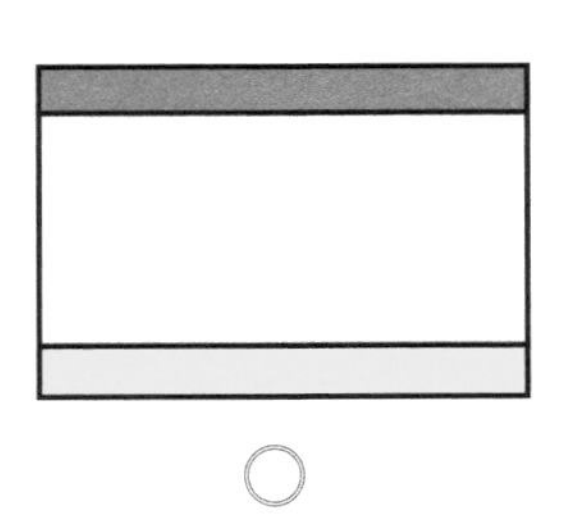
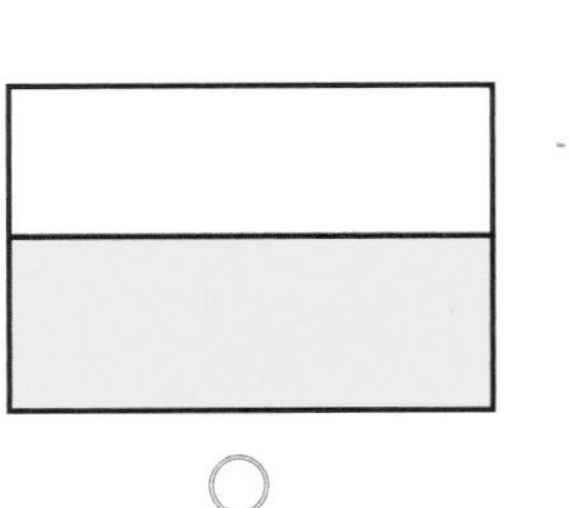
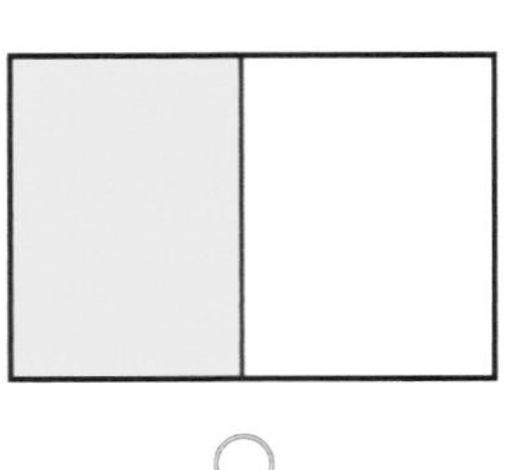

12

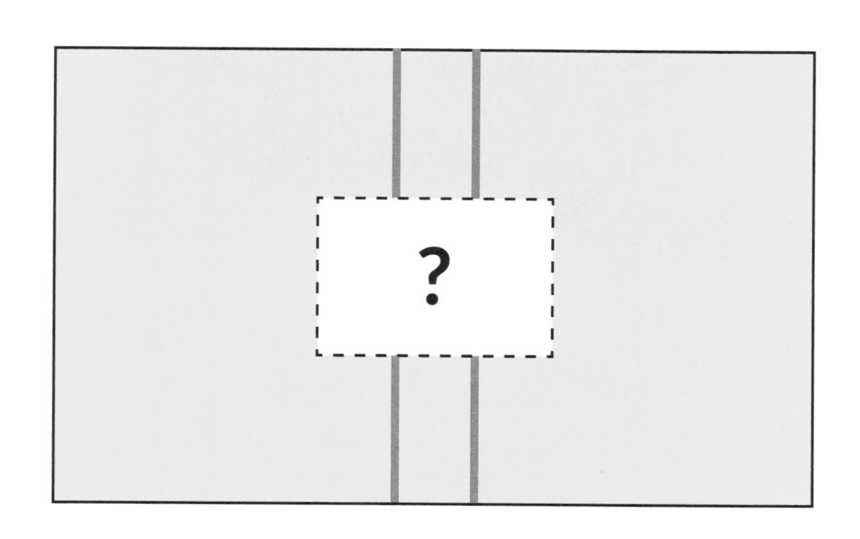

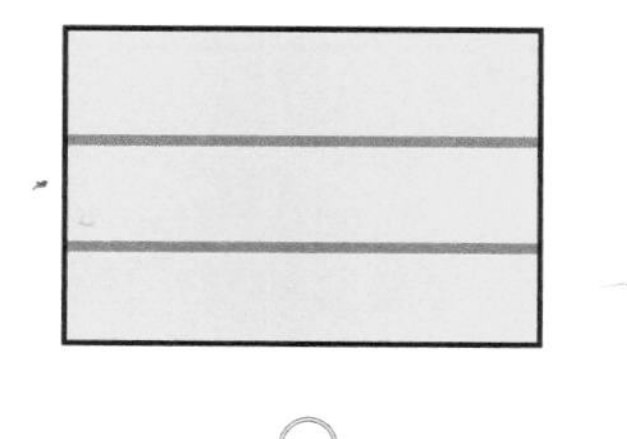
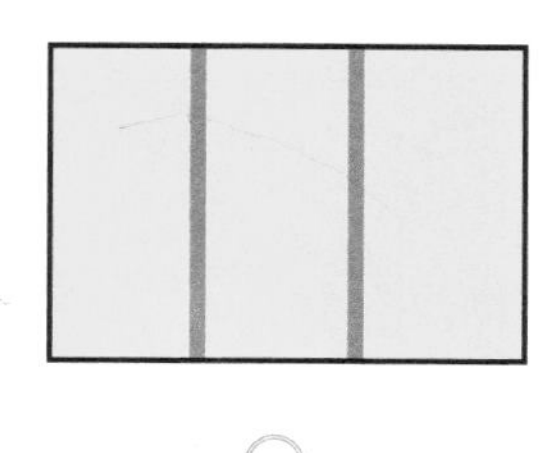
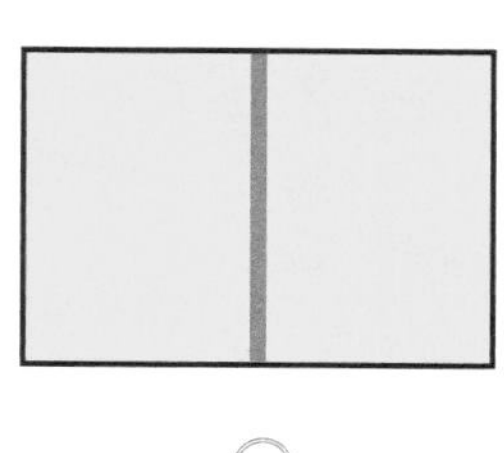
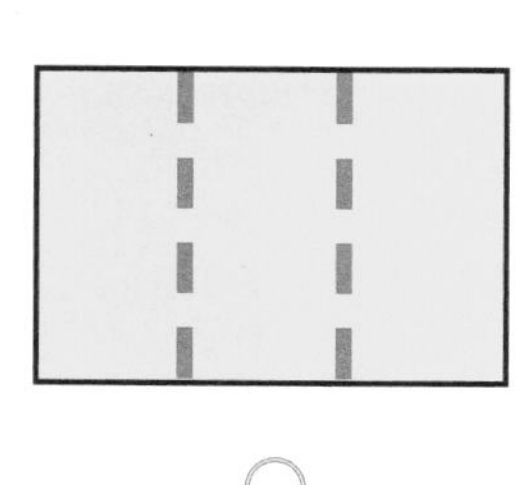
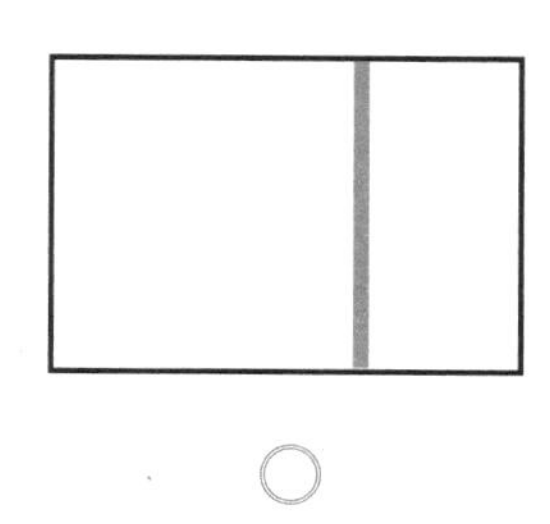

13

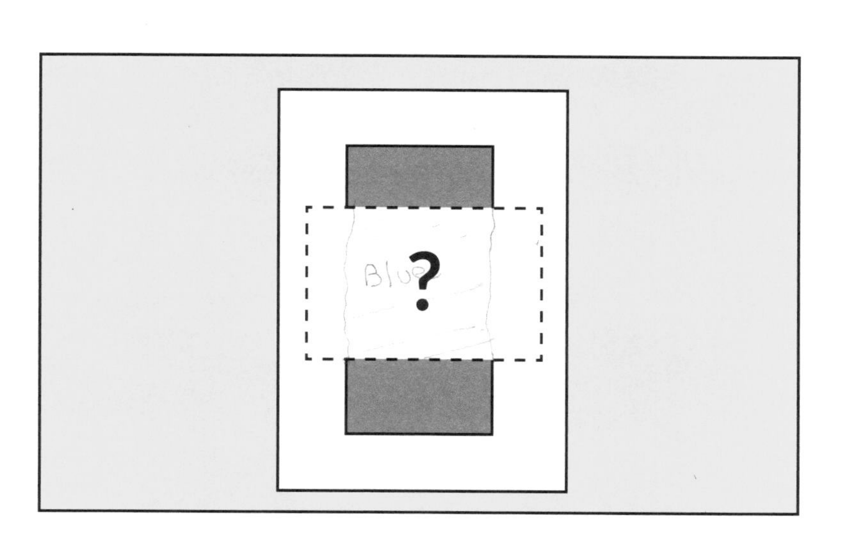

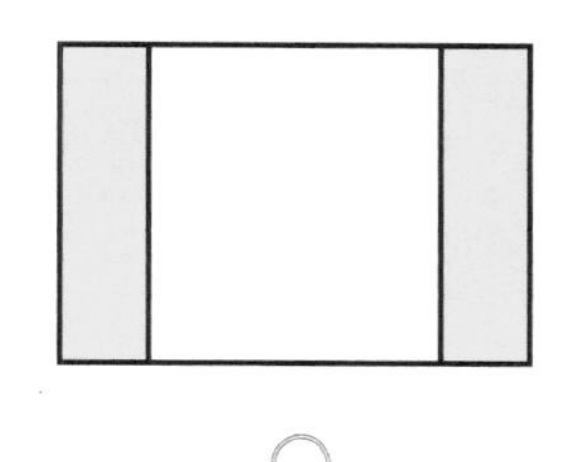
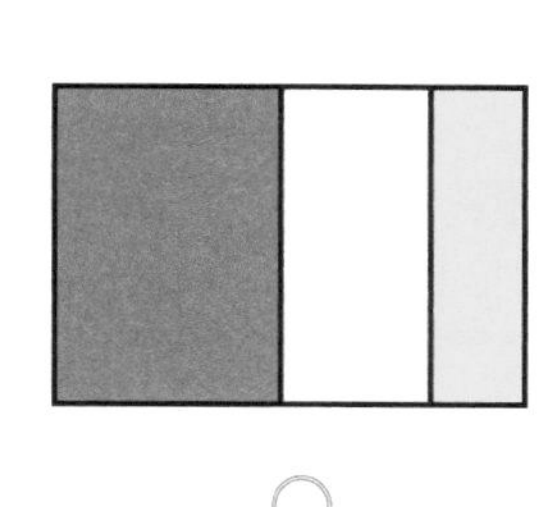
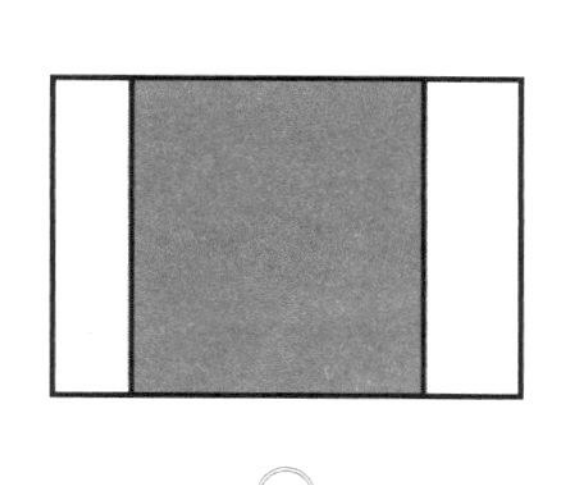
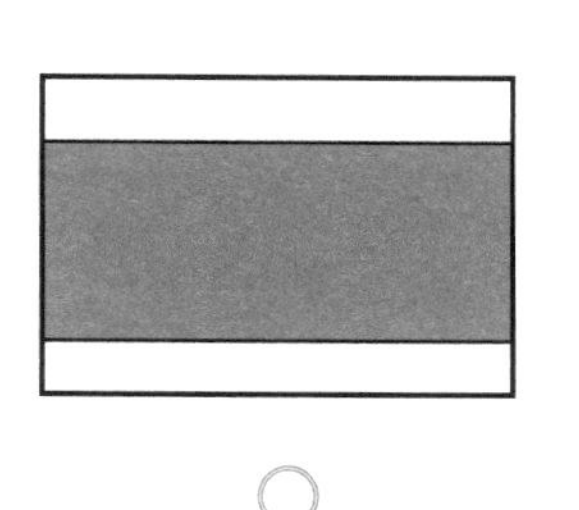
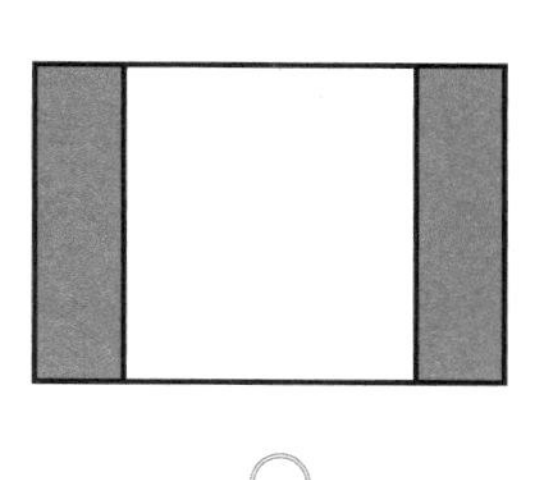

14

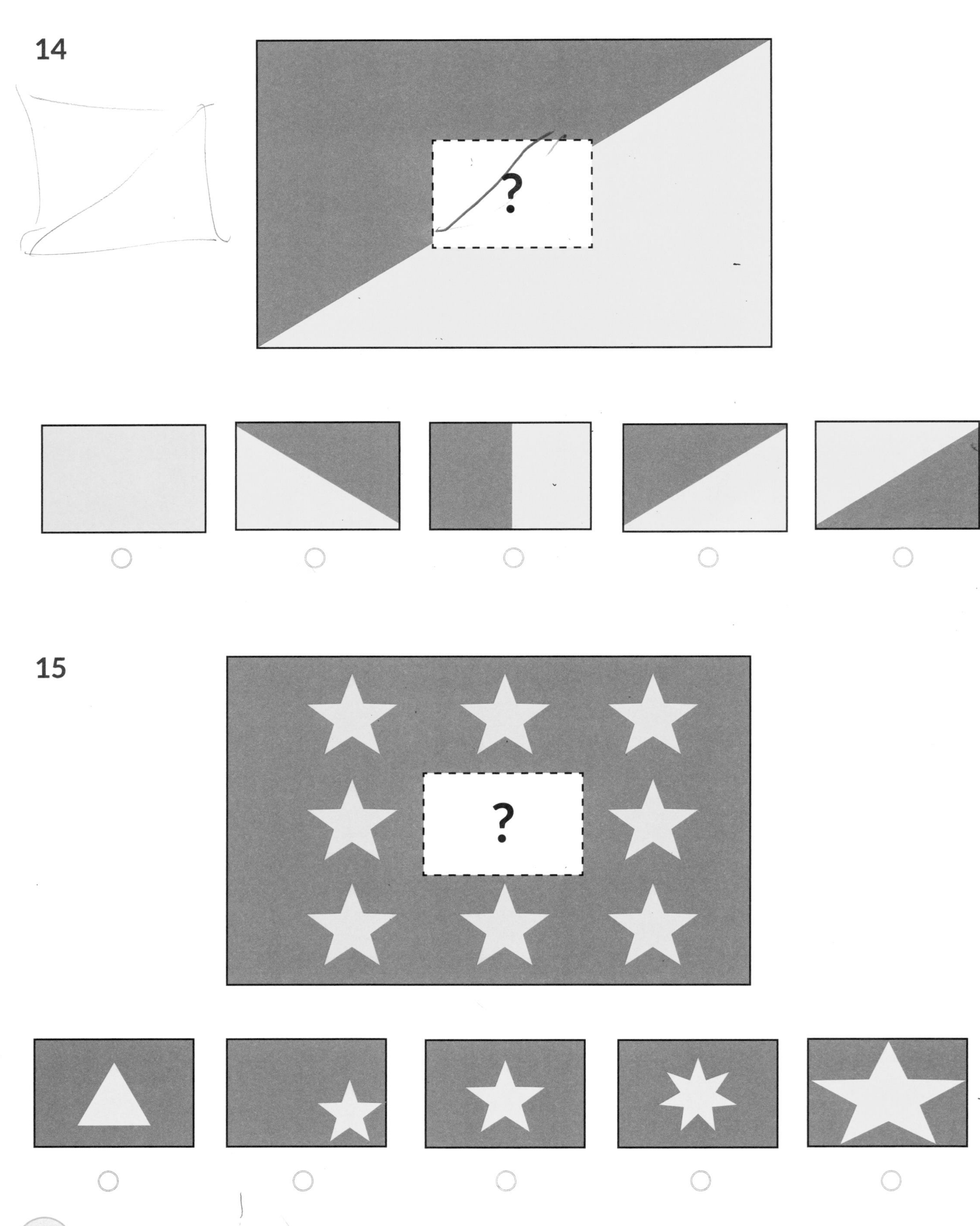

15

16

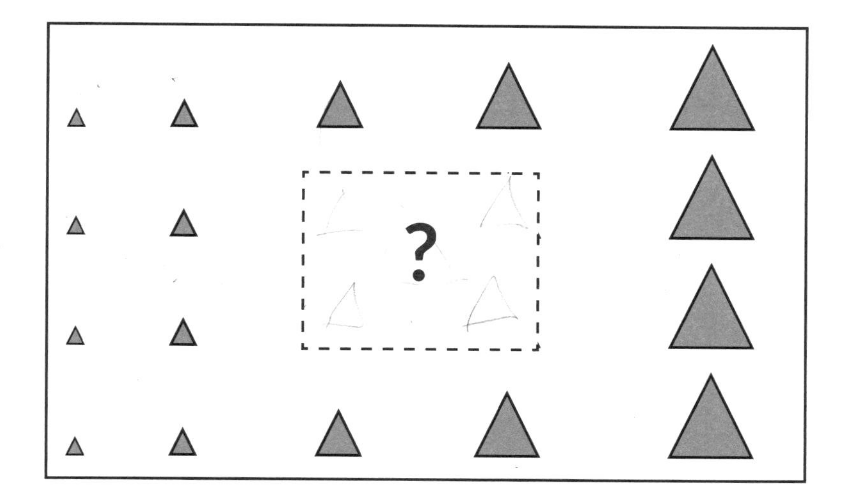

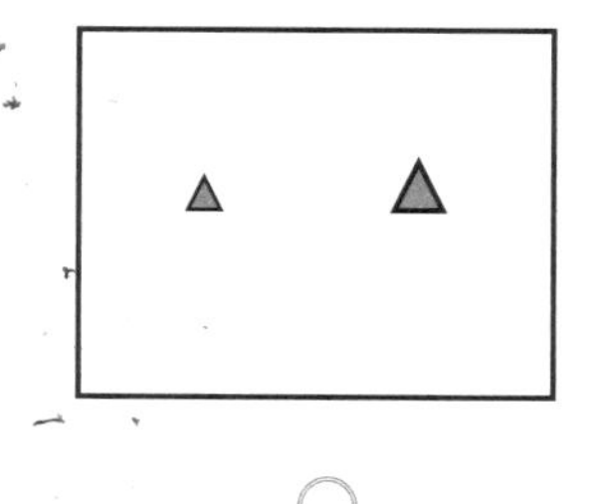
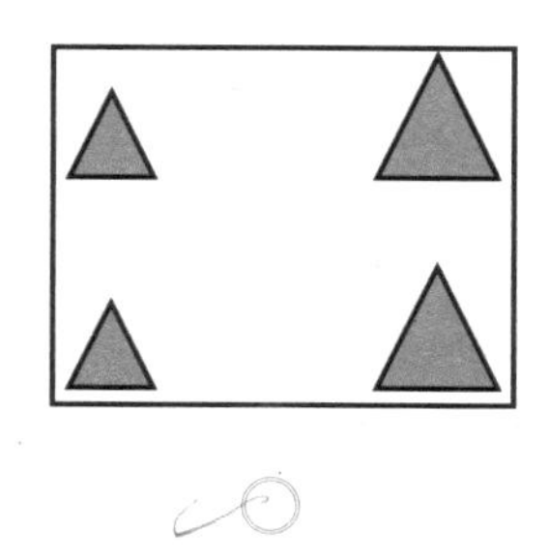
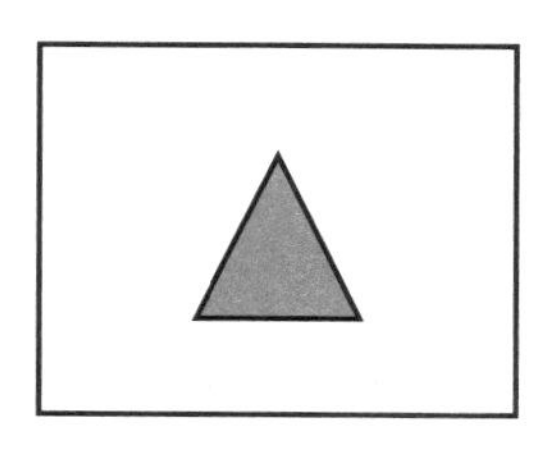
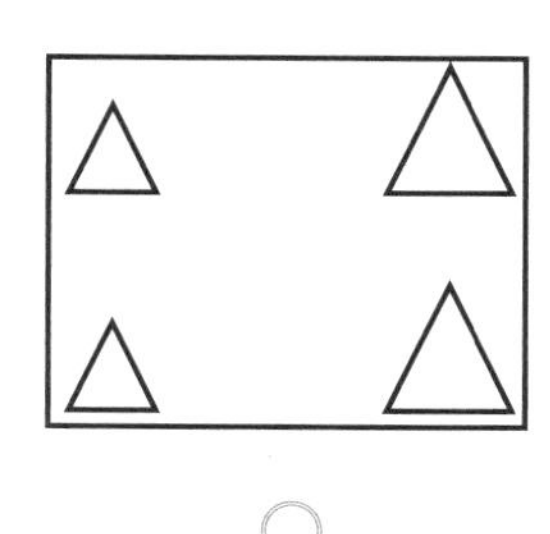
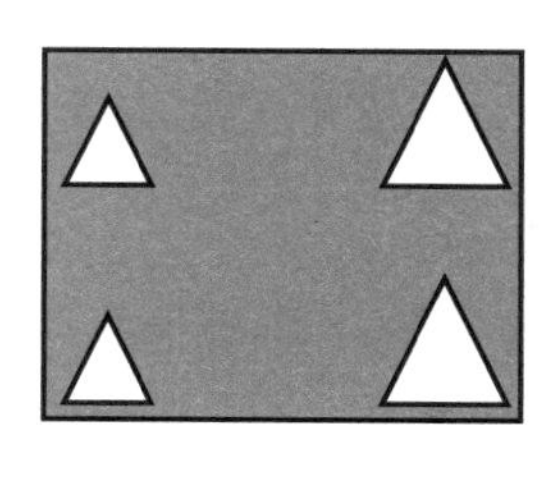

17

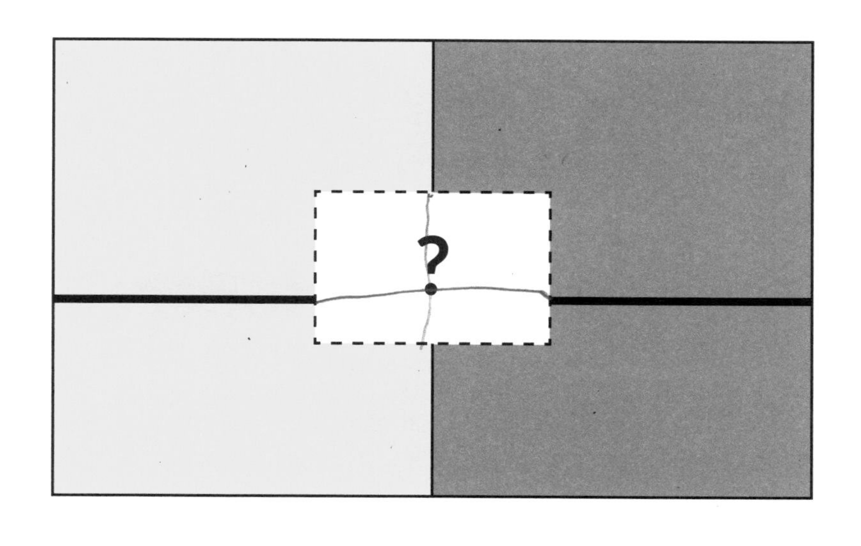

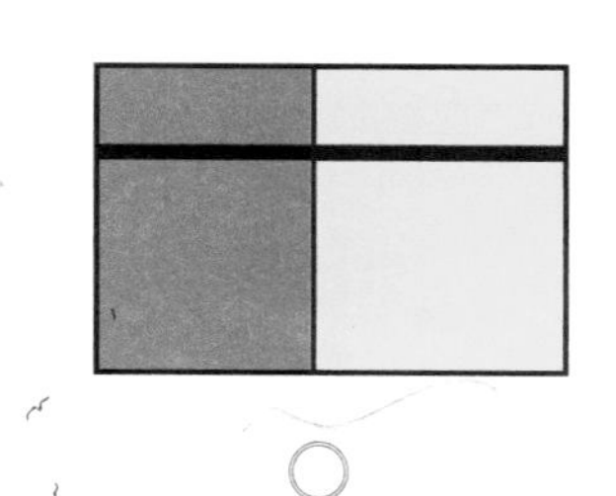
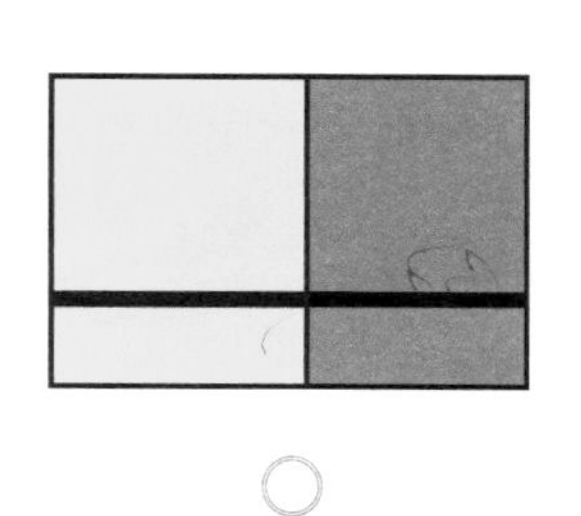
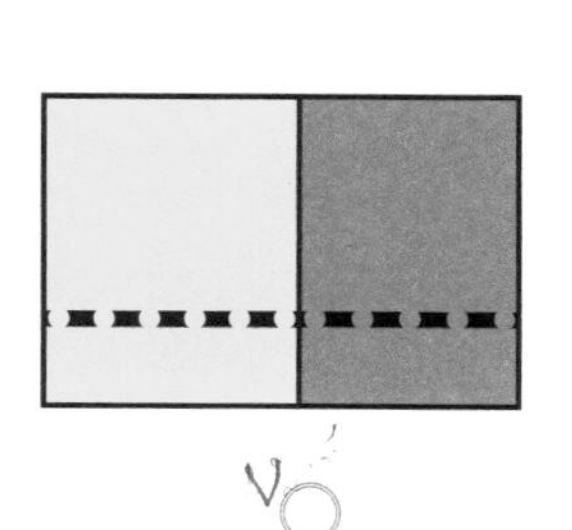
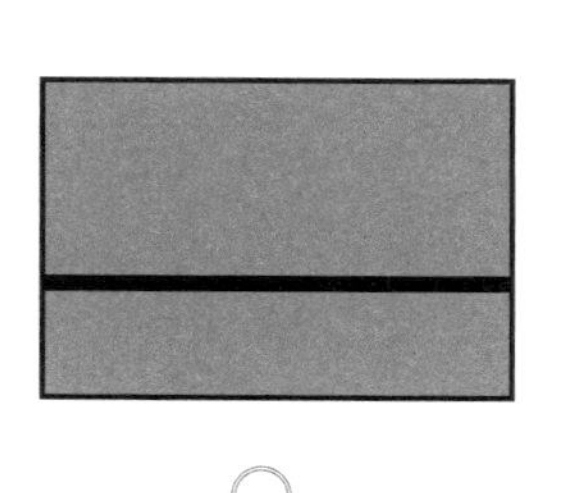
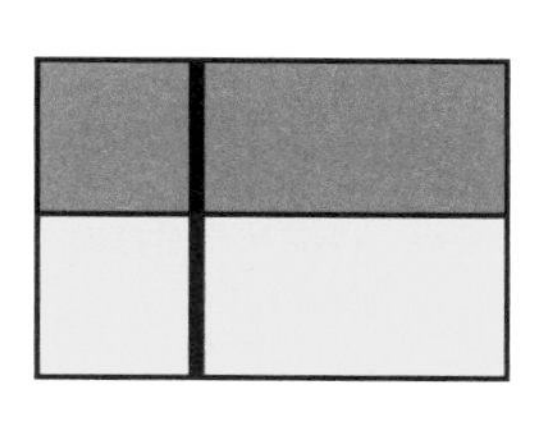

18

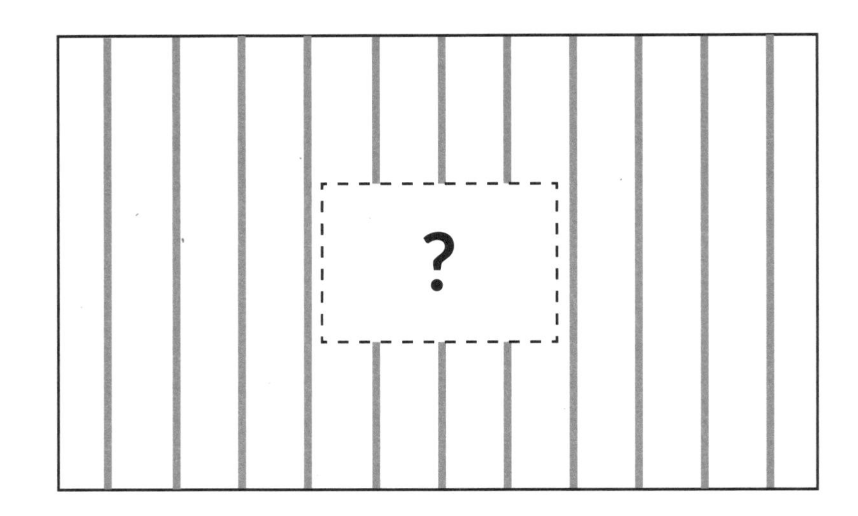

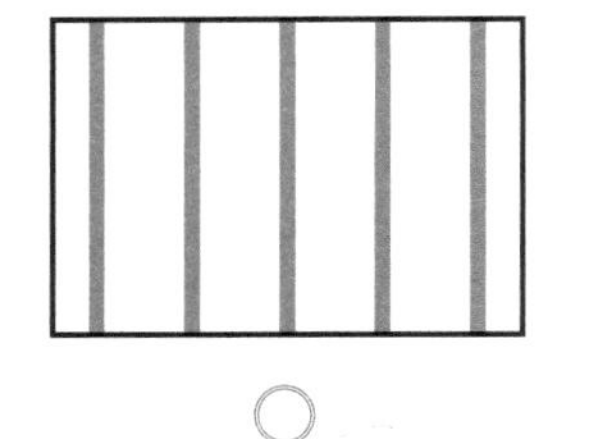

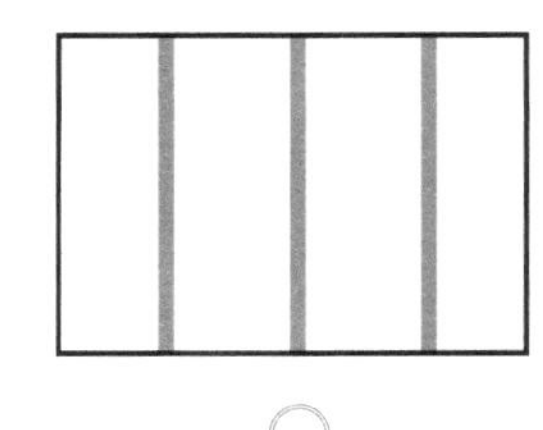
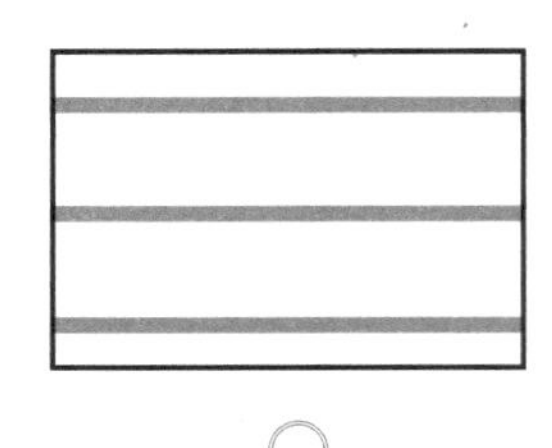
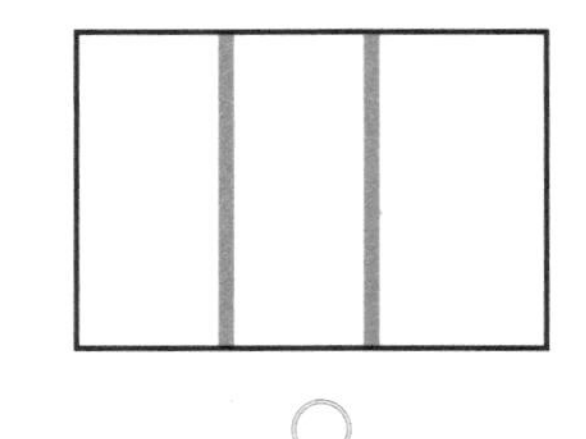

19

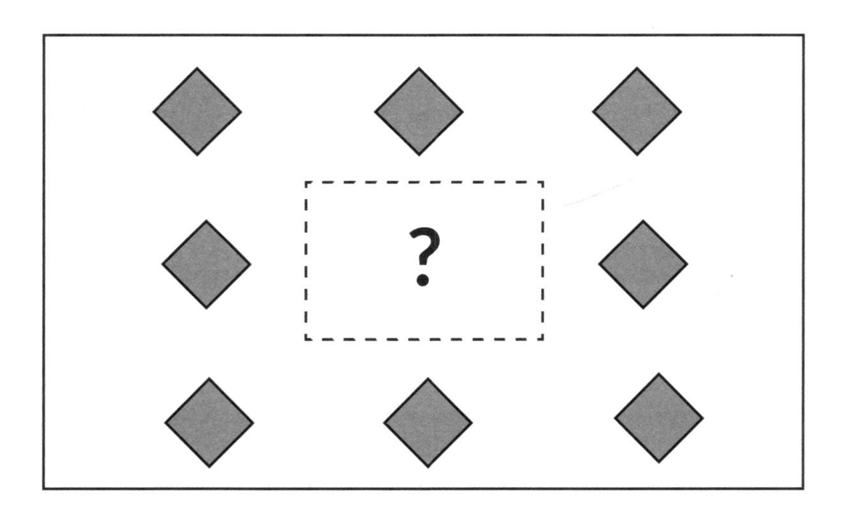

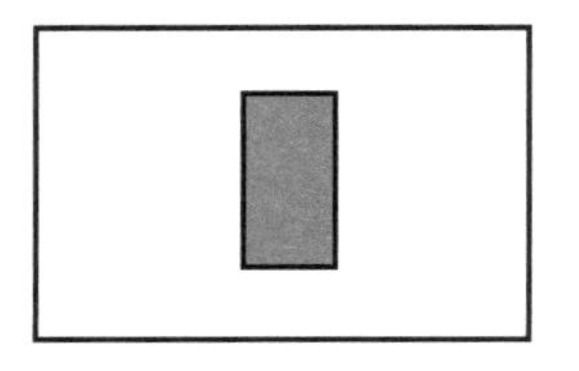
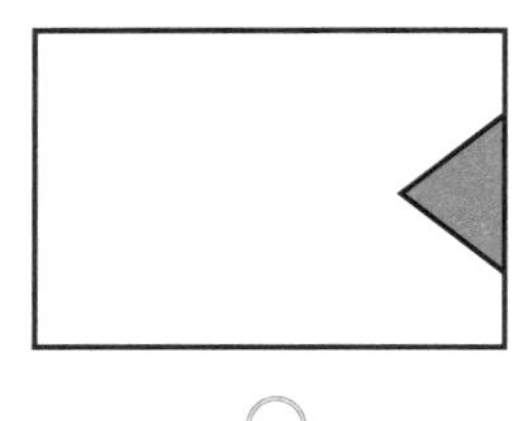
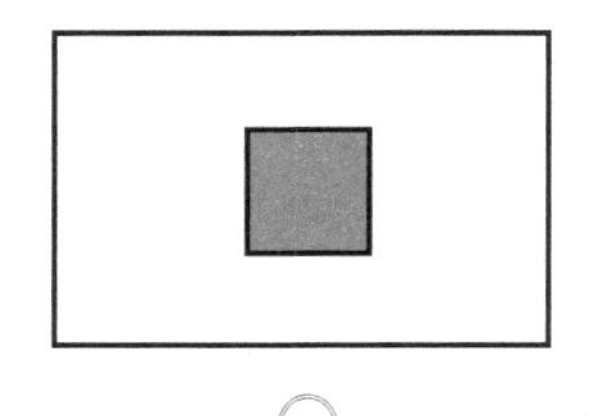
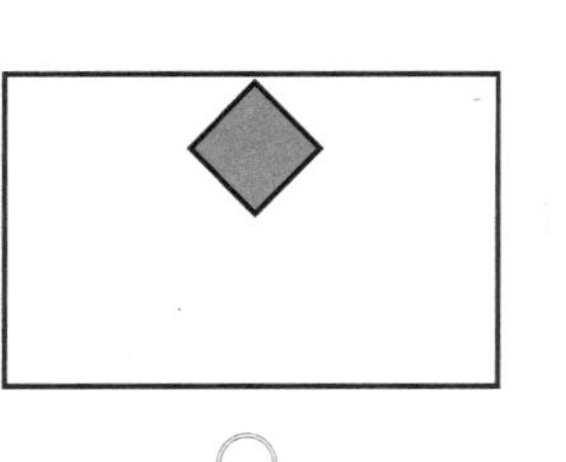
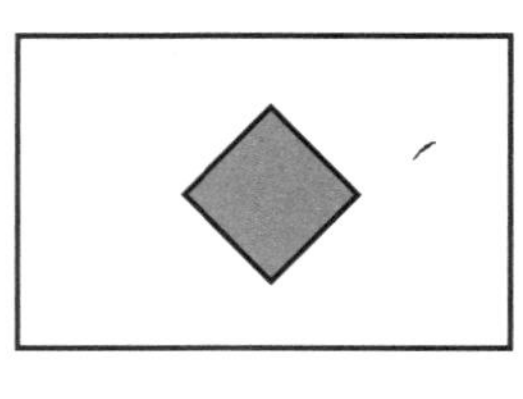

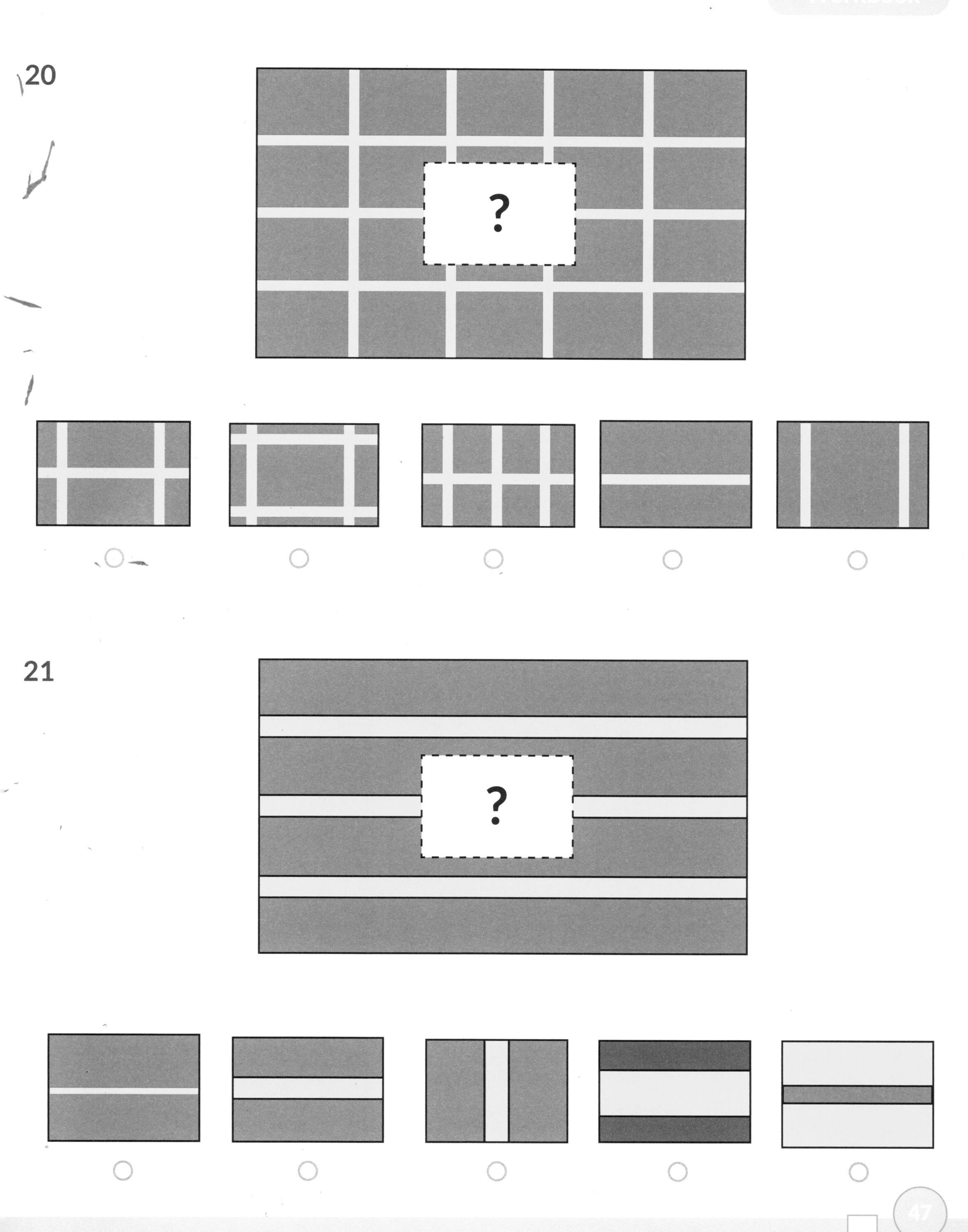
20
?
21
?

22

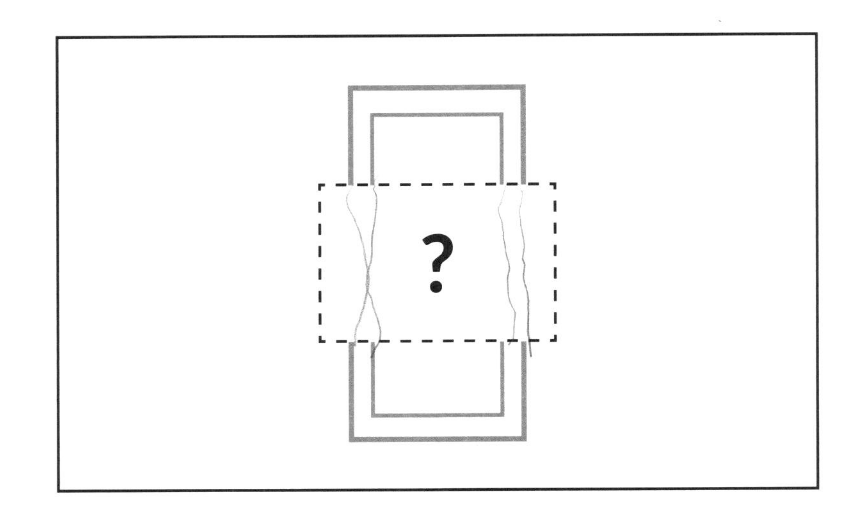

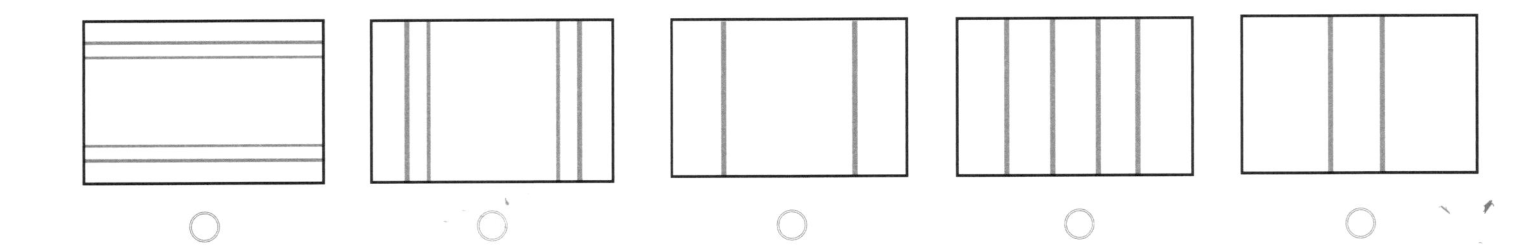

23

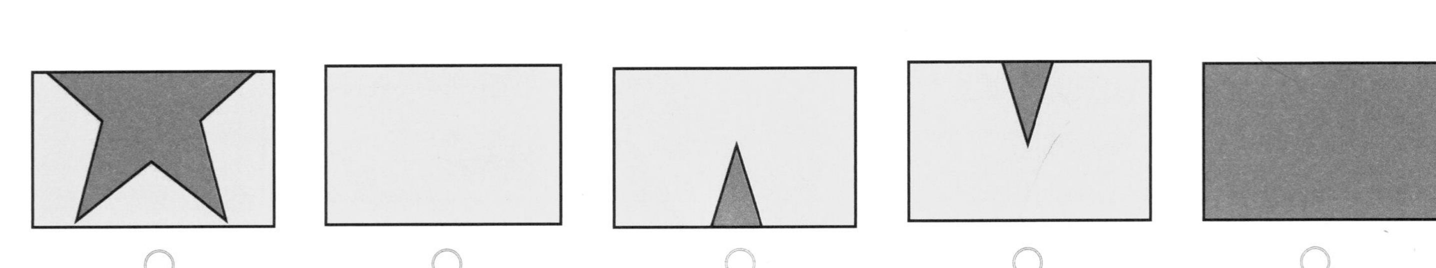

24

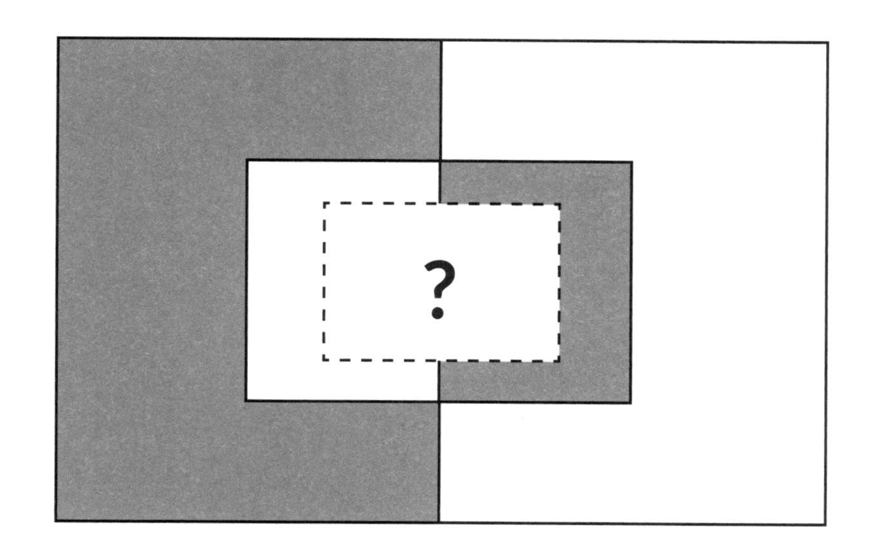

 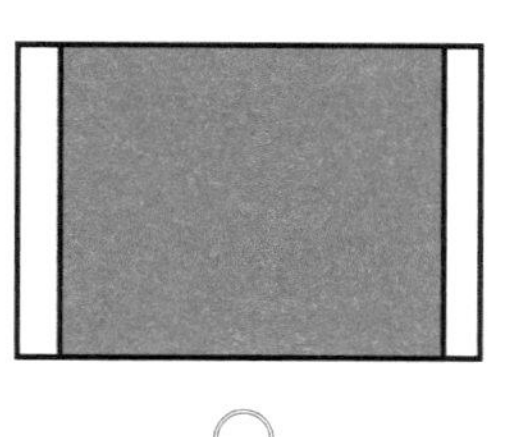 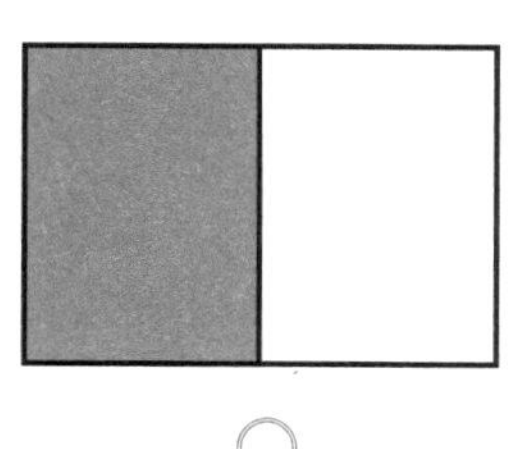 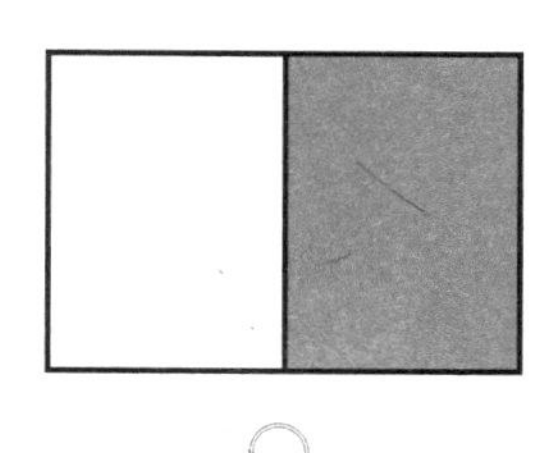 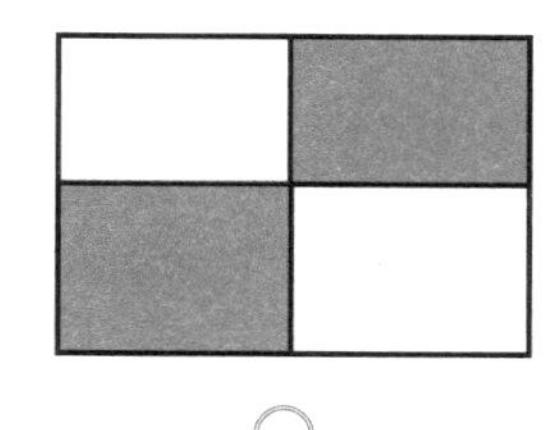

25

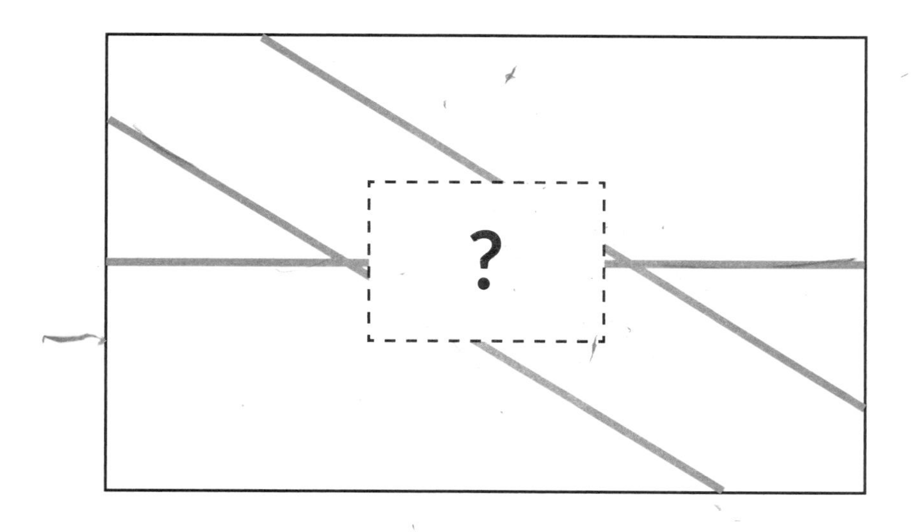

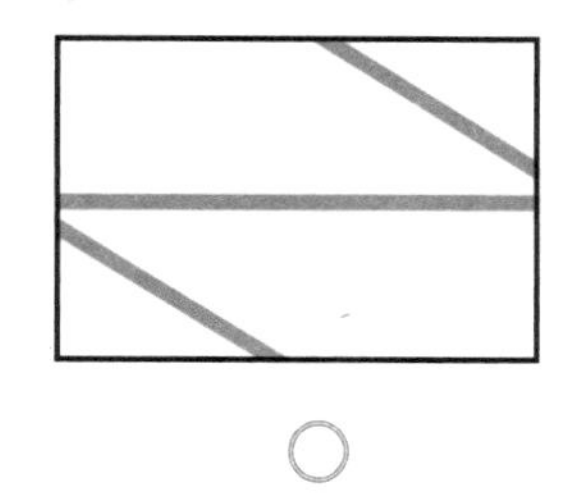 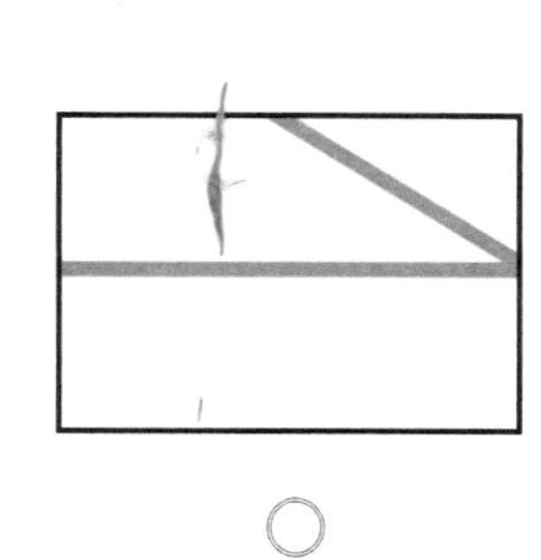 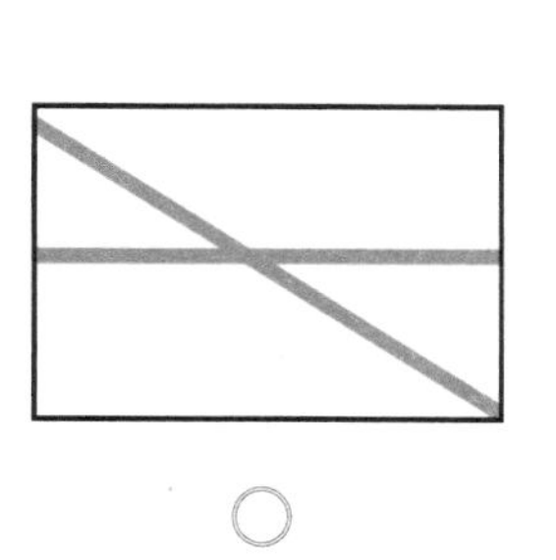 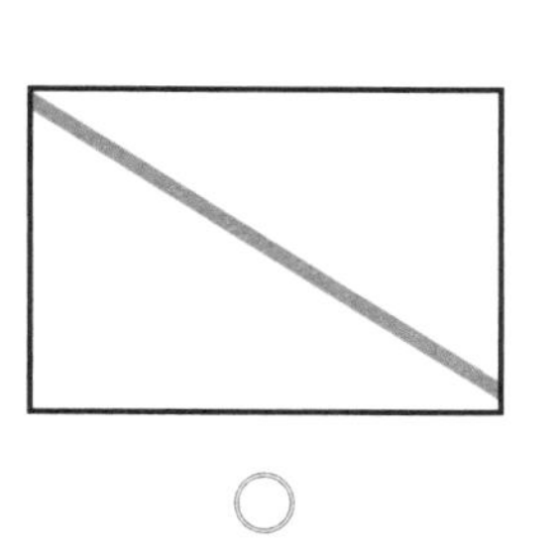 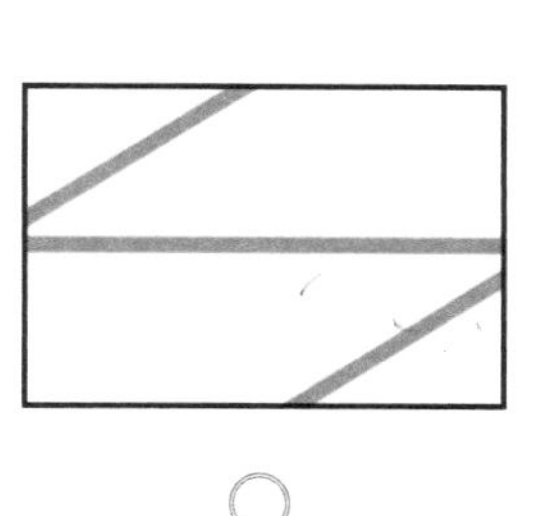

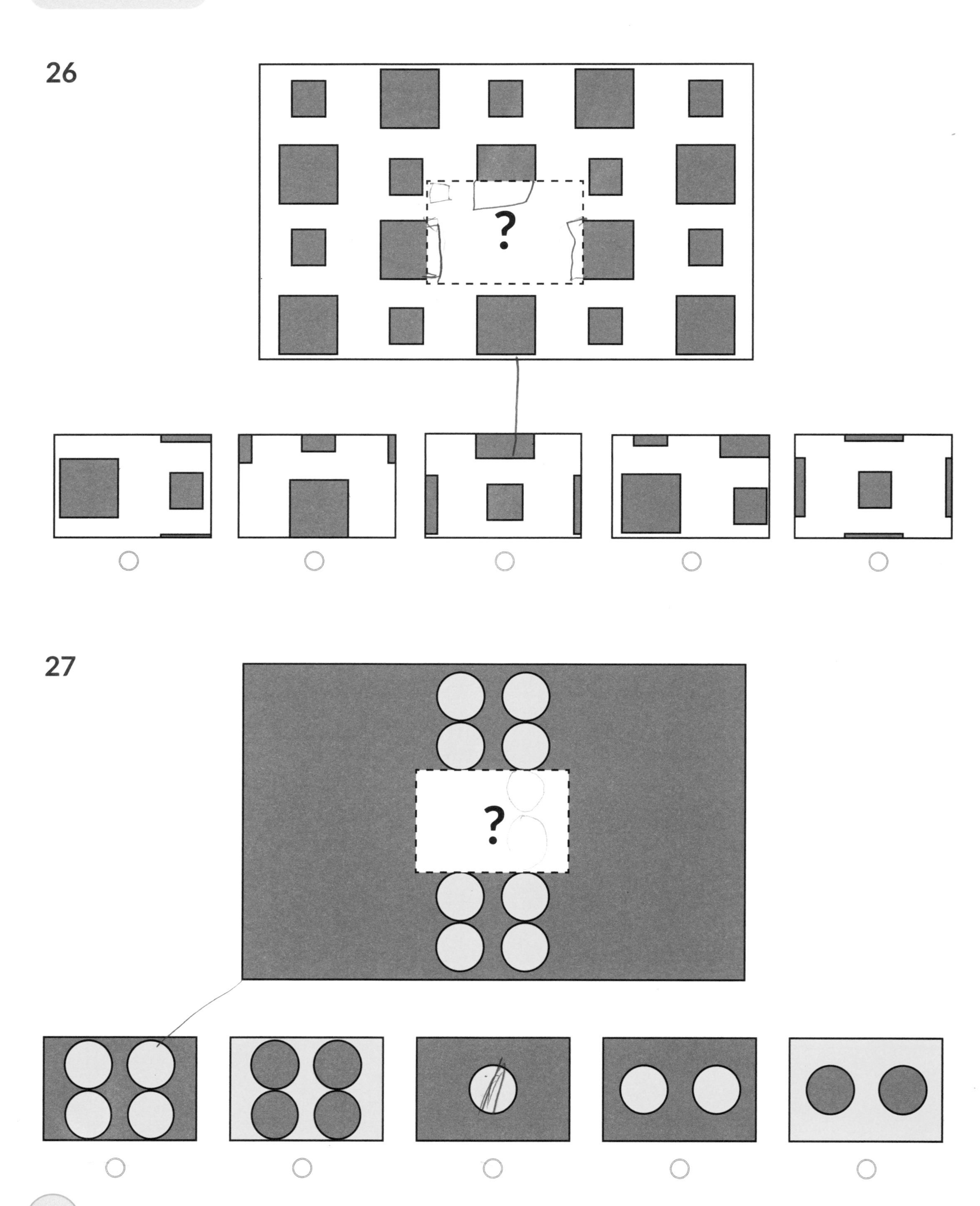
26
?
27
?

28

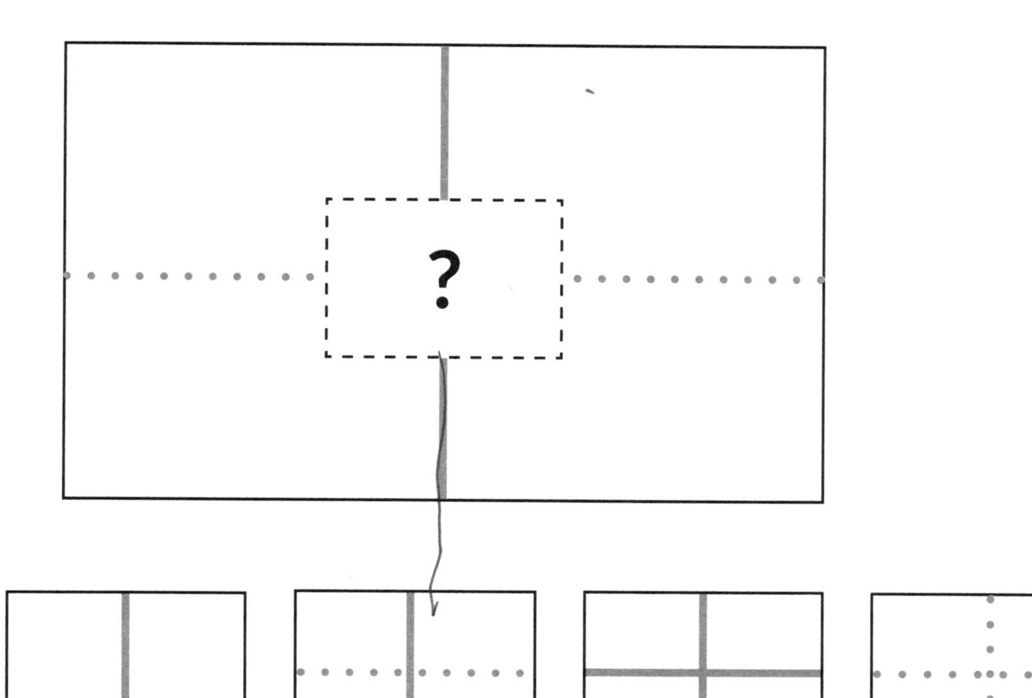

○ ○ ○ ○ ○

29

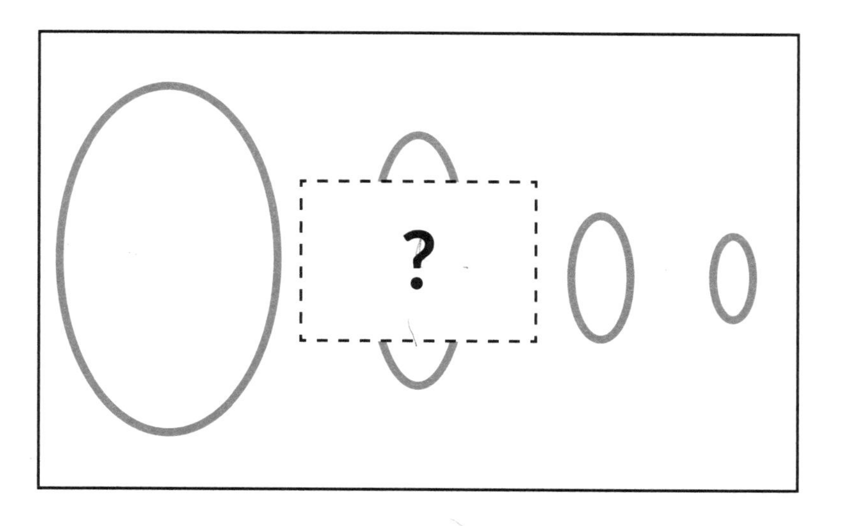

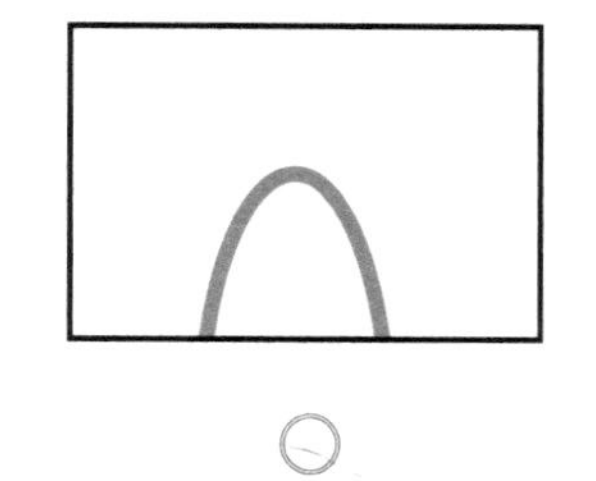 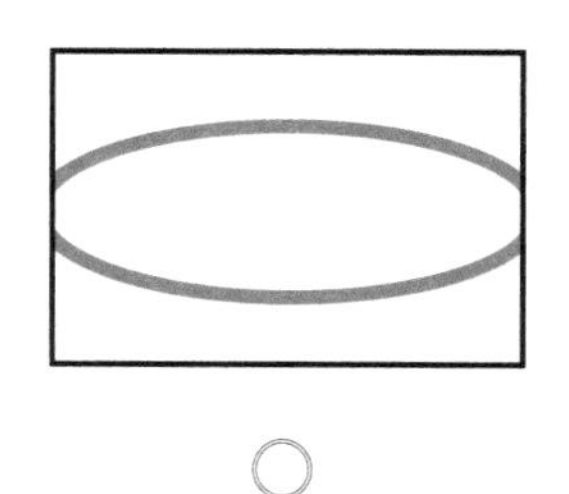 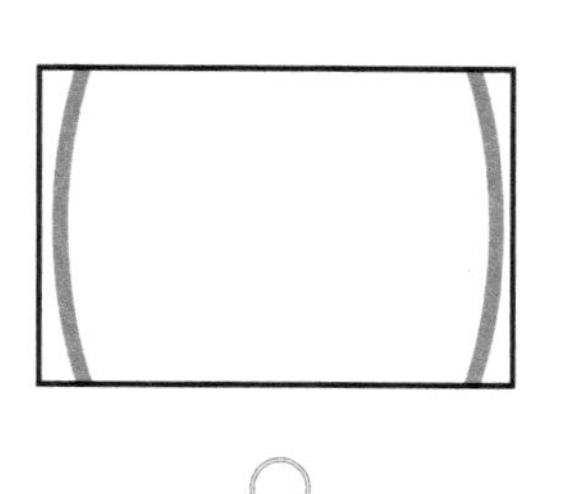 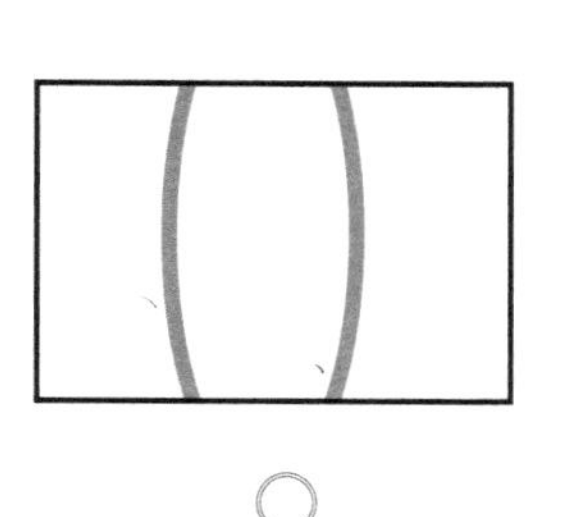 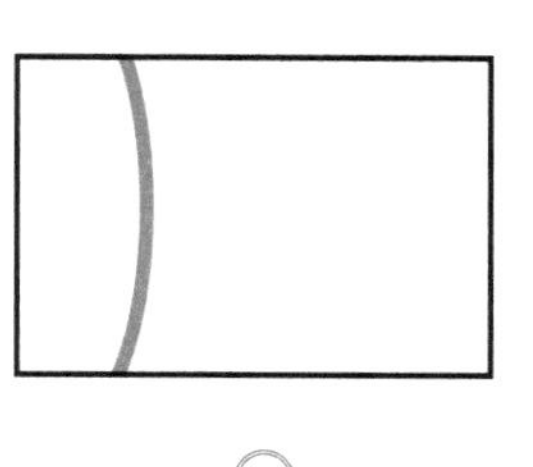

○ ○ ○ ○ ○

30

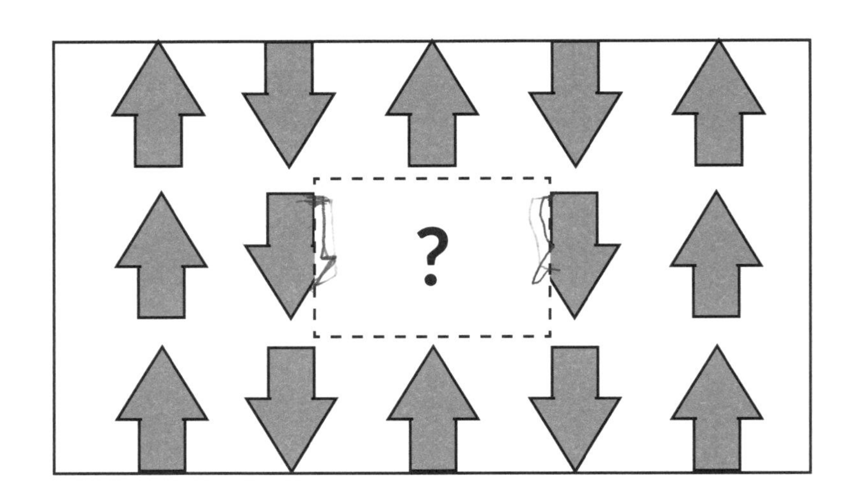

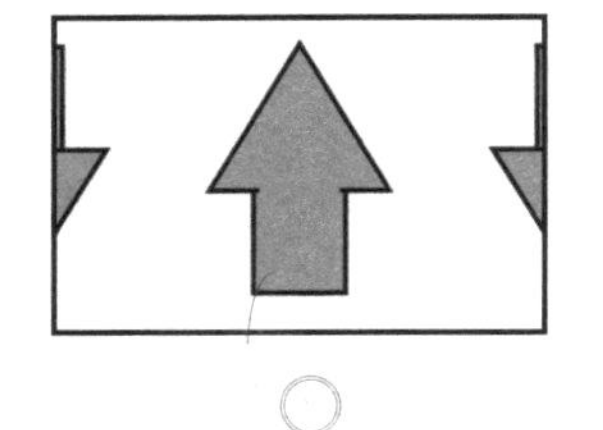
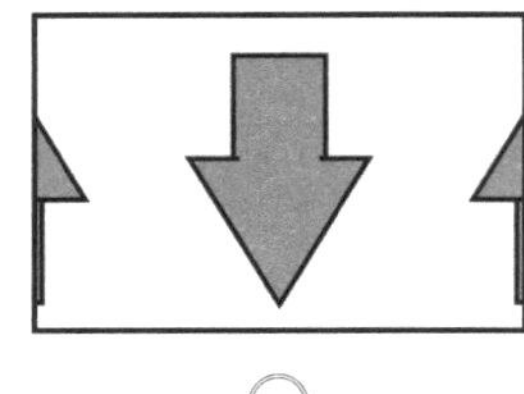
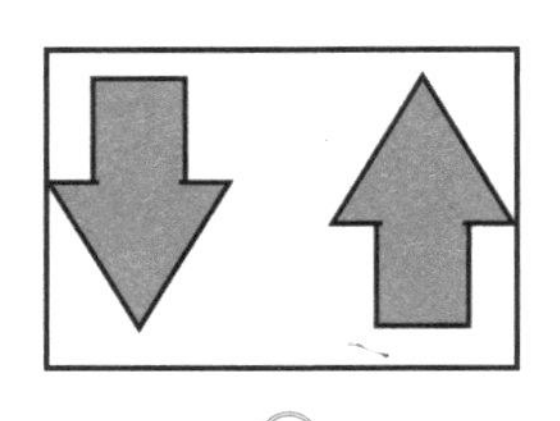
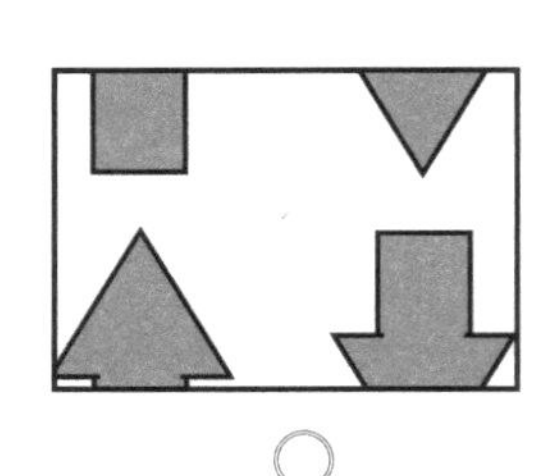
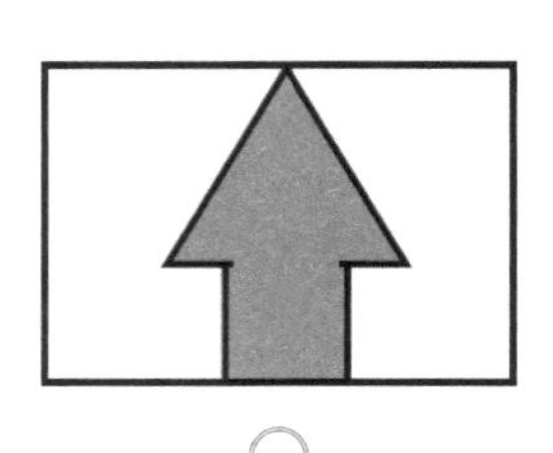

31

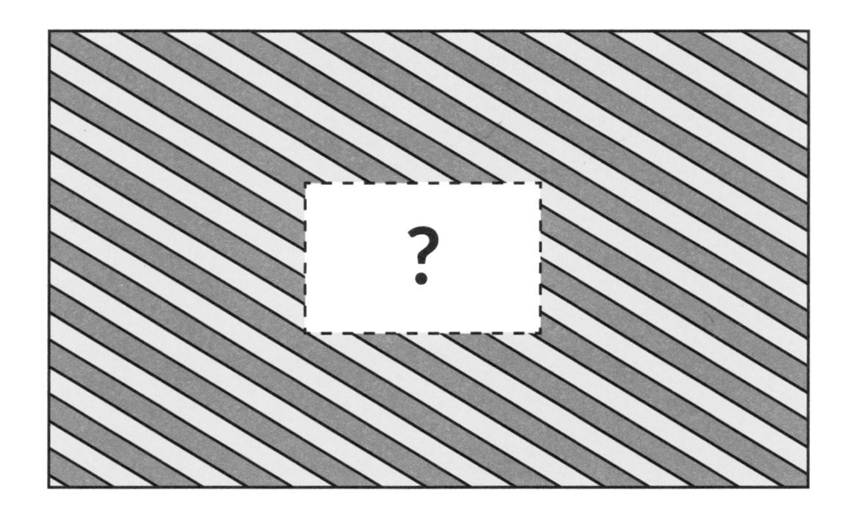

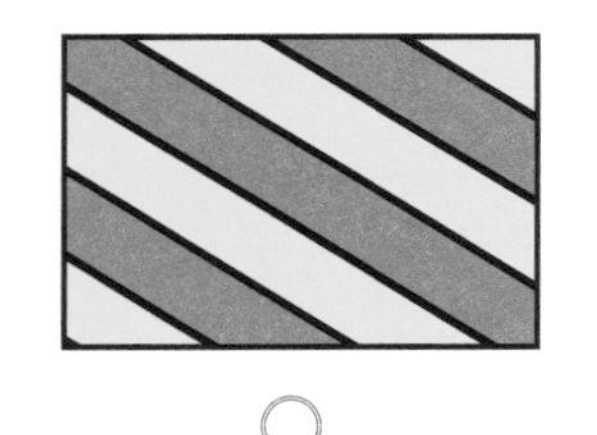
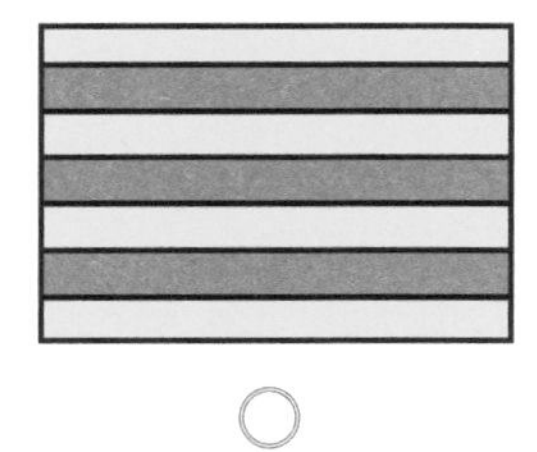
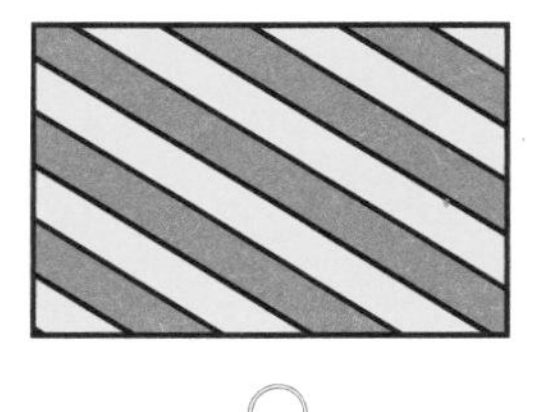
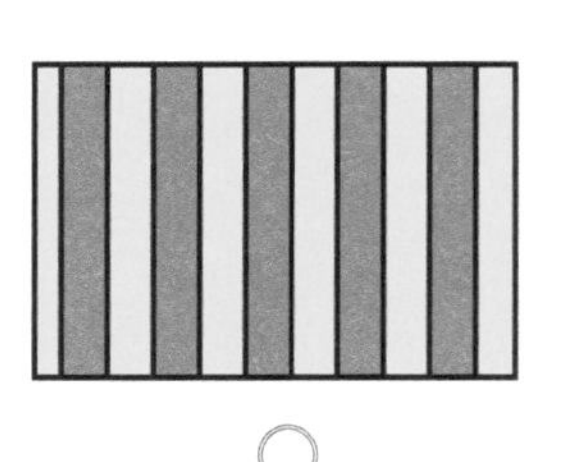
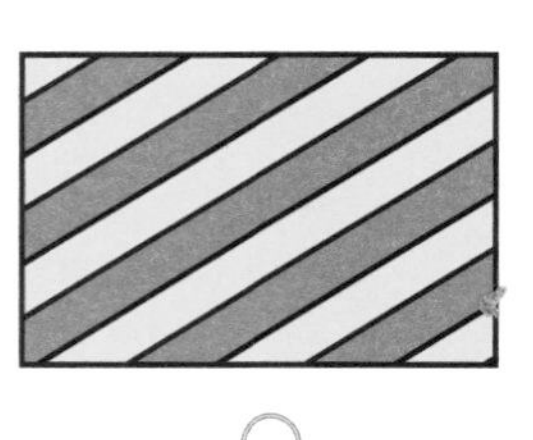

32

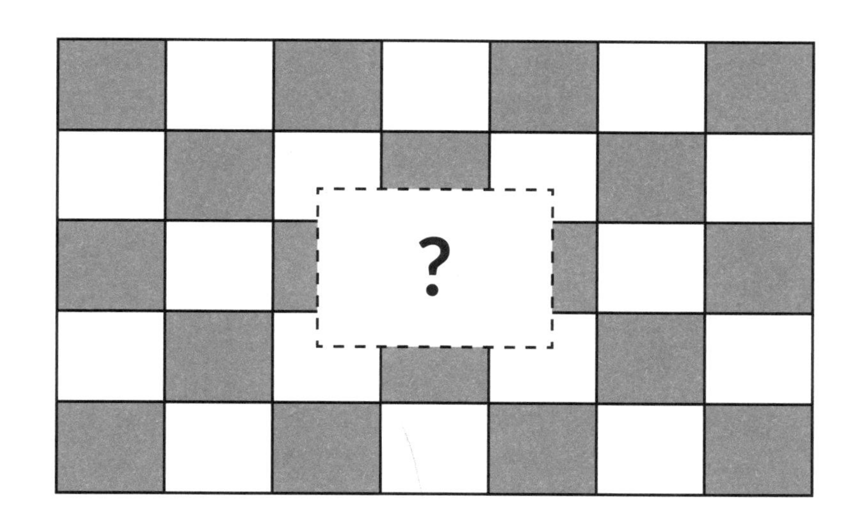

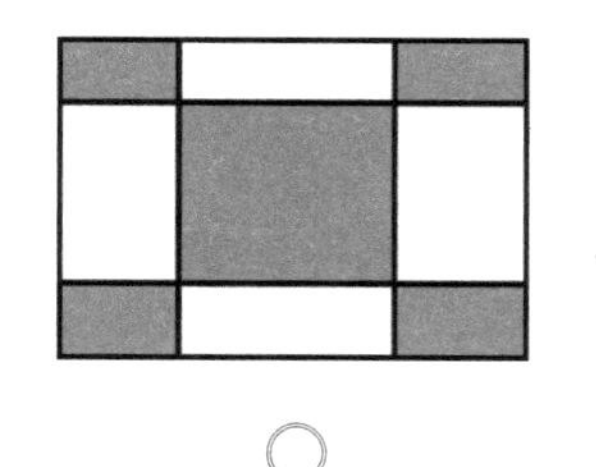
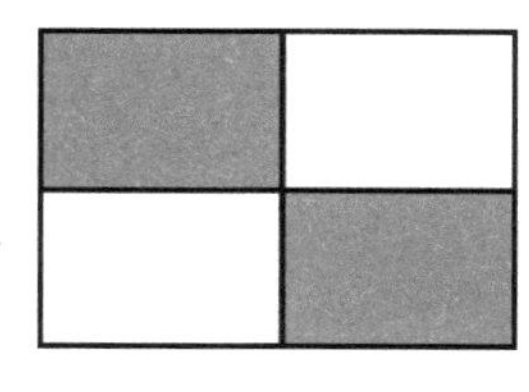
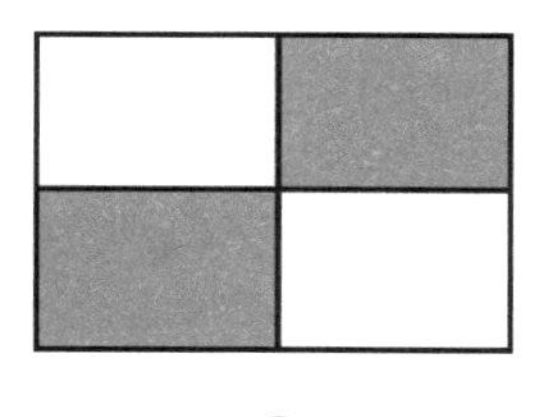
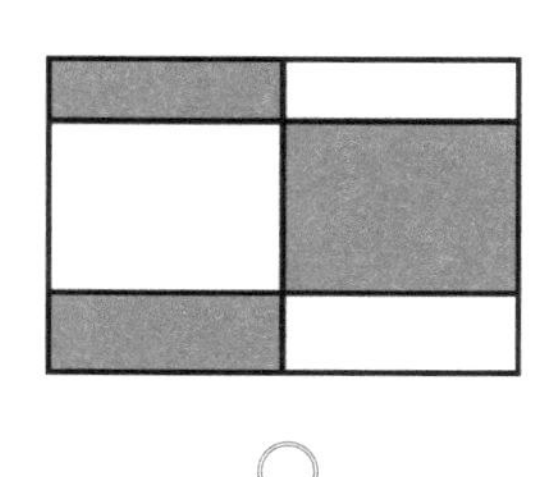
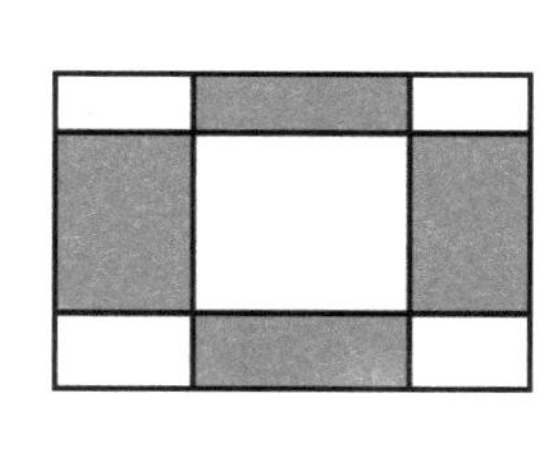

33

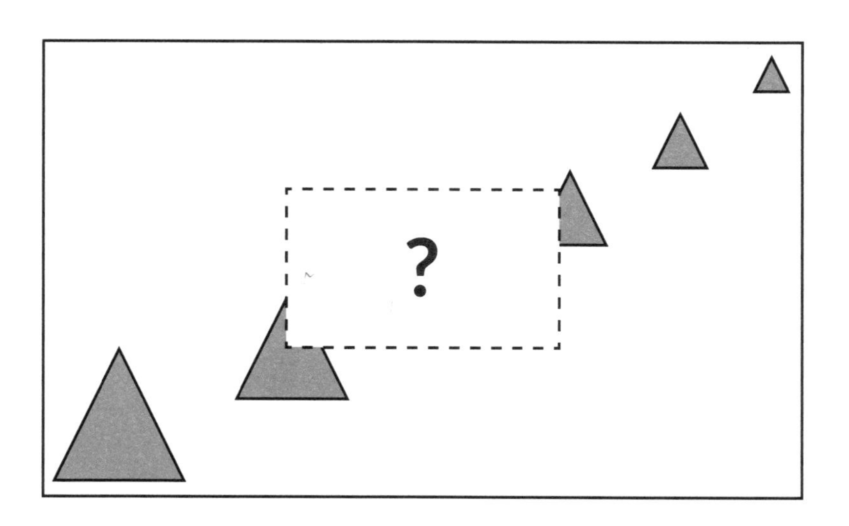

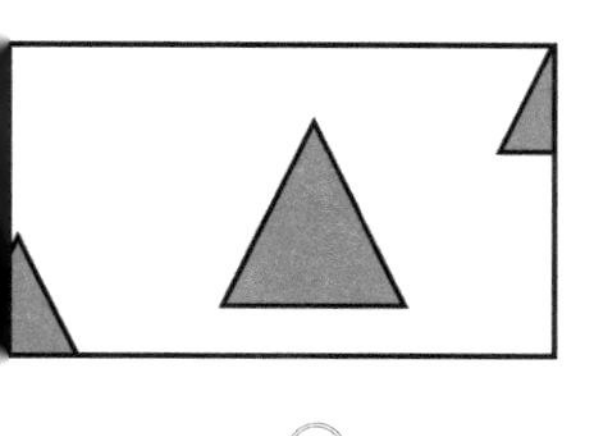
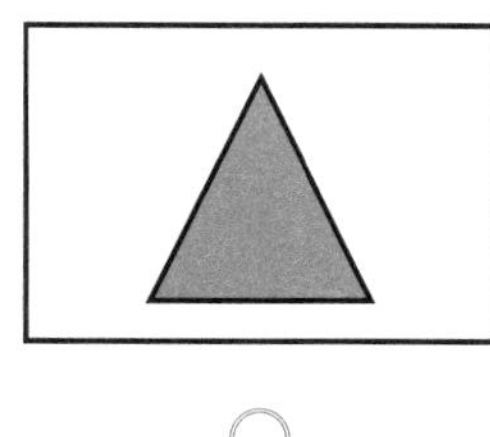
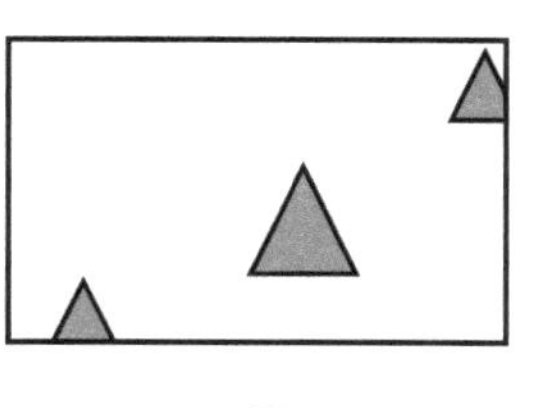
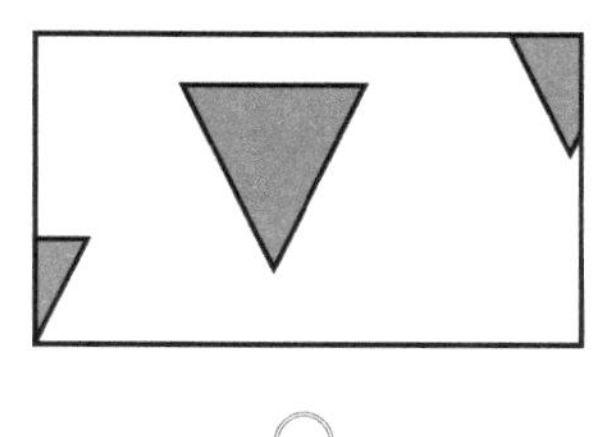
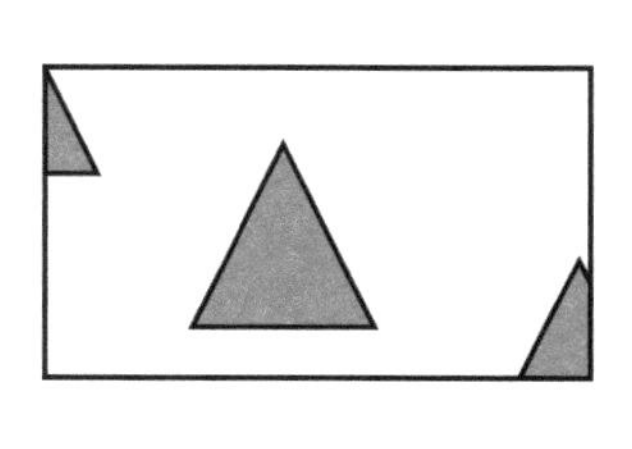

MAY SAYS, "YOU'RE DOING GREAT. LET'S DO SOME MORE!"

Directions: Look at these pictures that are inside the boxes. These belong together in some way. One box is missing. (Point to the bottom box that has a question mark.)

Now, look below at the row of answer choices. (Point to the row of answer choices.)

Which one would go here? (Point to the bottom box that has a question mark again.)

Parent note: Analogies are a new kind of "puzzle" for most young kids. They compare sets of items, and the way they are related can easily be missed at first. Work through these together with your child so (s)he sees how the top set is related. Together, try to come up with a "rule" to describe how the top set is related. Then, look at the picture on the bottom. (The one next to the question mark.) Take this "rule," use it together with the picture on the bottom, and figure out which of the answer choices would follow that same rule.

1

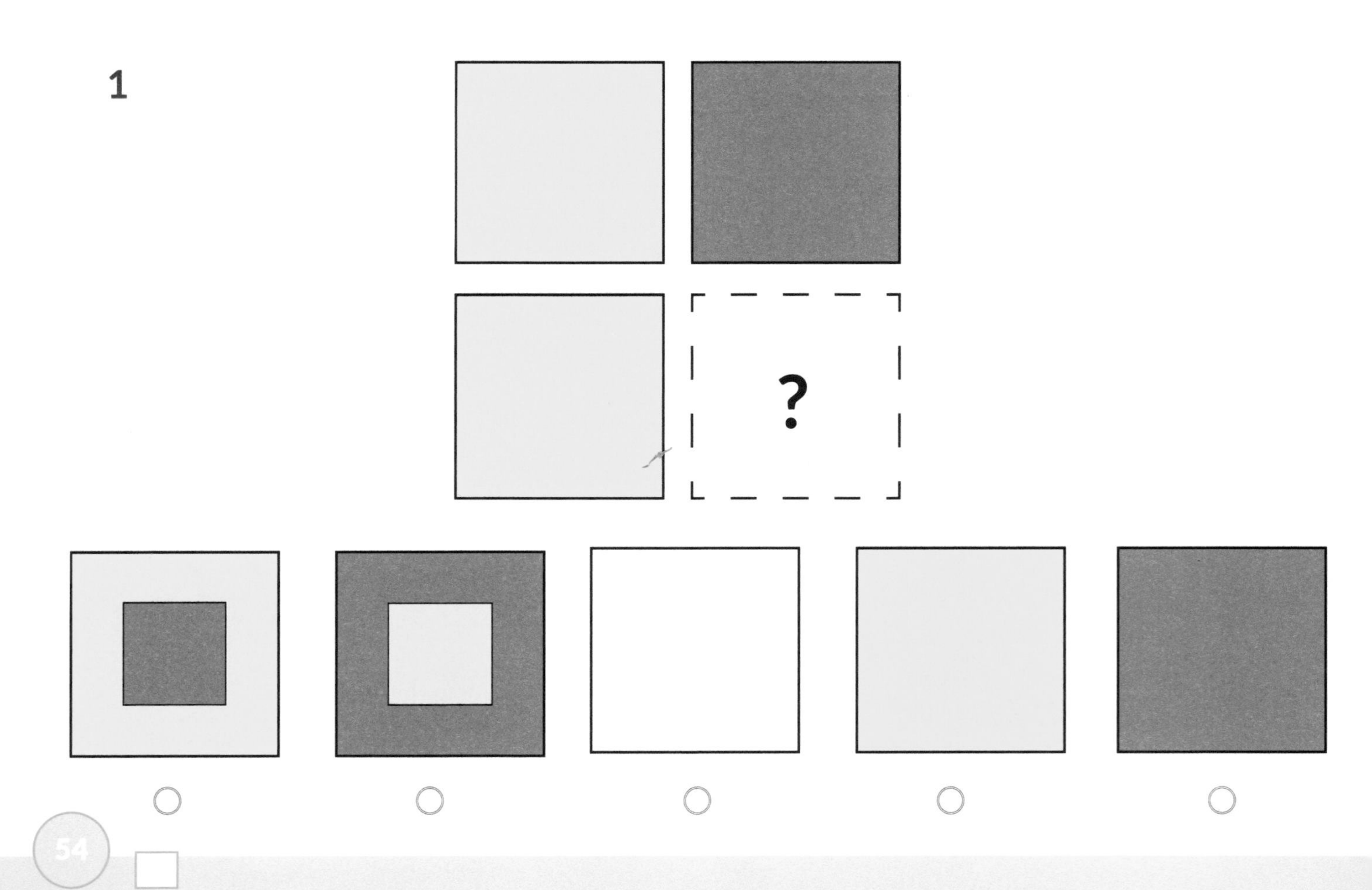

2

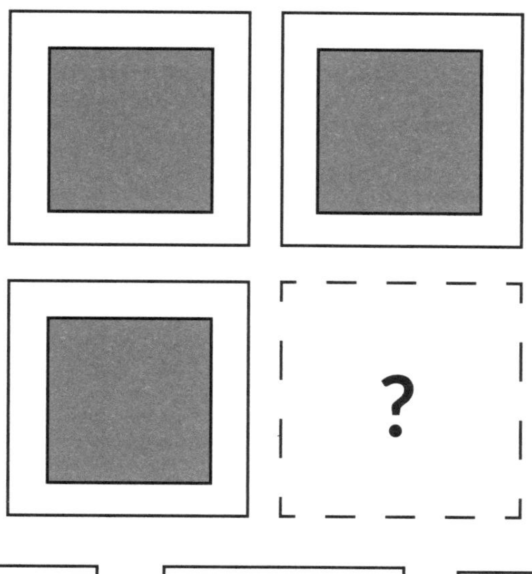

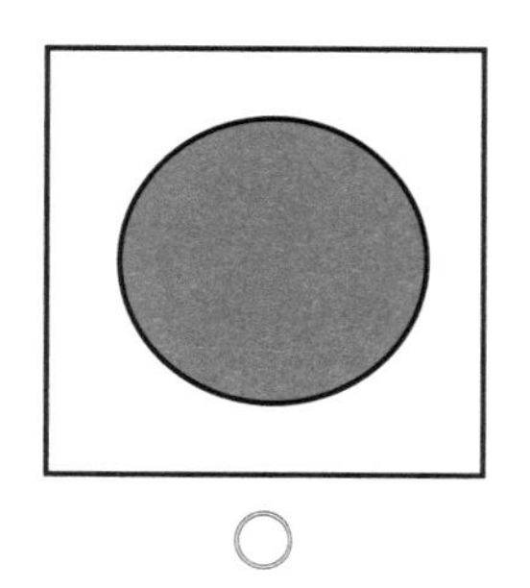
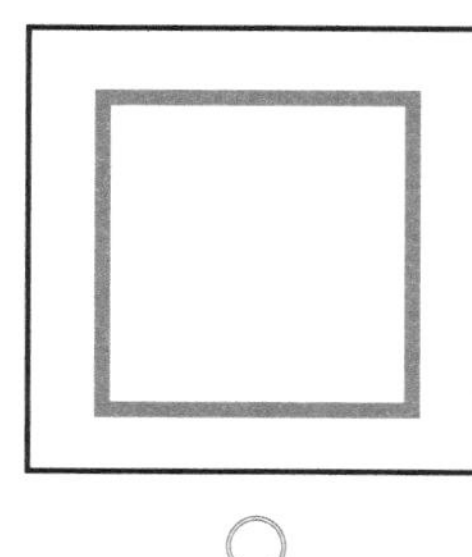
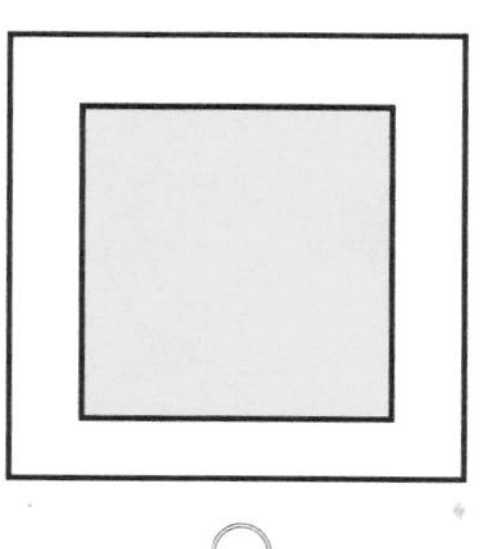
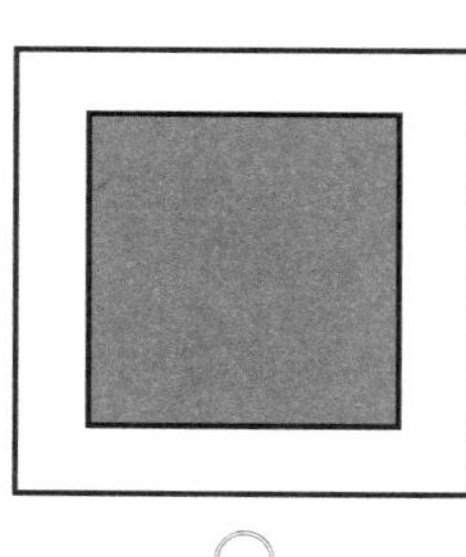
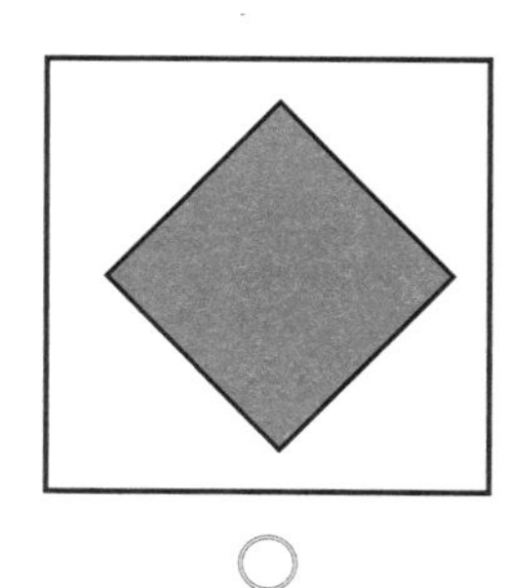

3

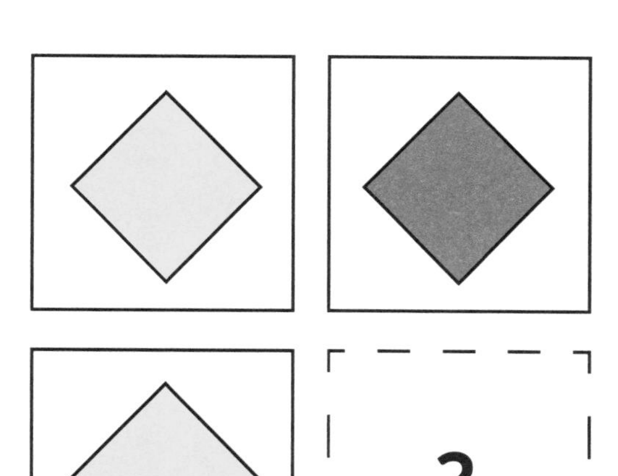

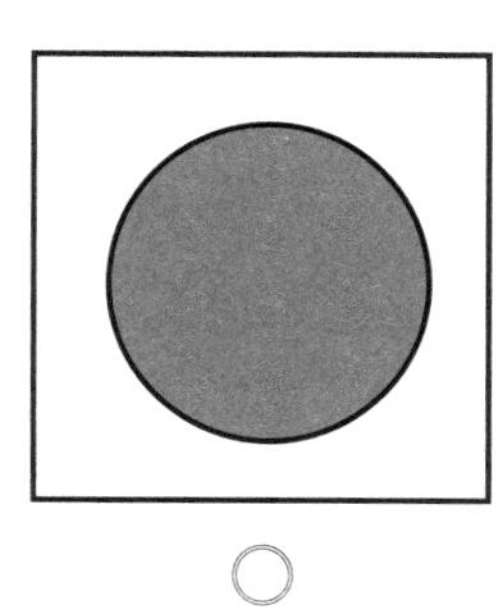
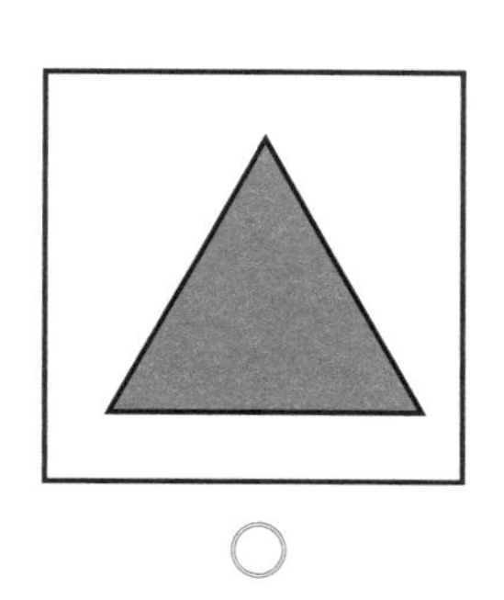

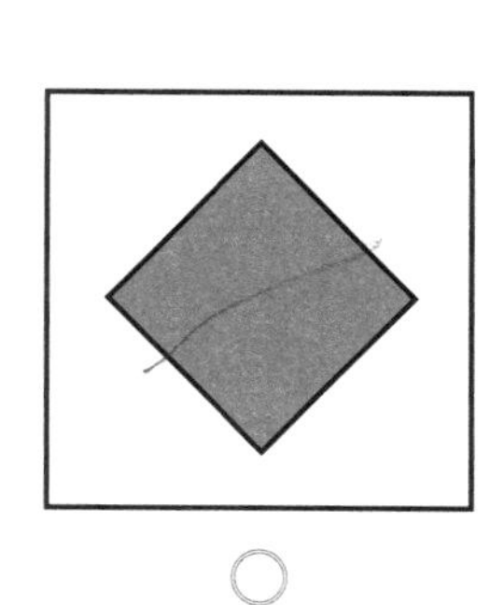

4

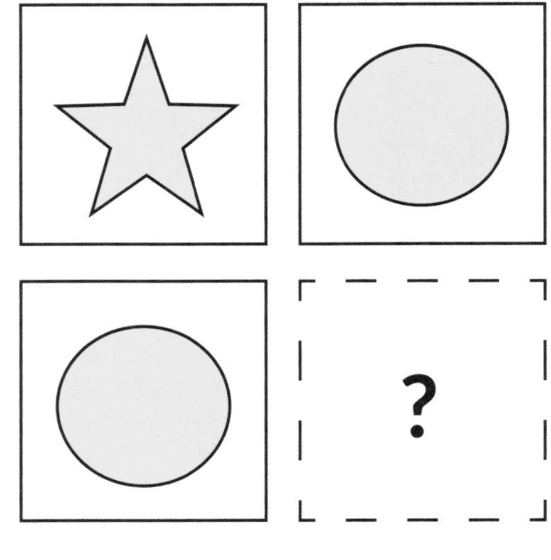

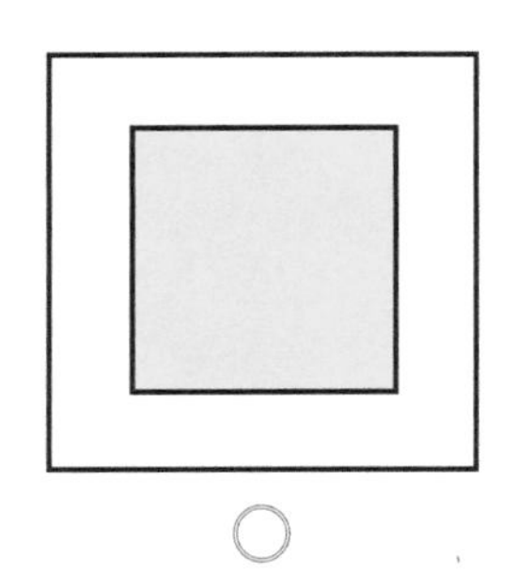
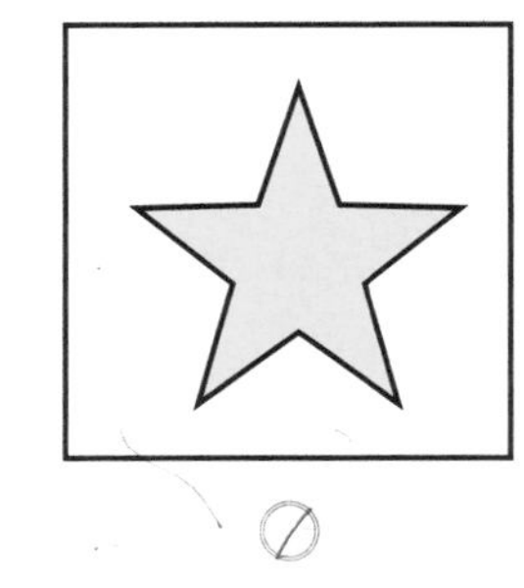

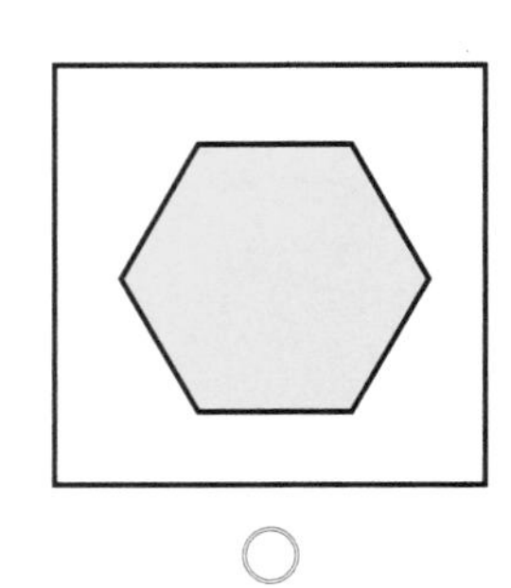

5

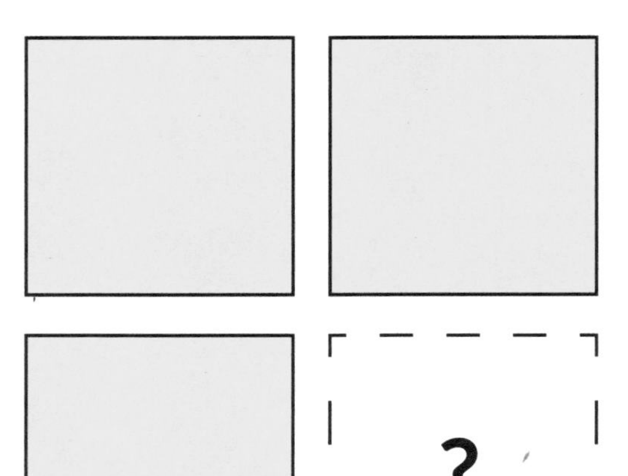

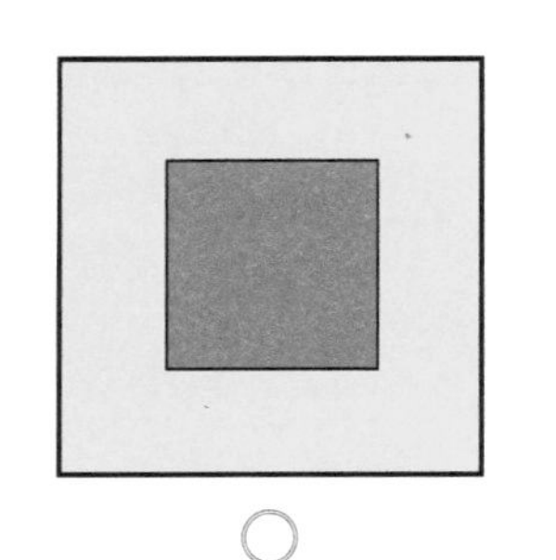

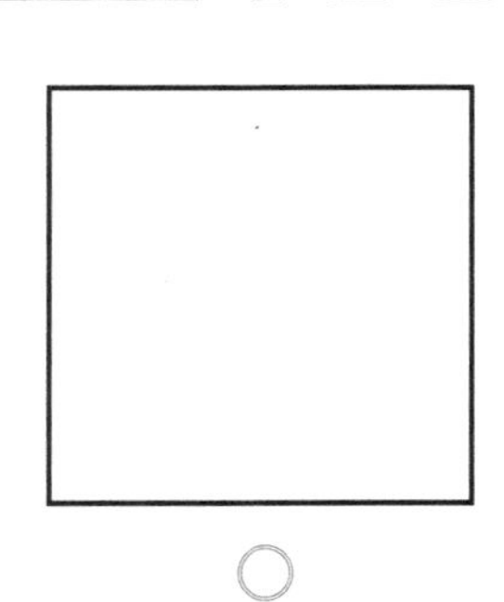
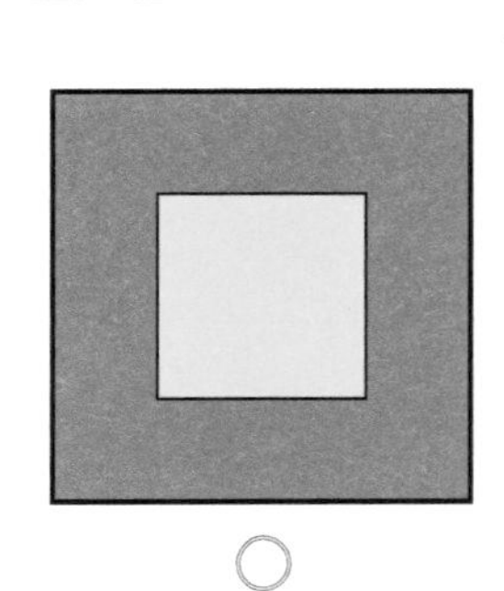

6

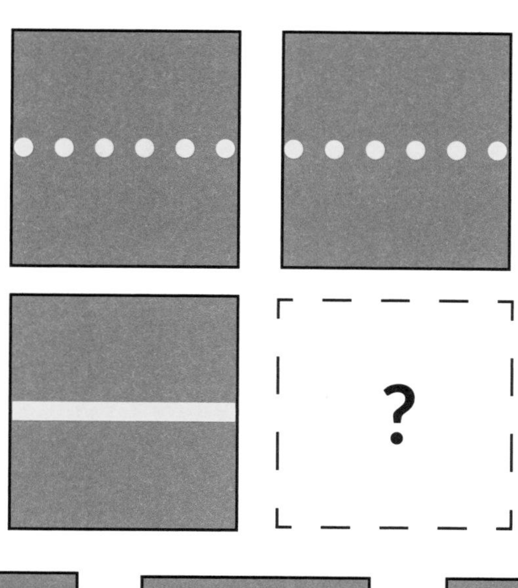

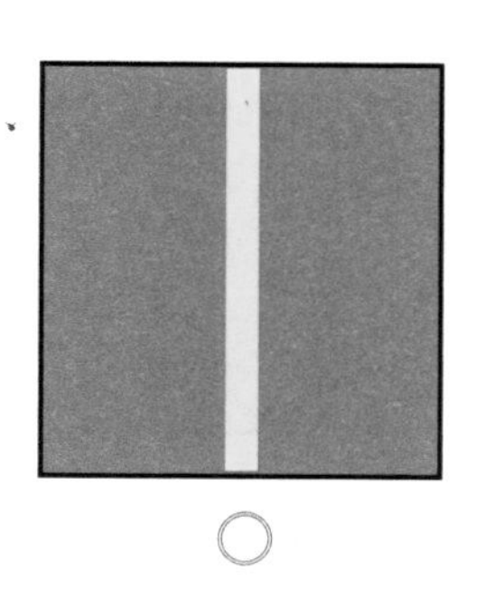
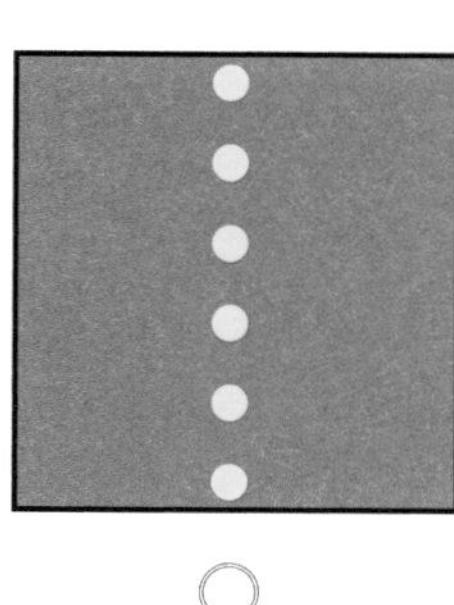
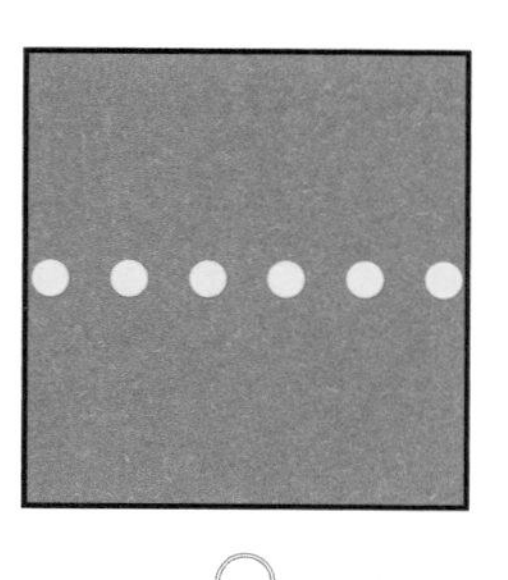

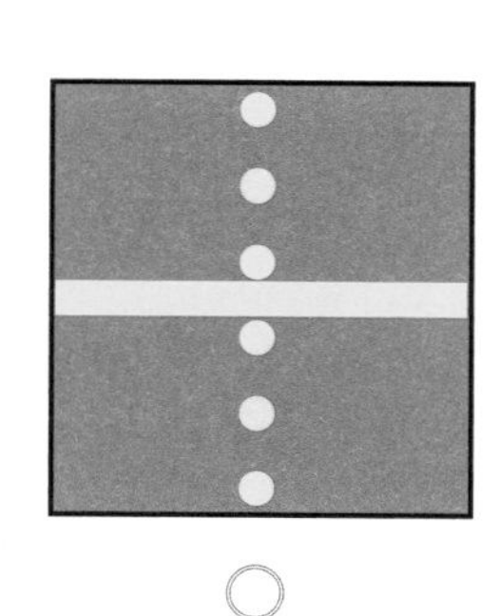

7

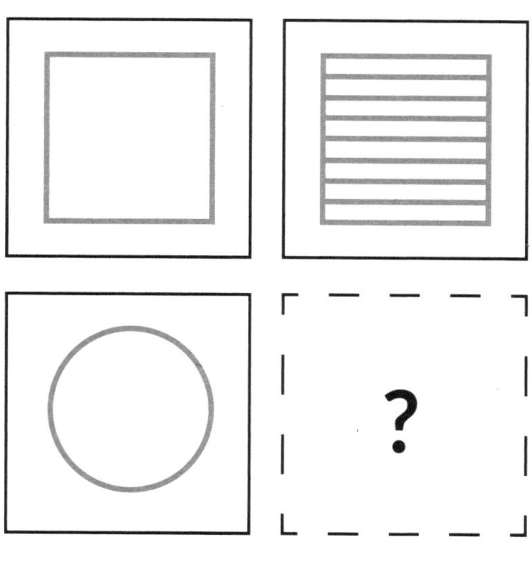

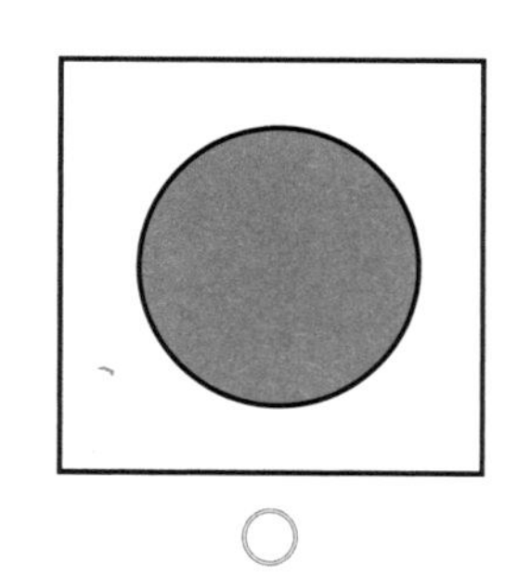
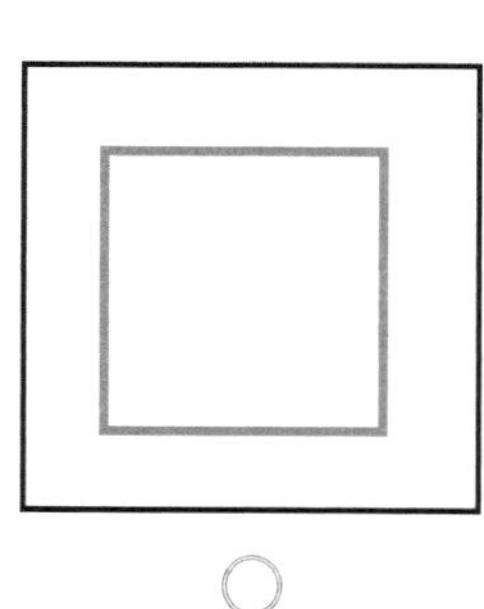
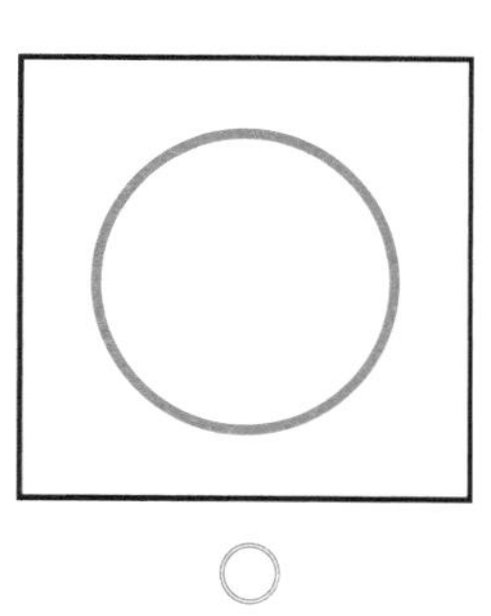
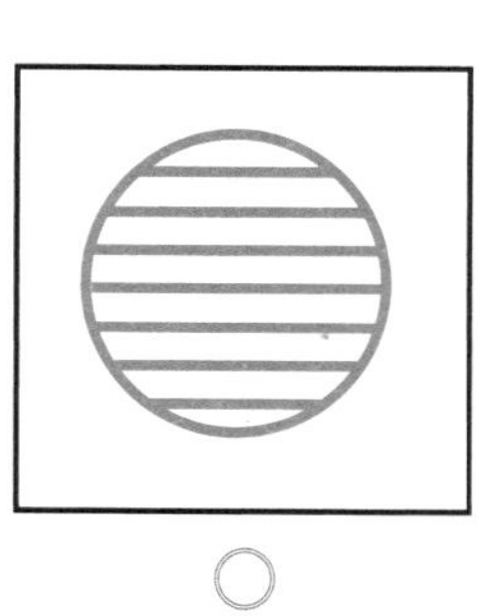

8

?

9

10

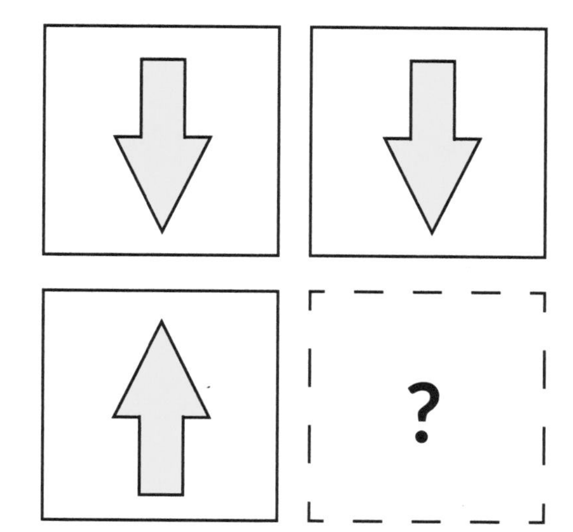

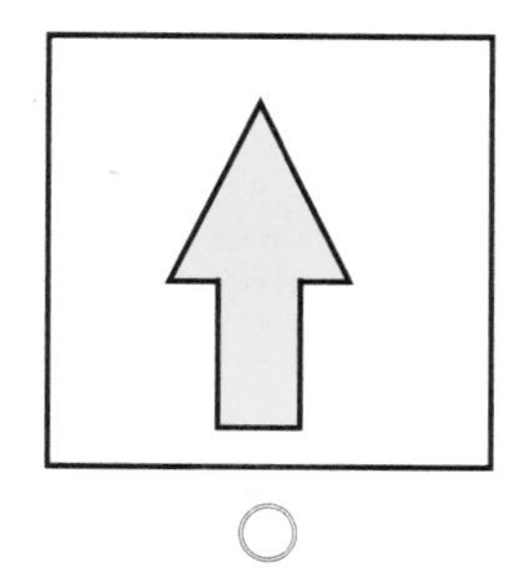 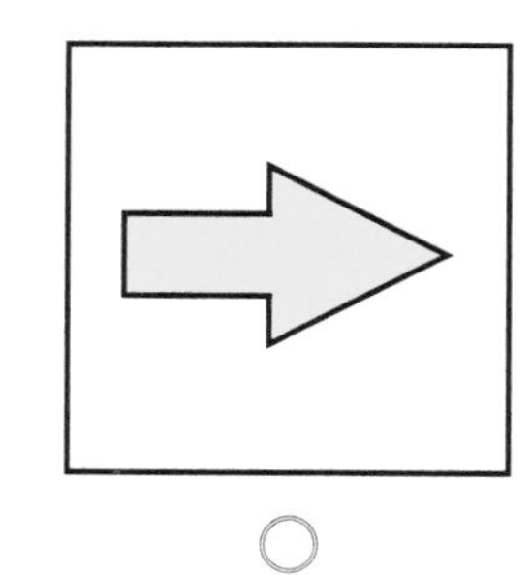 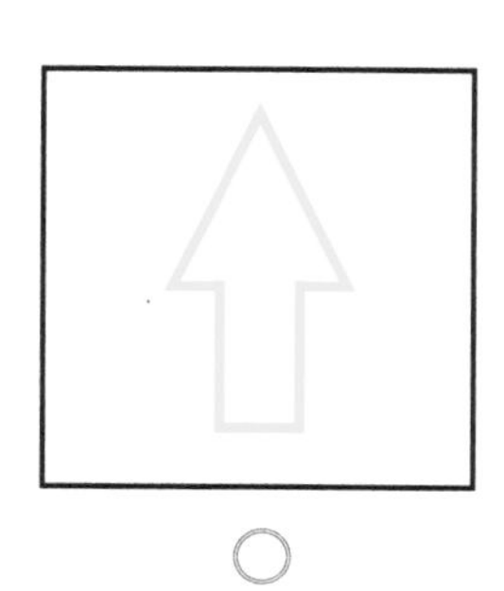 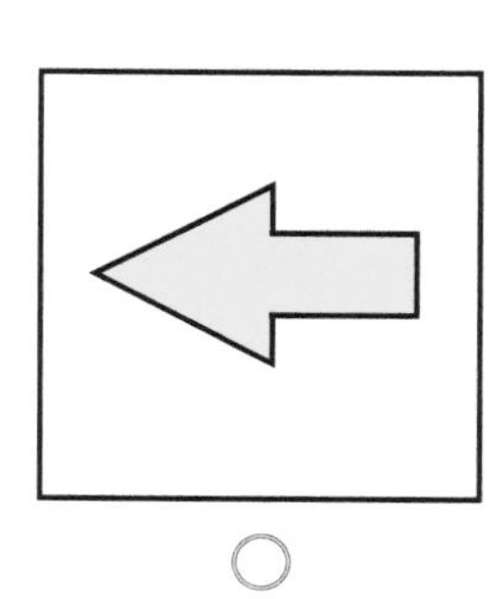 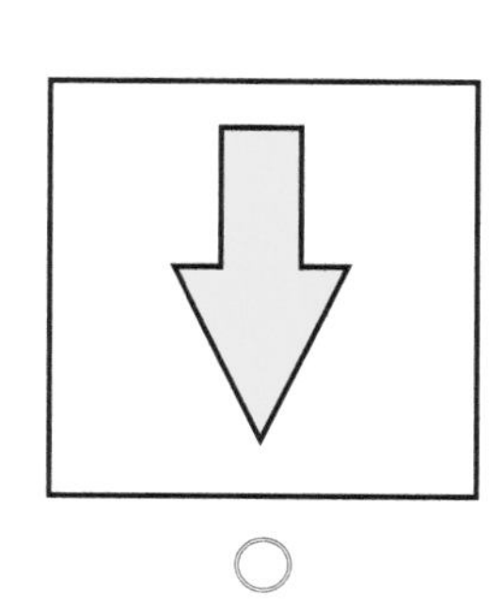

11

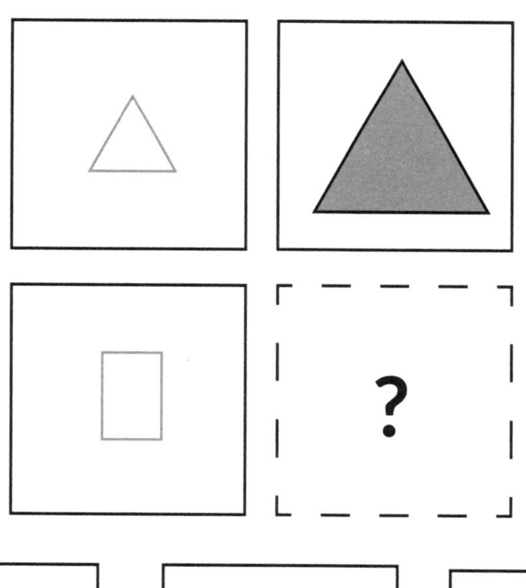

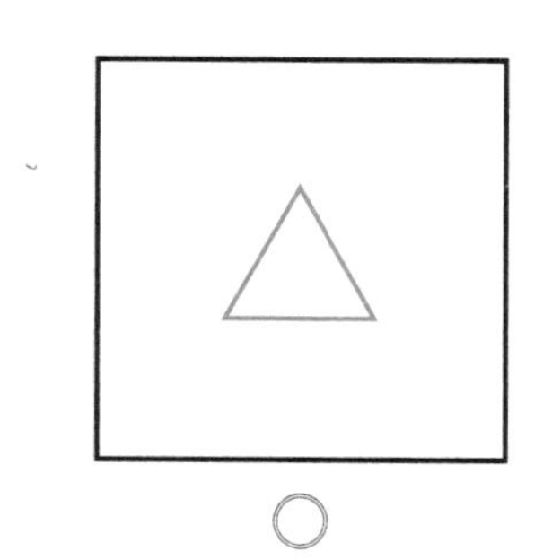 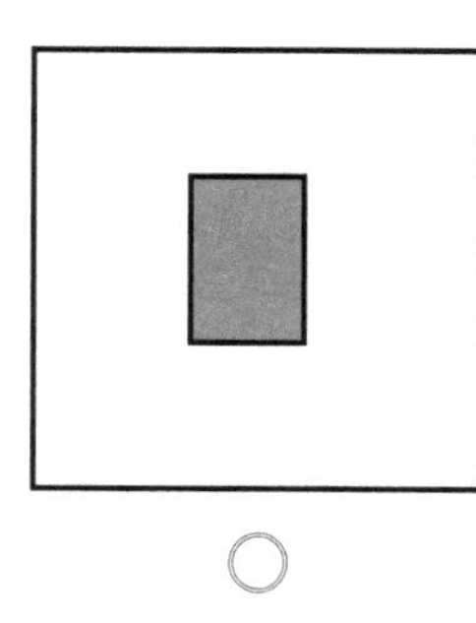 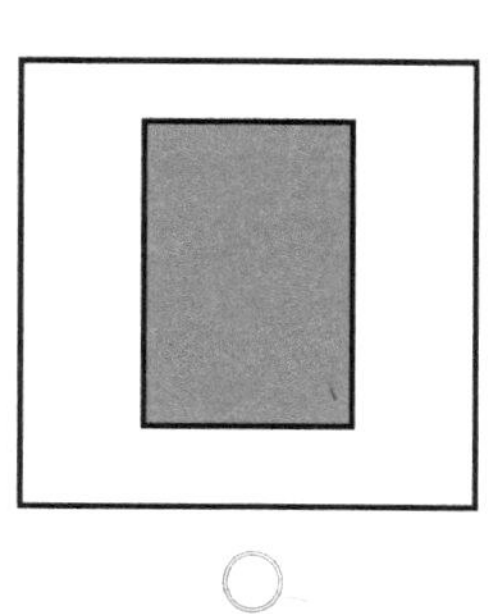 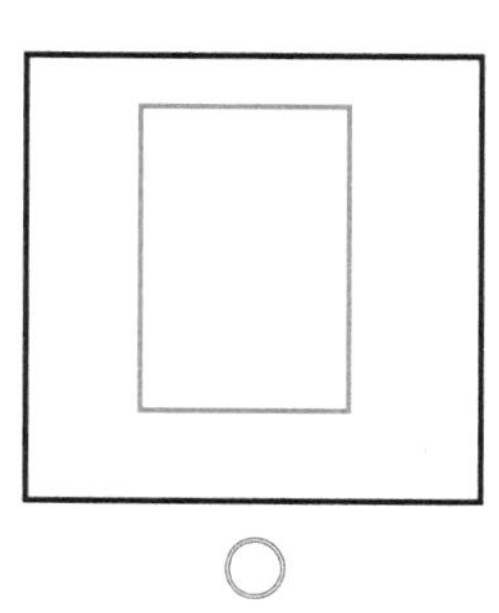 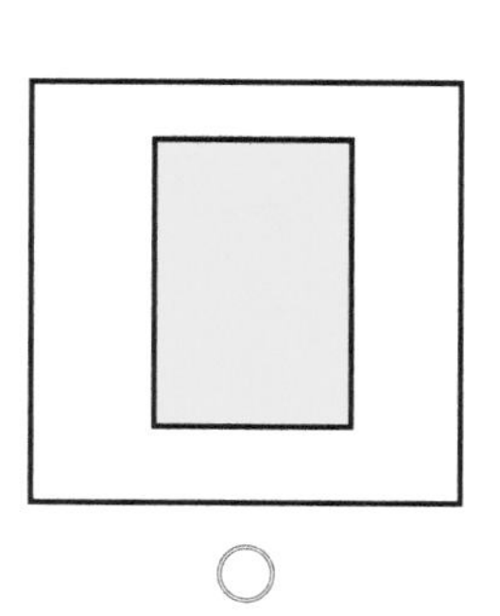

12

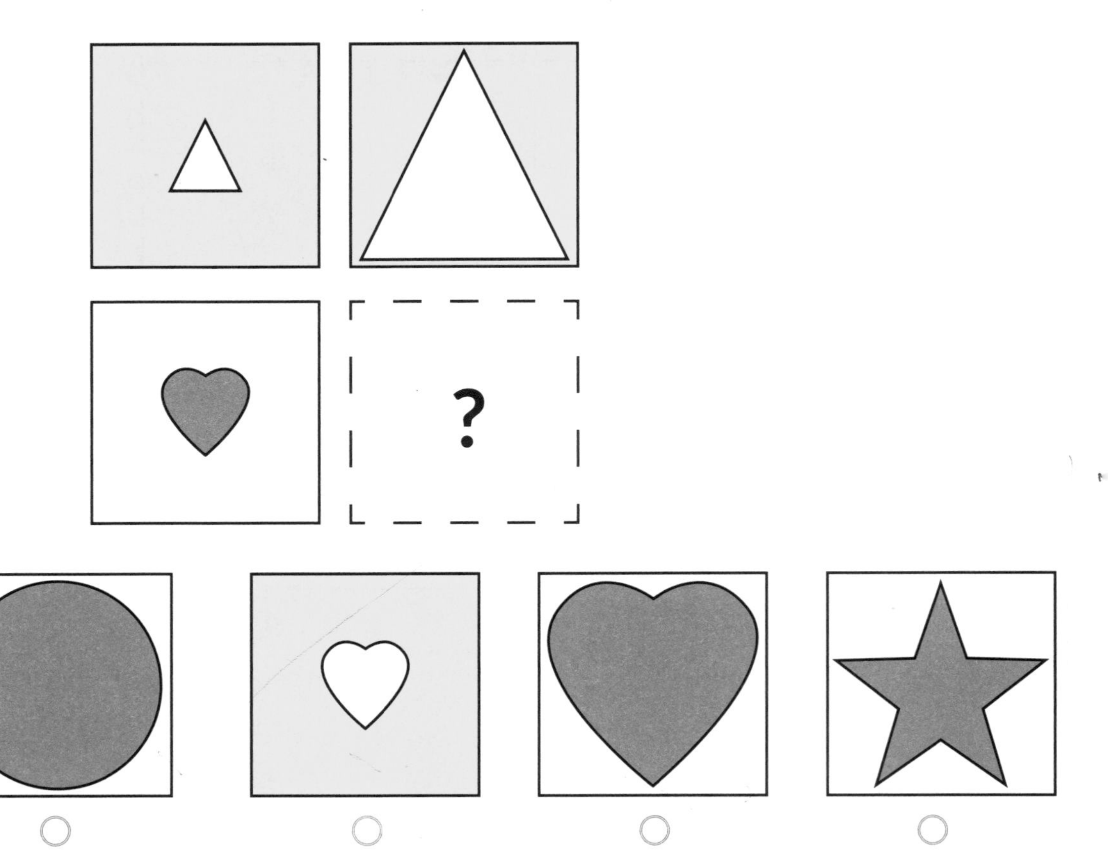

13

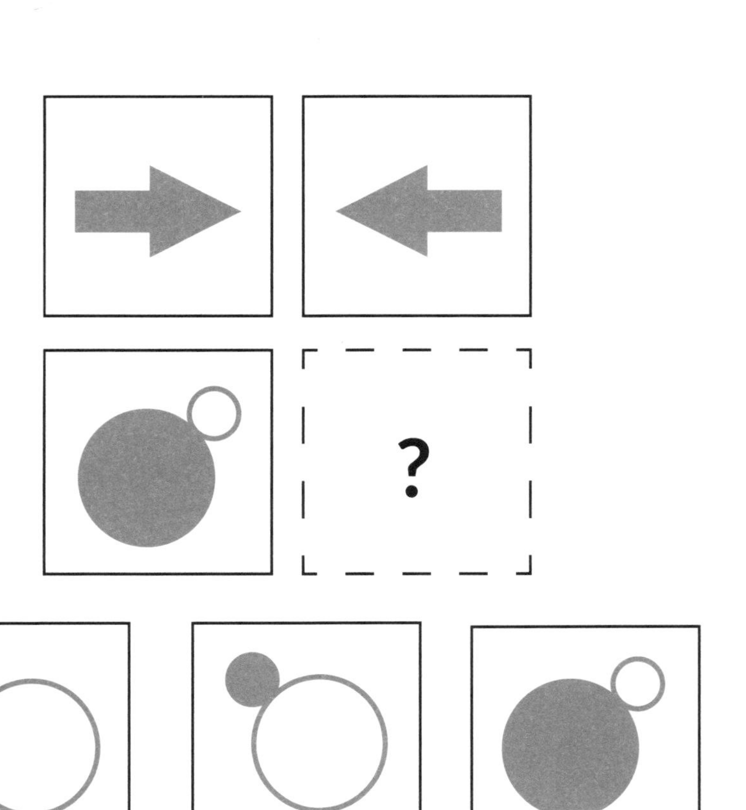

14

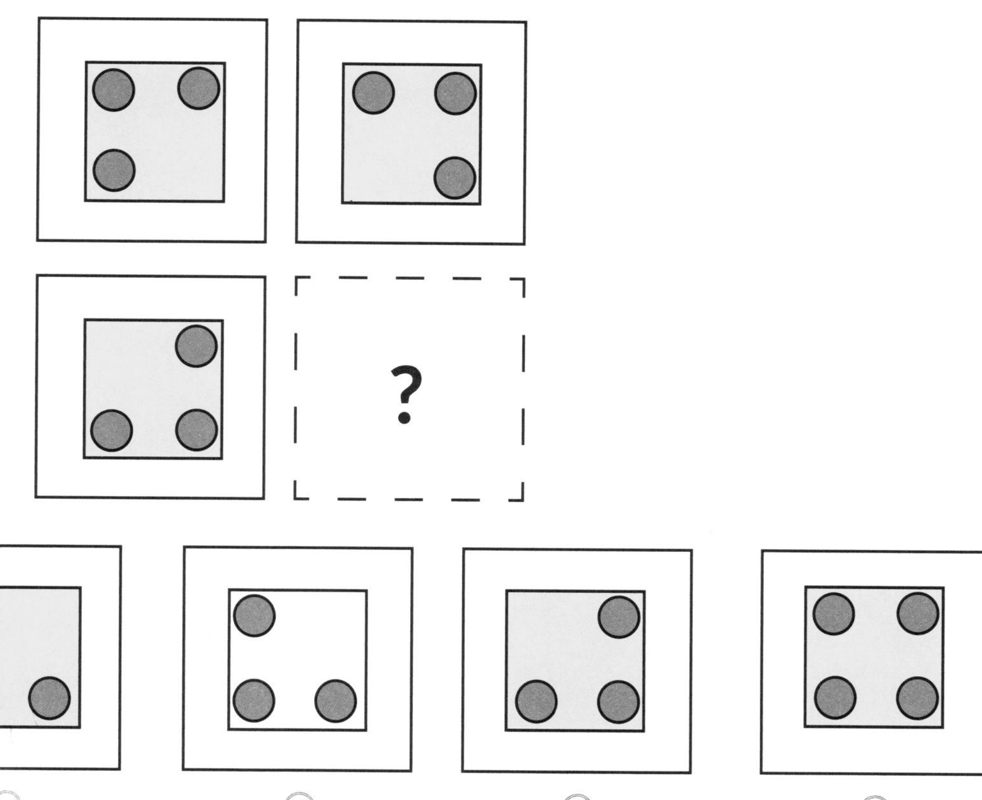

15

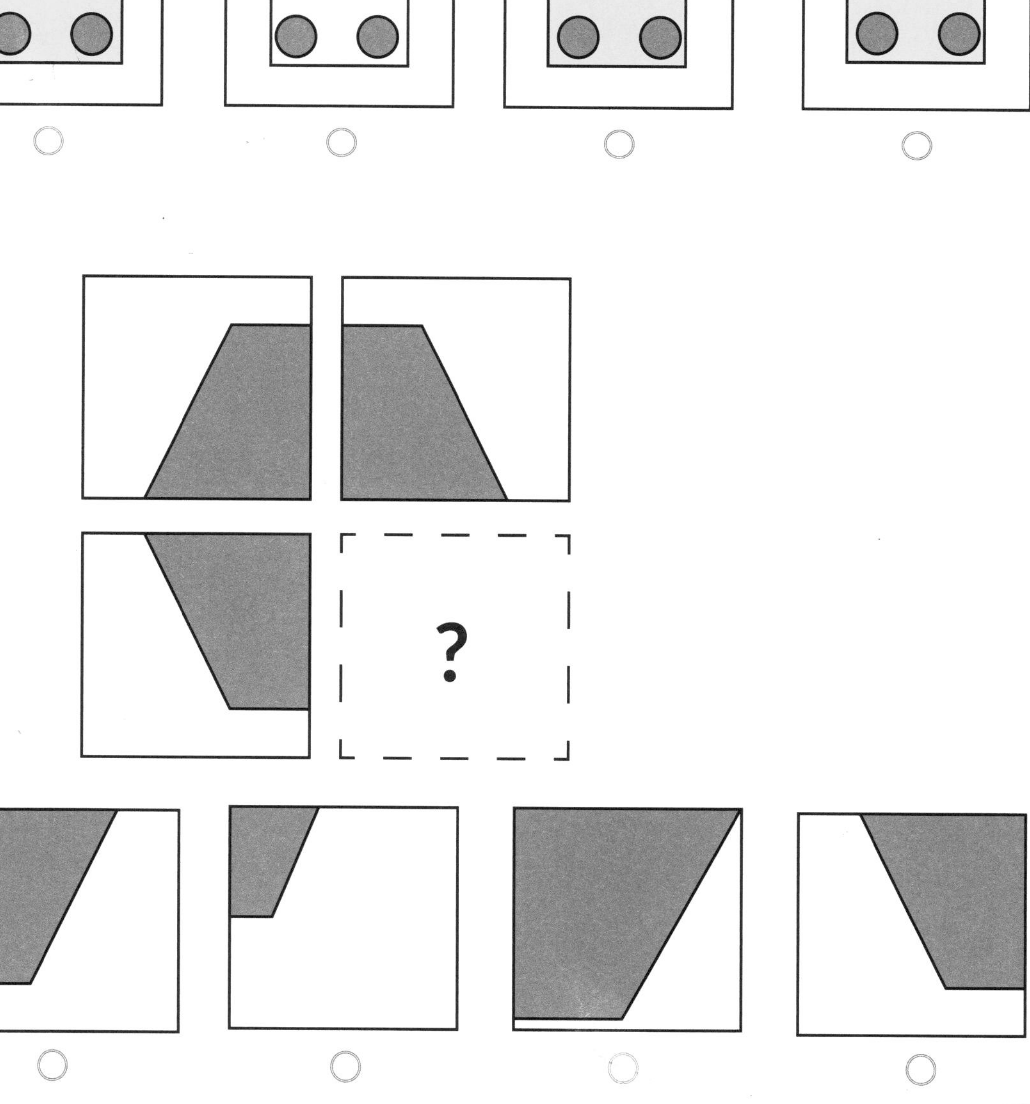

16

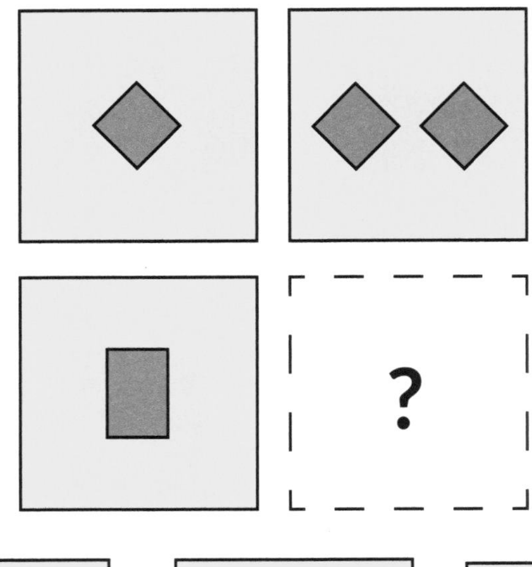

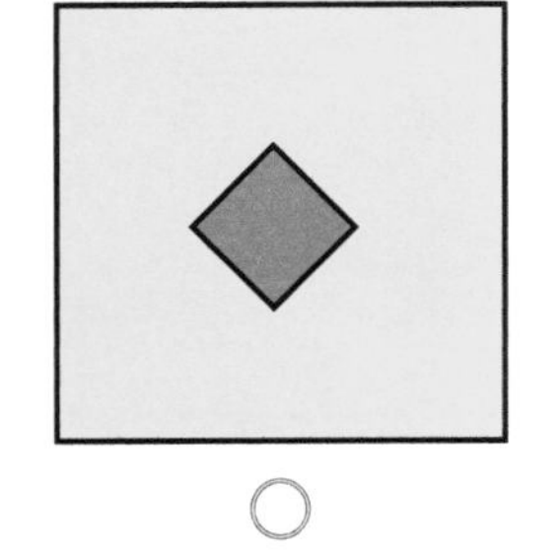
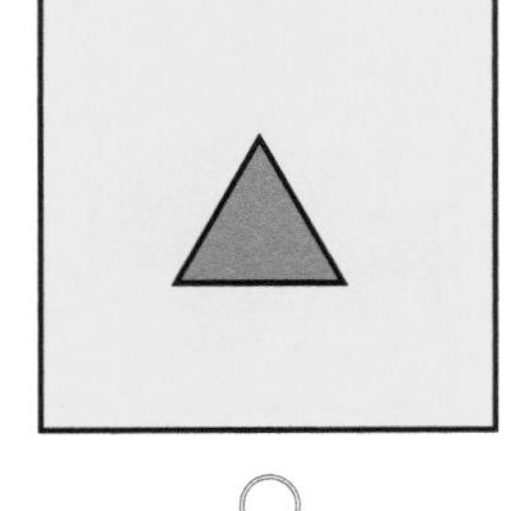

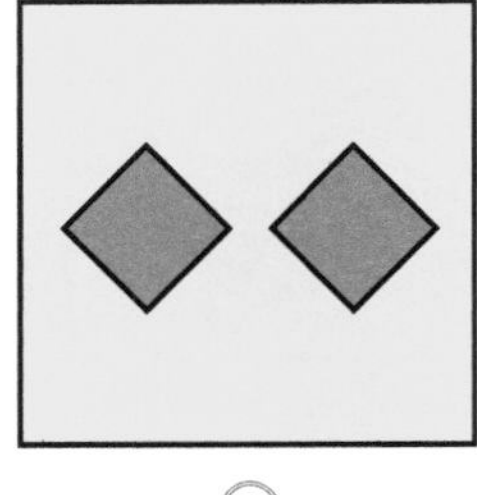
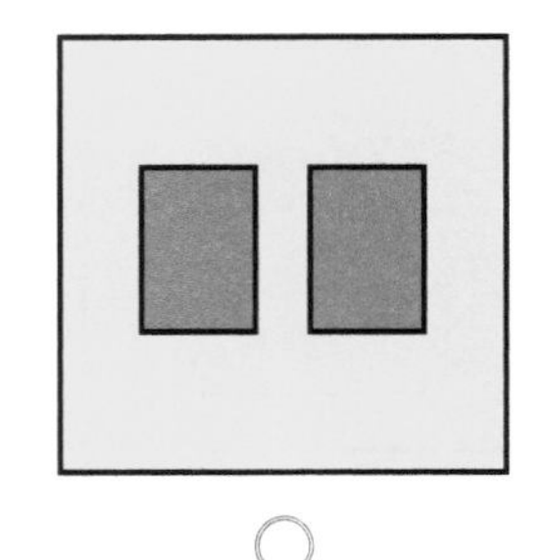

17

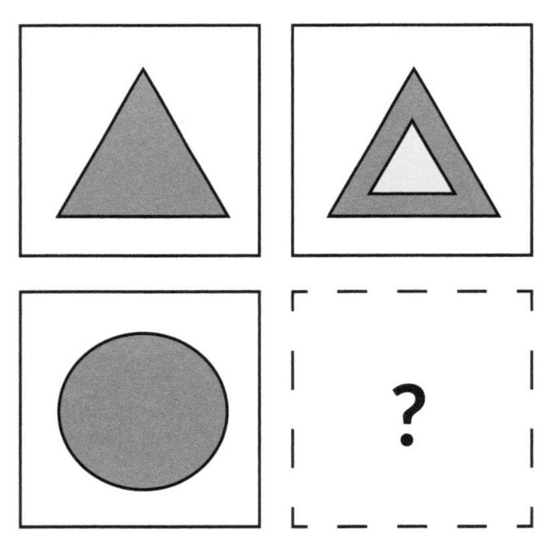

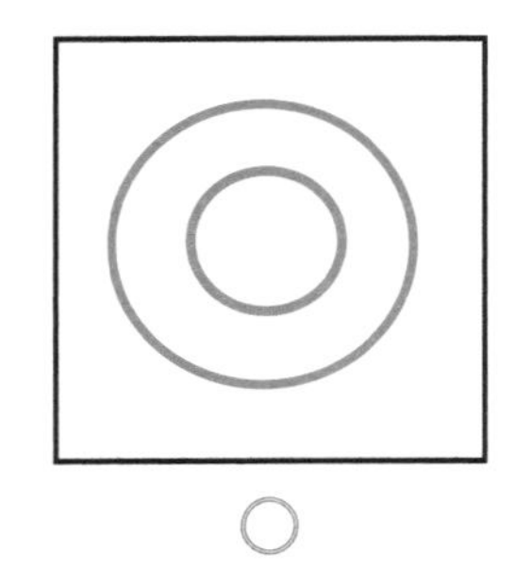
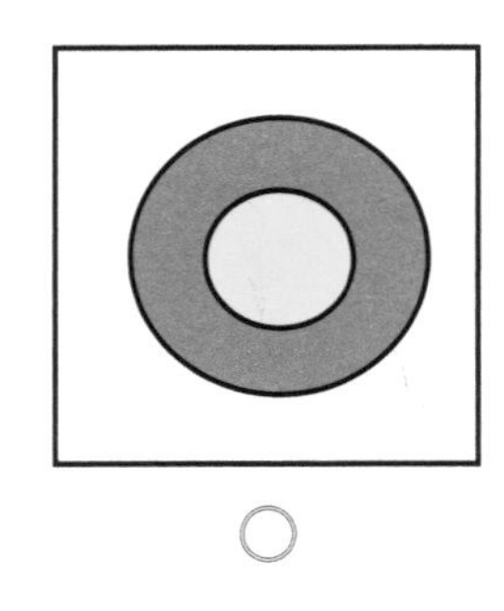
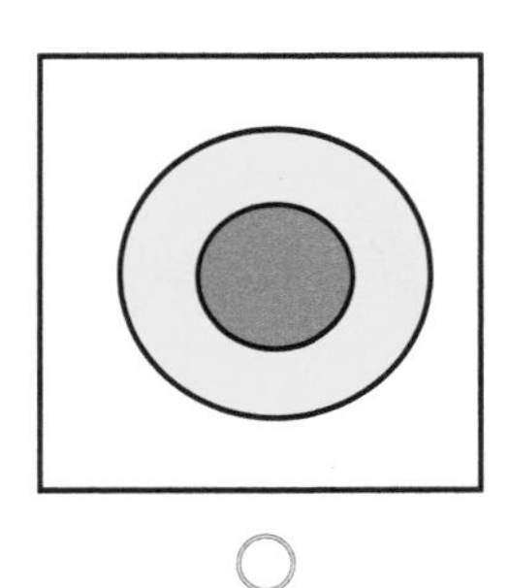
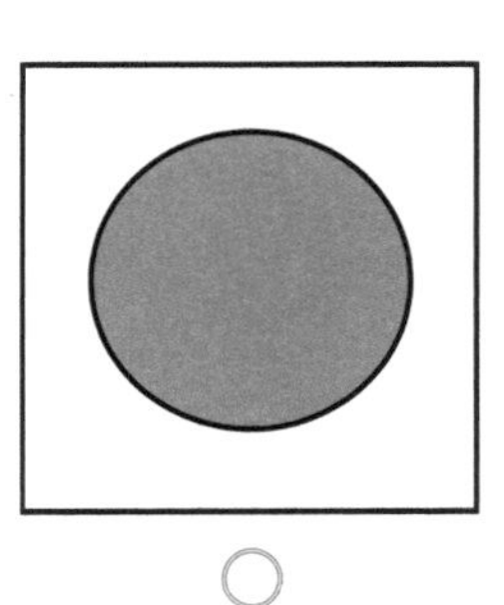
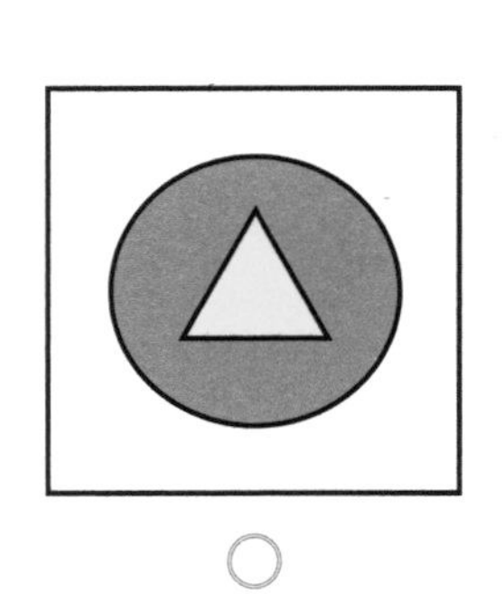

18

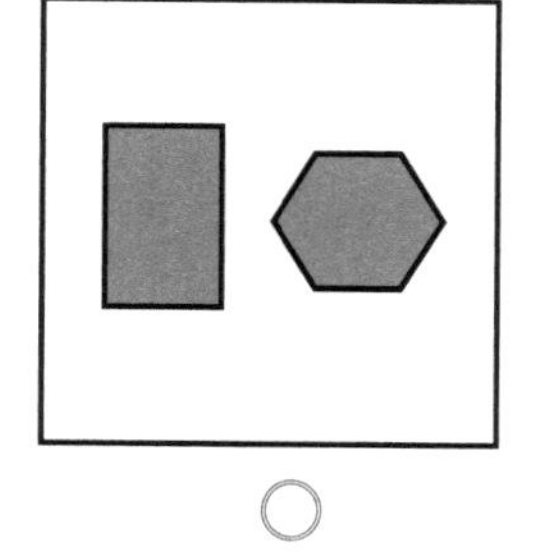

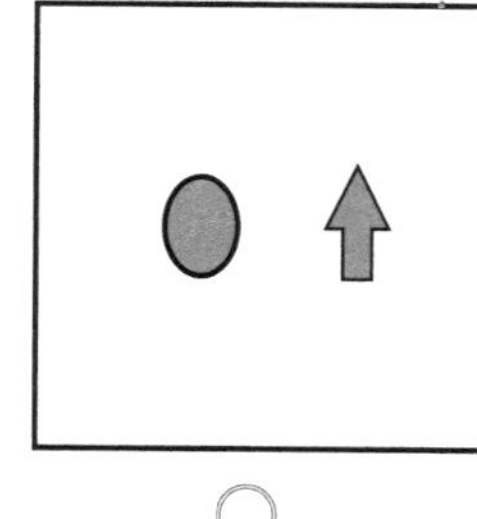

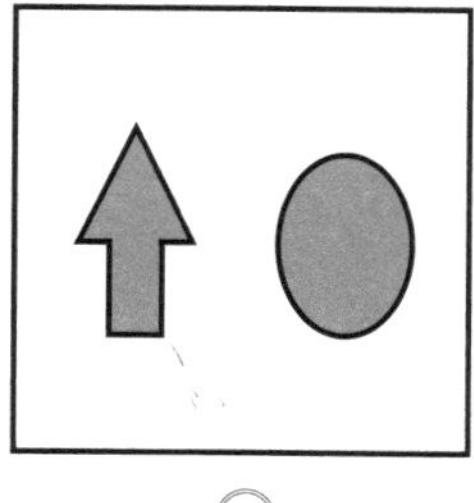

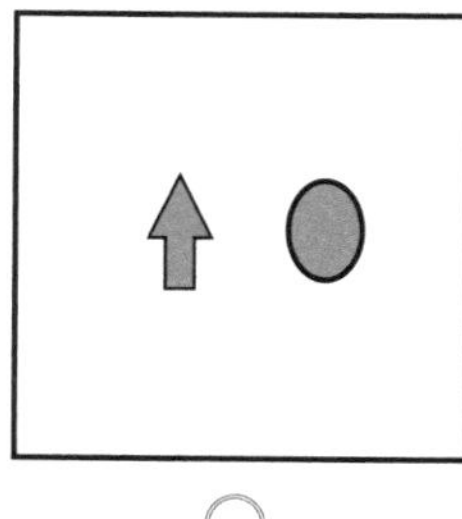

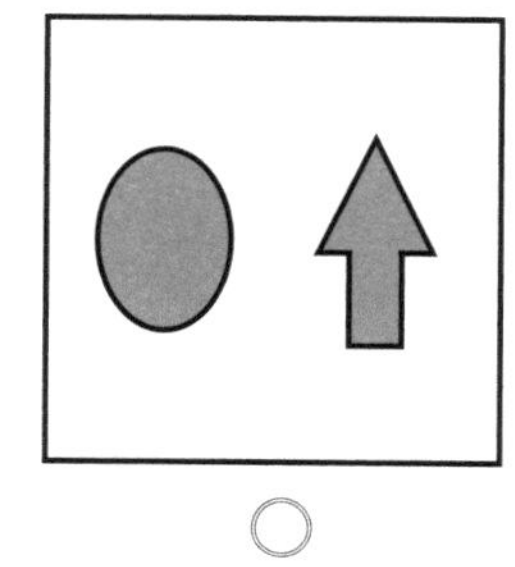

19

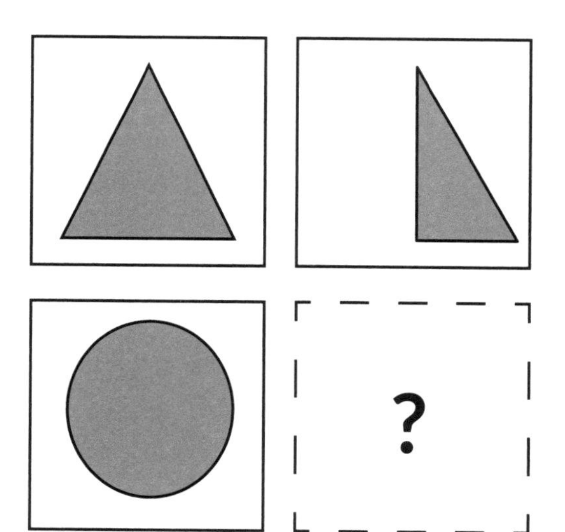

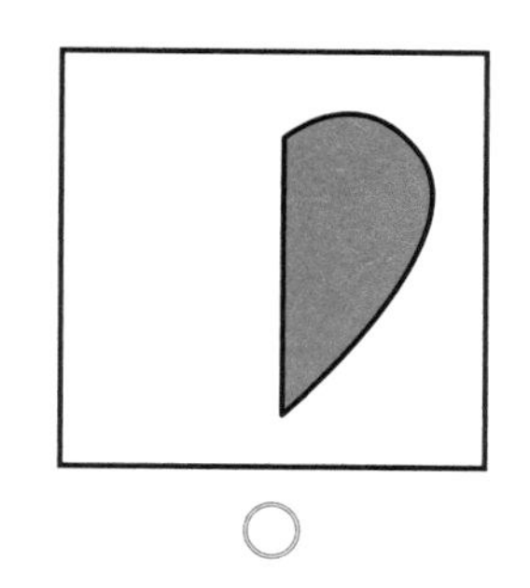

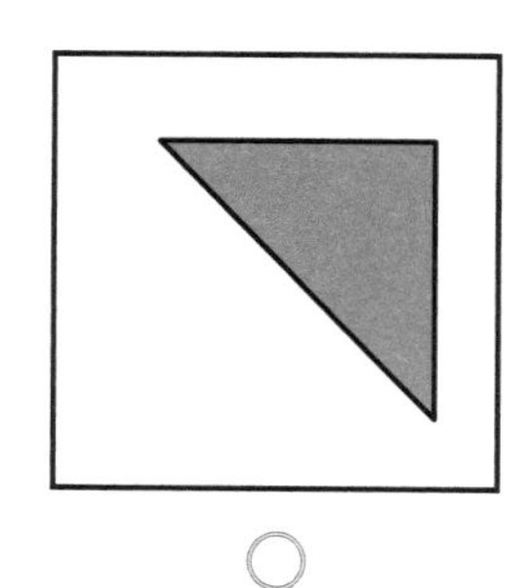

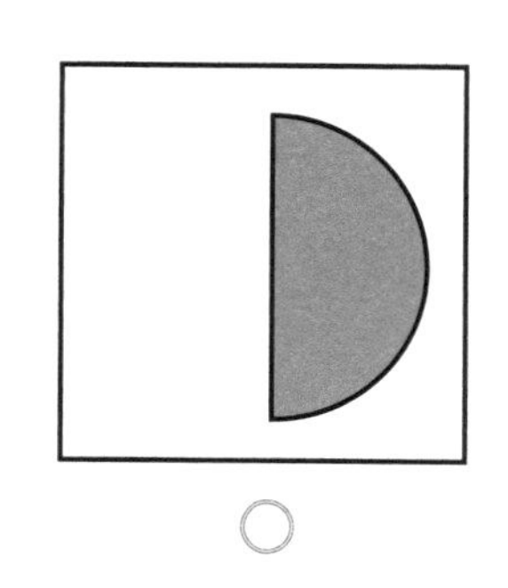

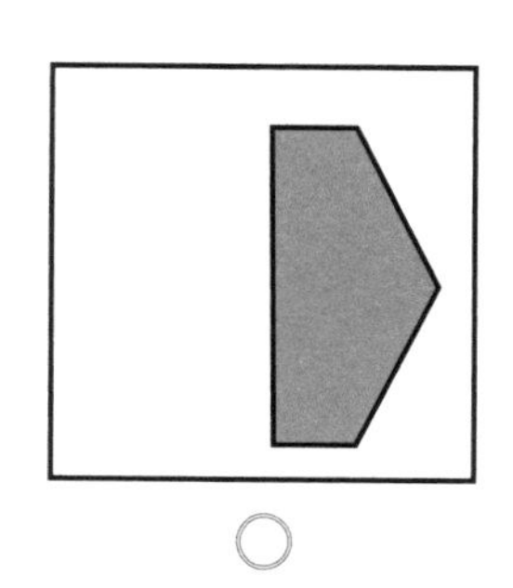

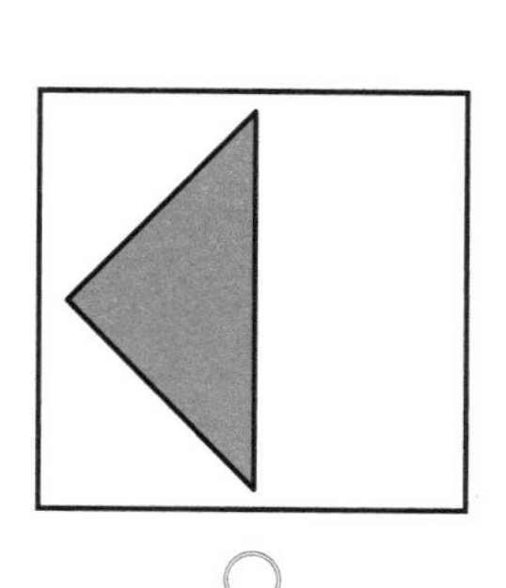

20

?

21

?

22

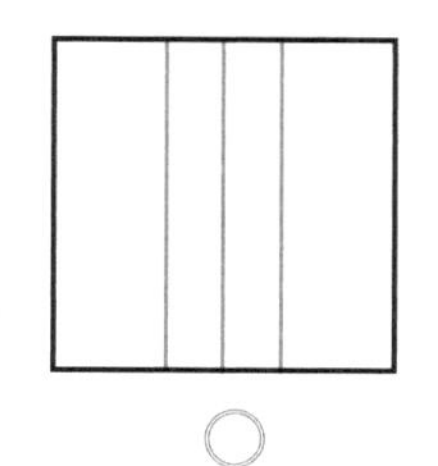

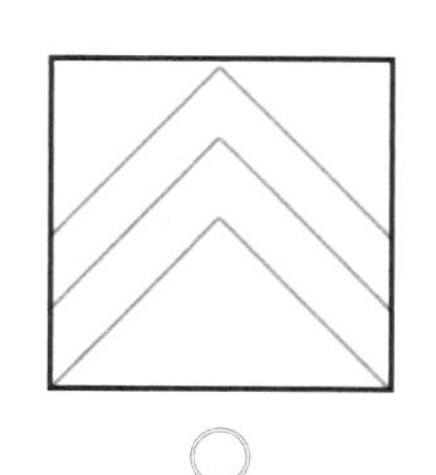
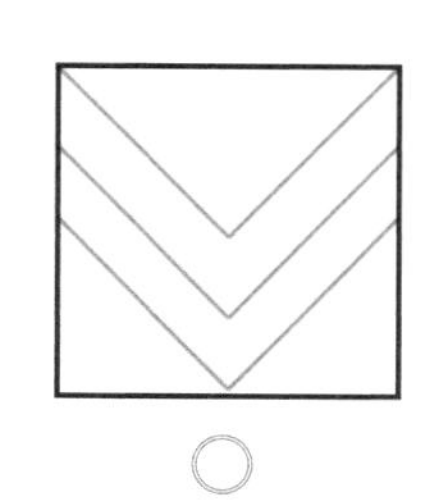
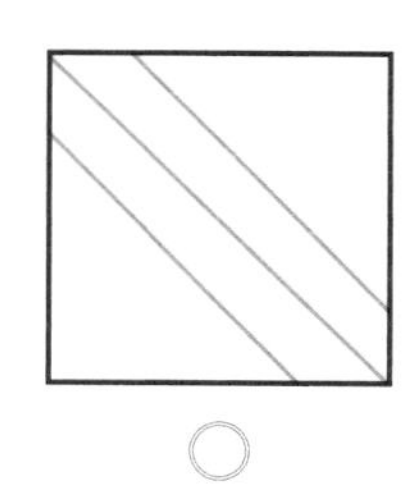

23

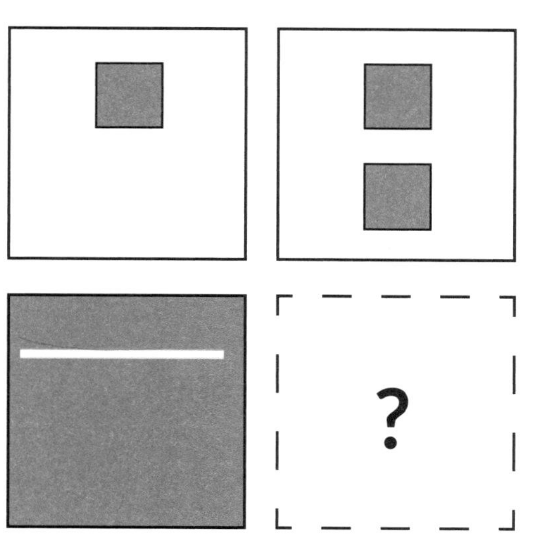

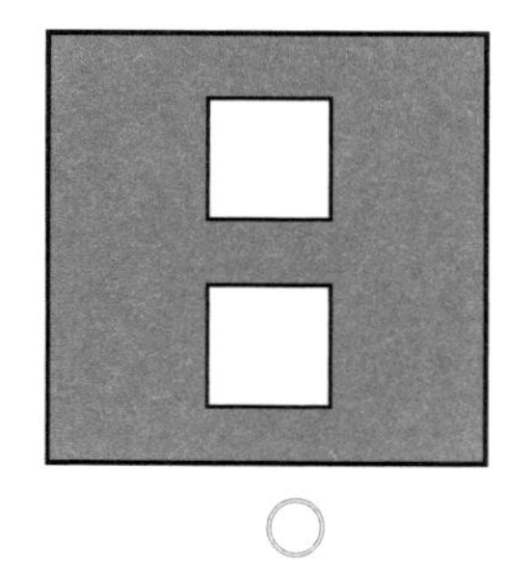

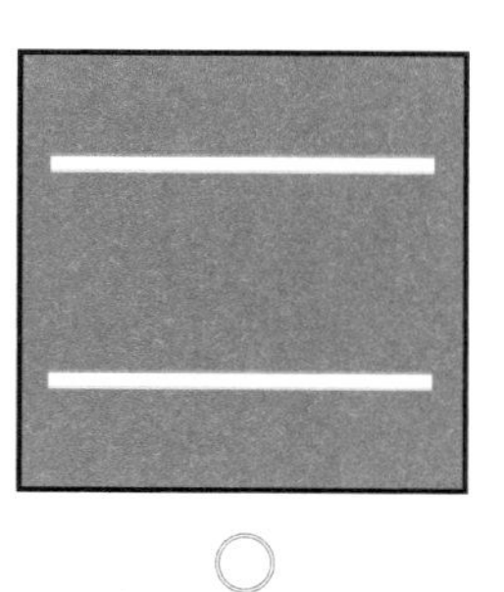
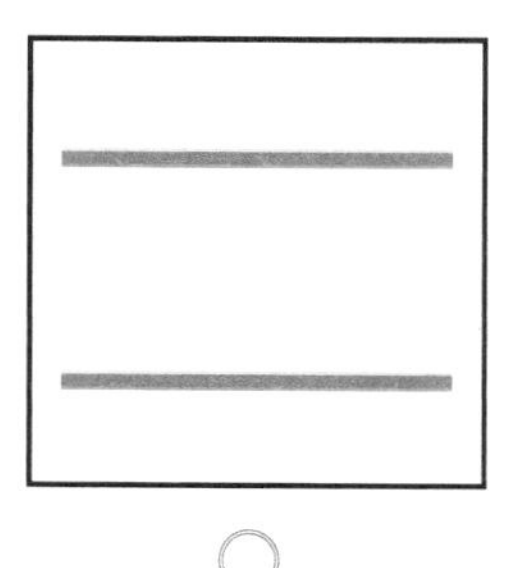
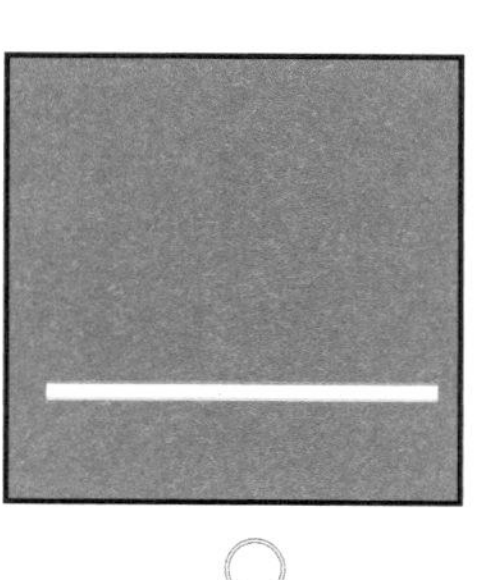

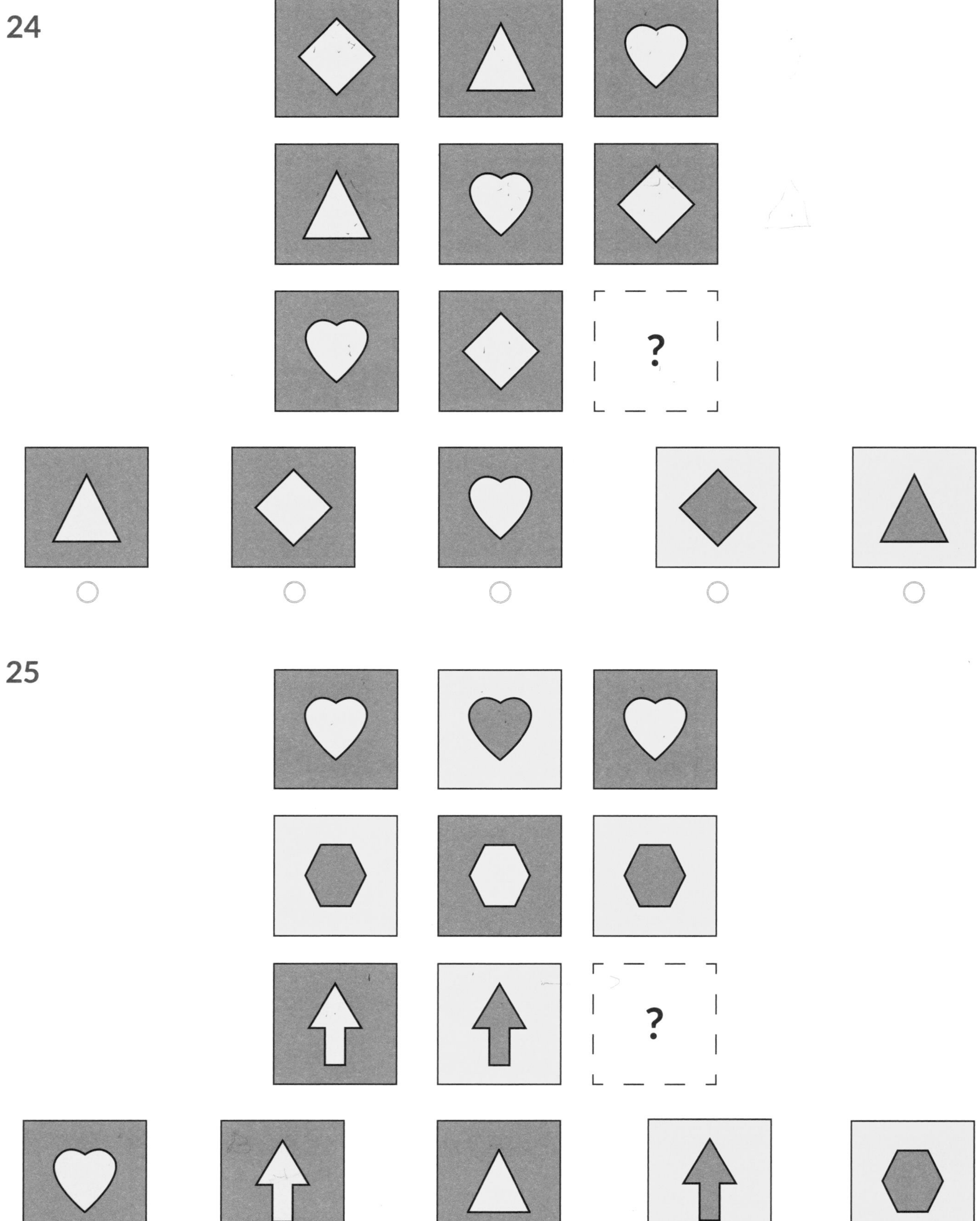
24
?
25
?

26

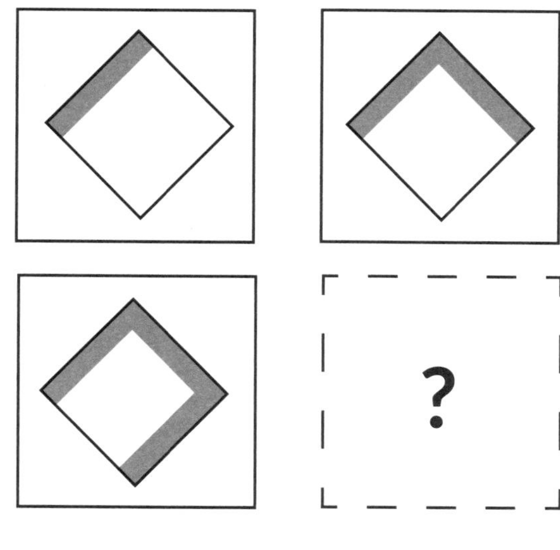

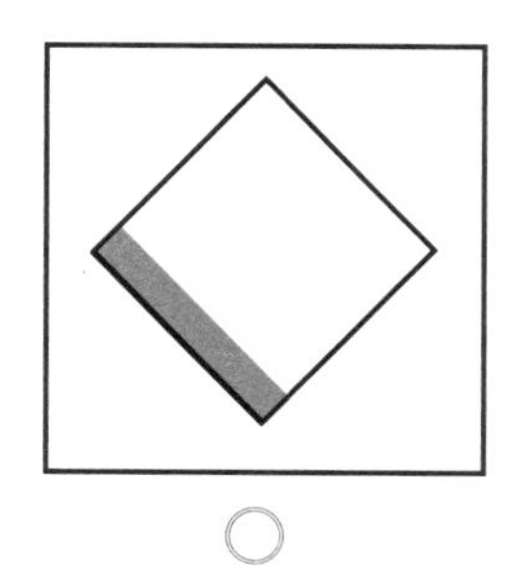
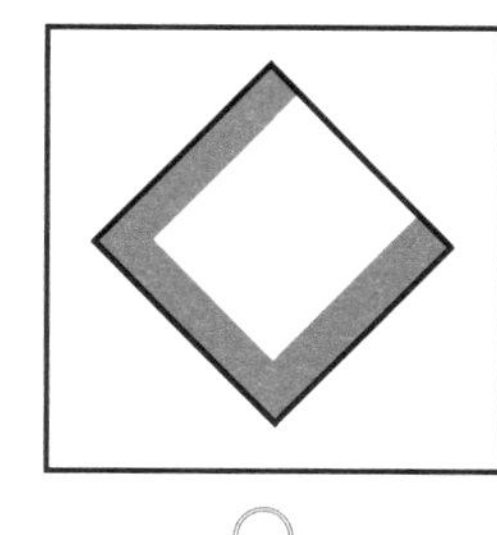
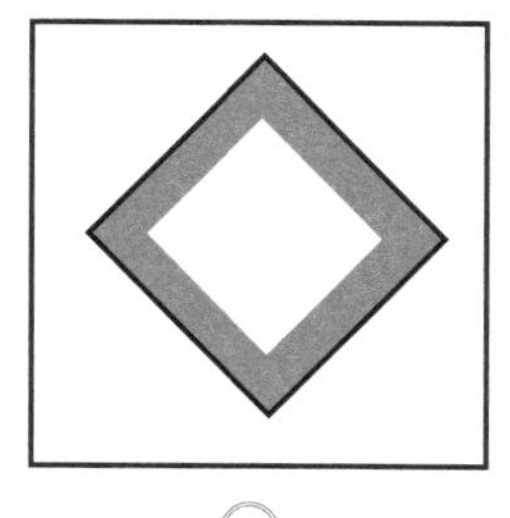
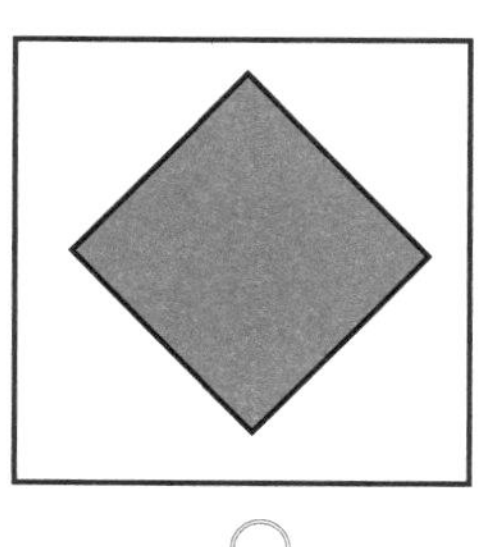
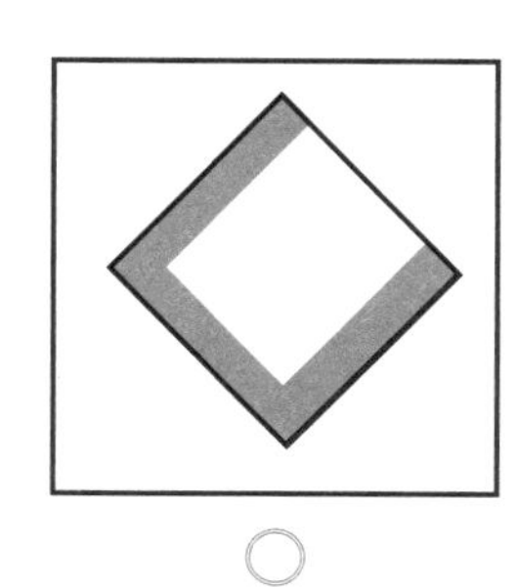

27

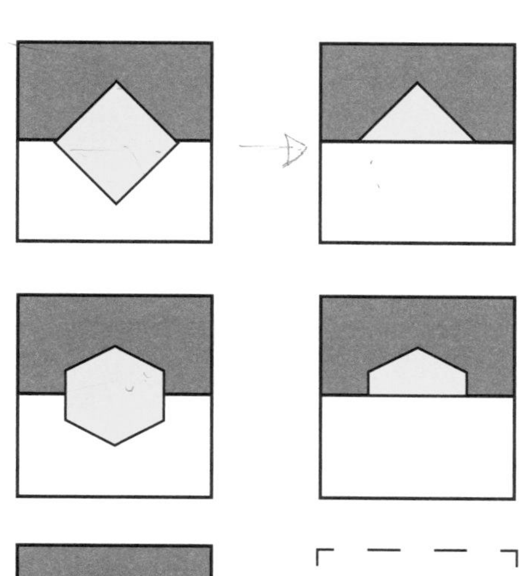

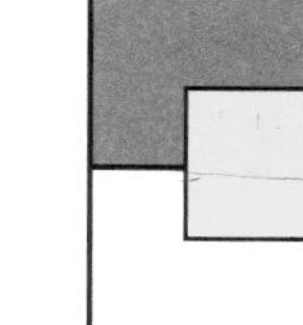
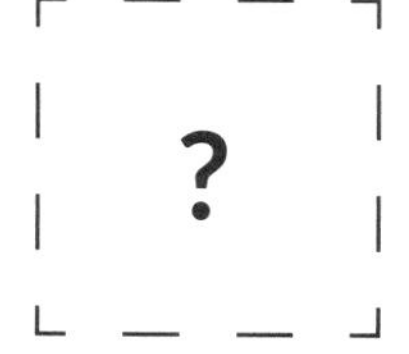

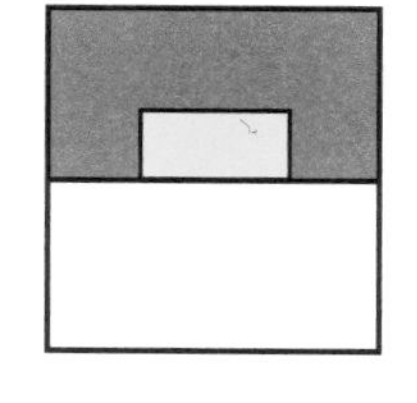
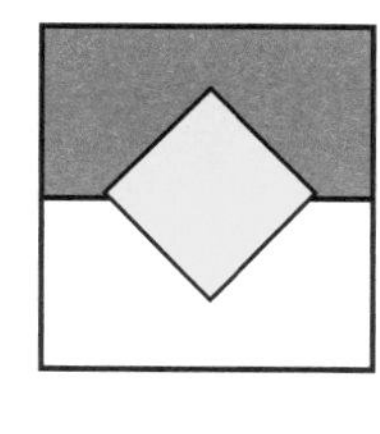
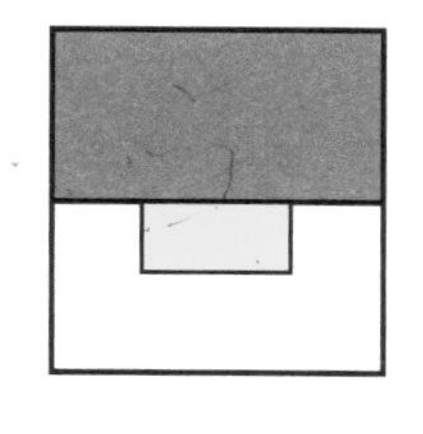
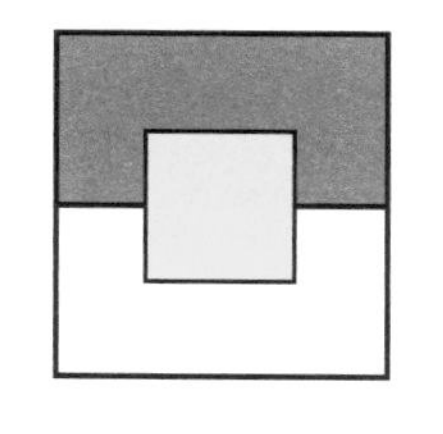
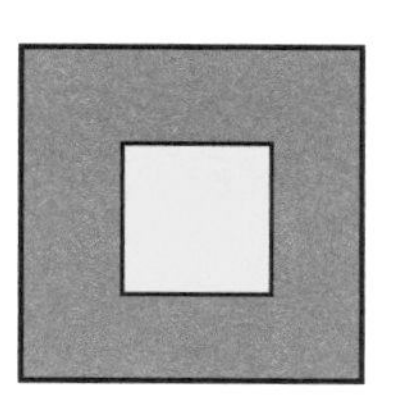

28

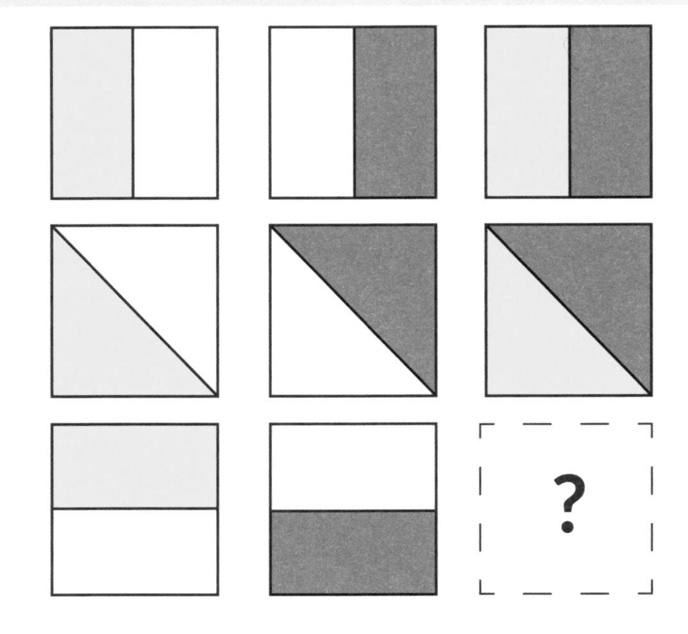

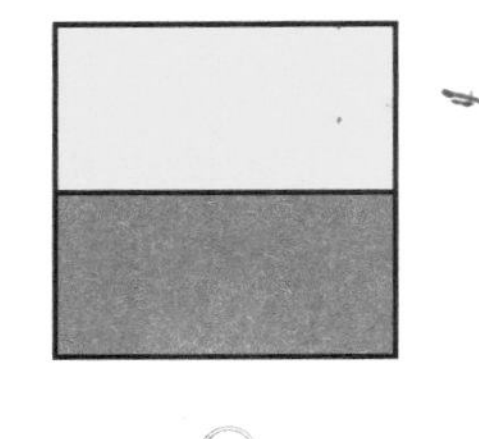
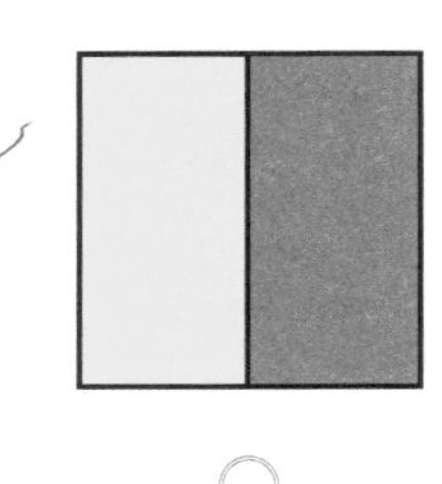
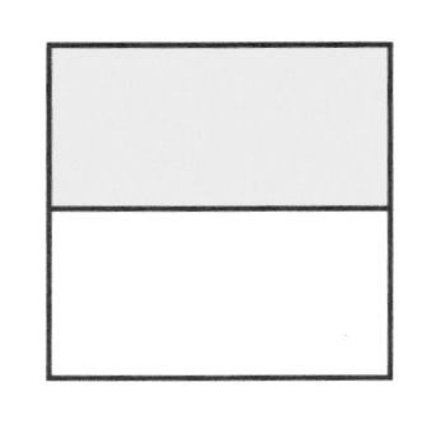
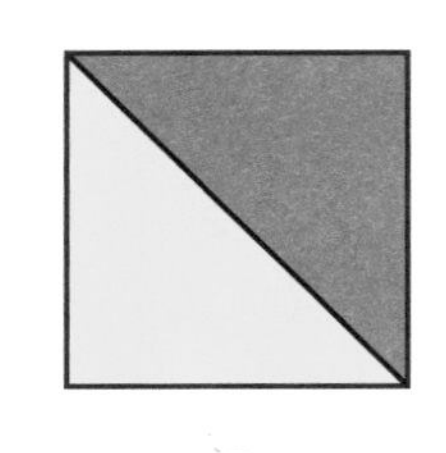

29

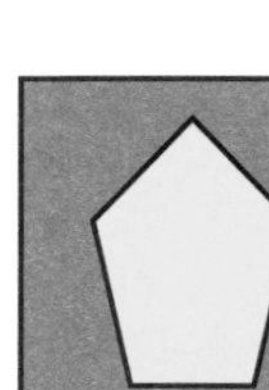
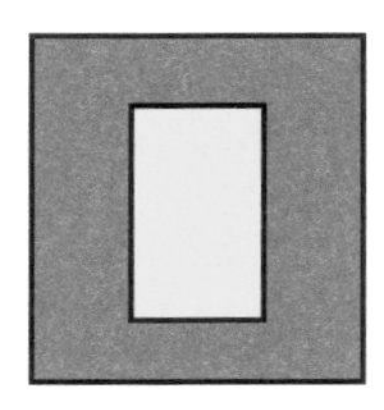

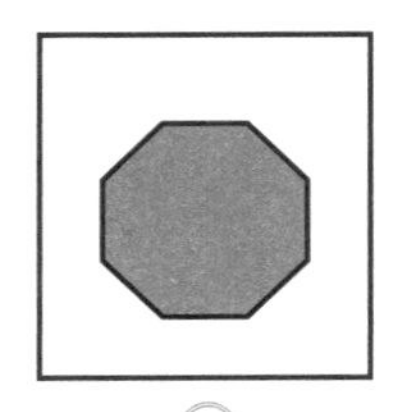

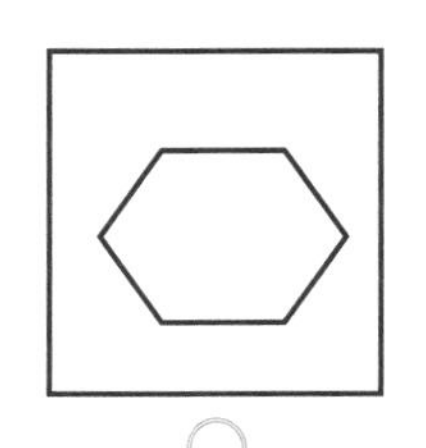

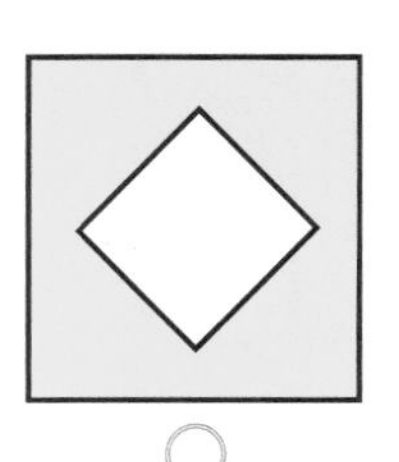

30

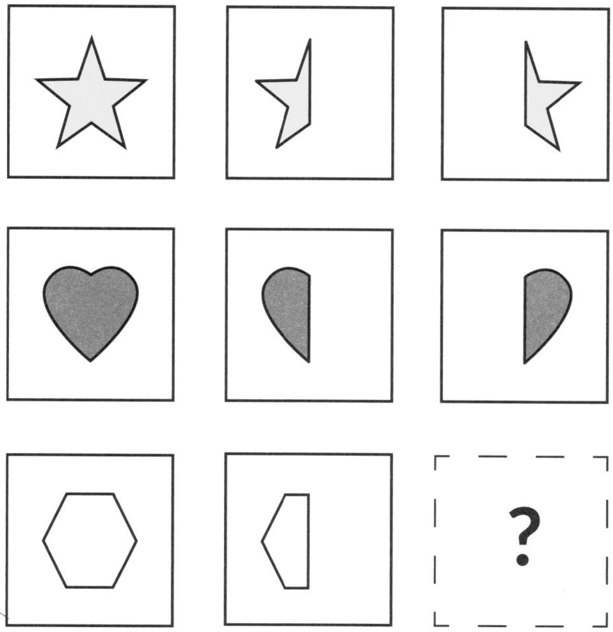

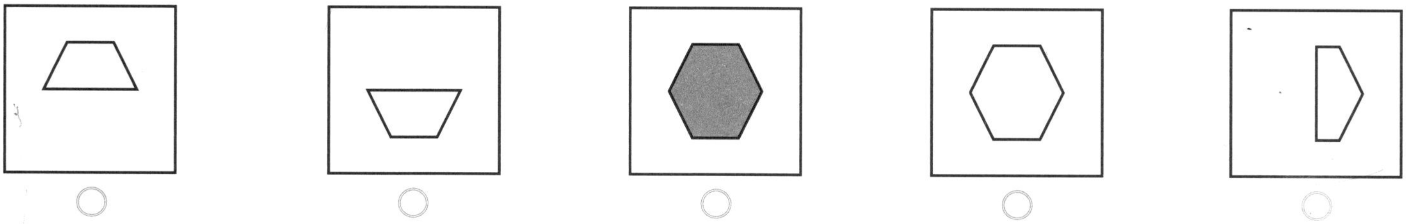

?

31

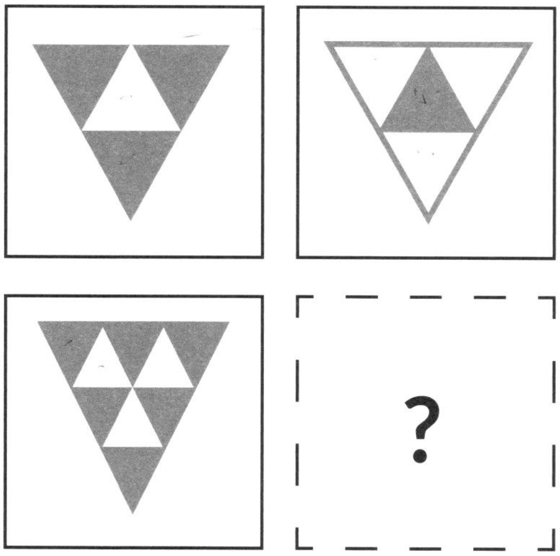

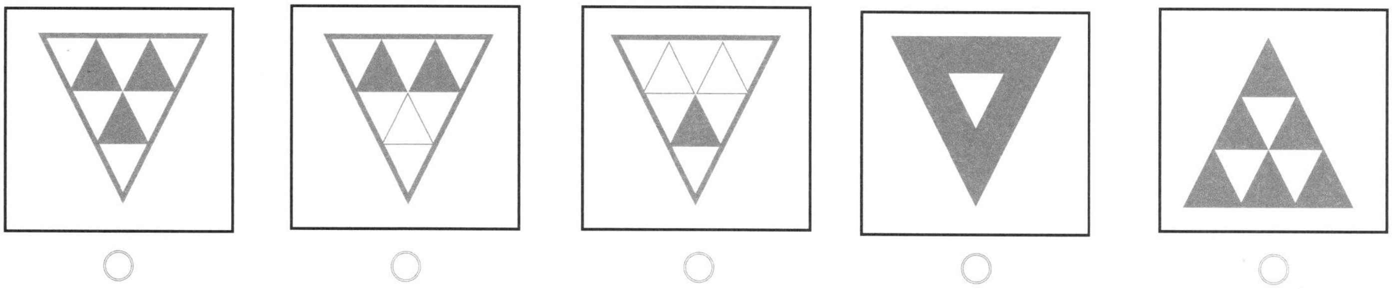

?

1

?

2

?

3

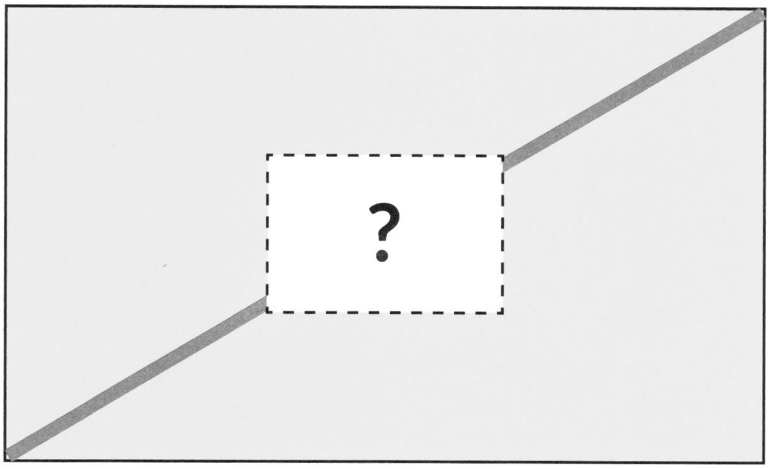

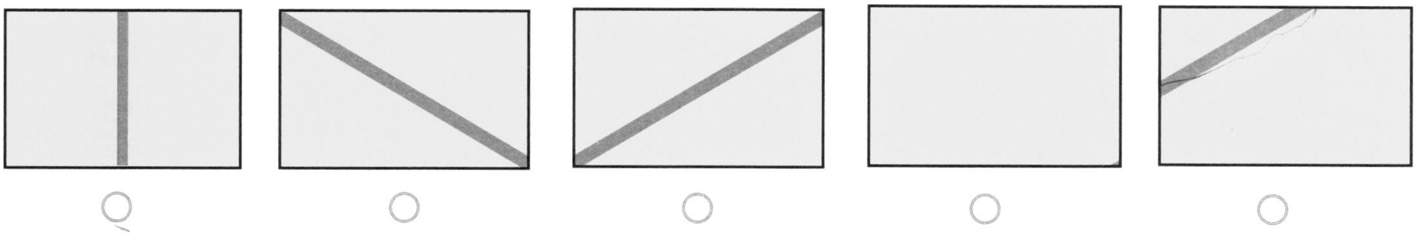

?

4

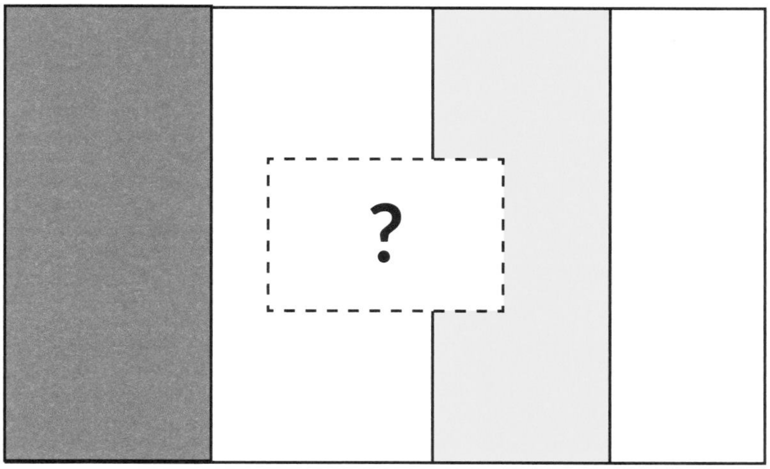

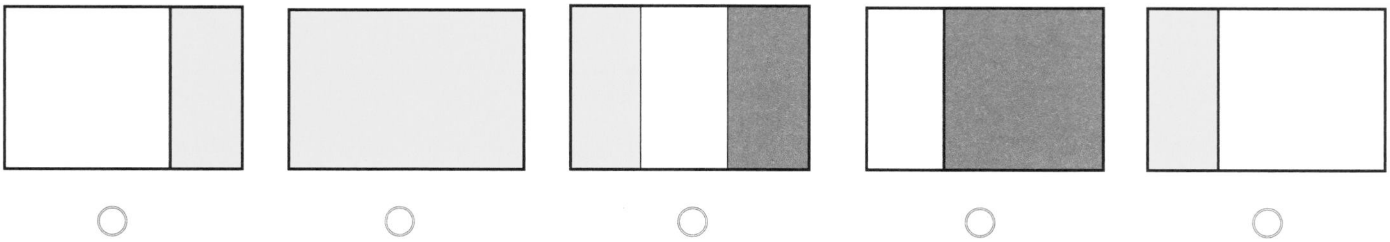

?

5

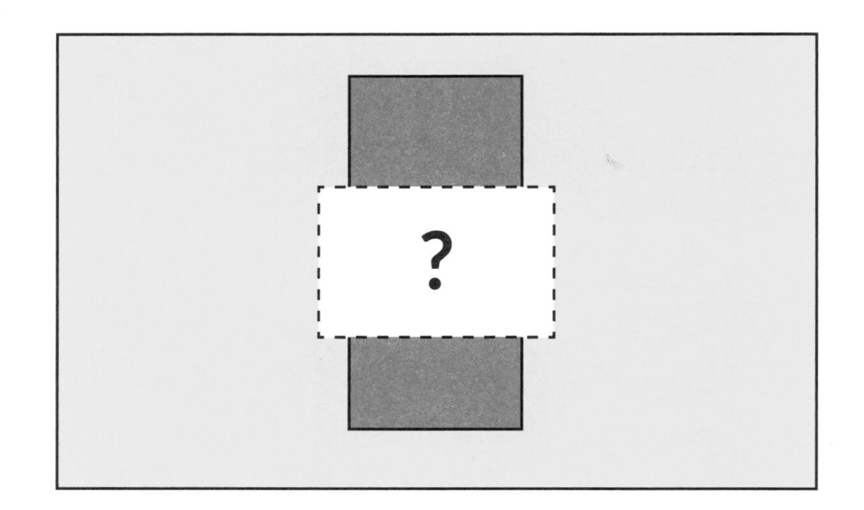

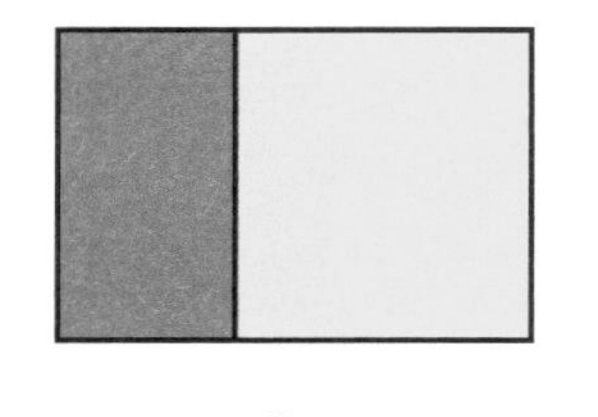
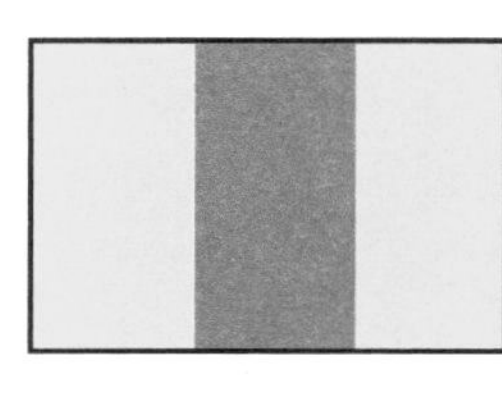
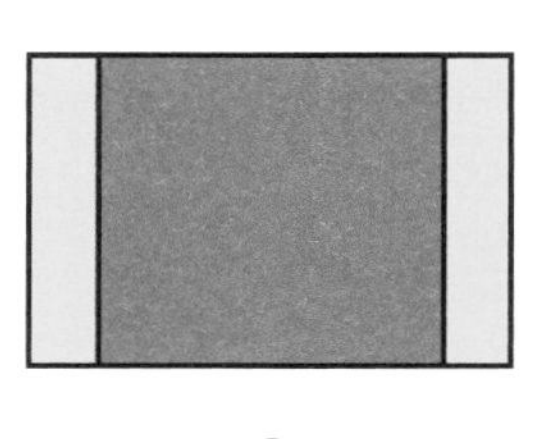
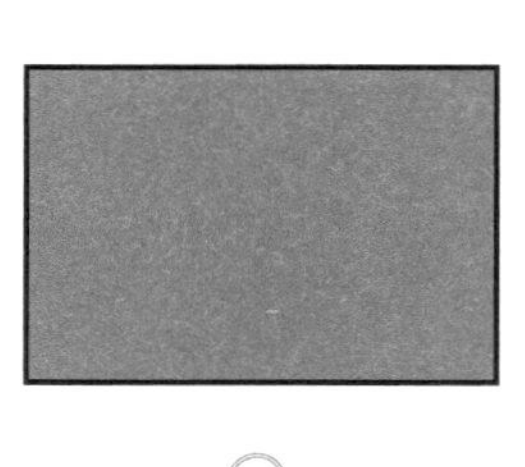

6

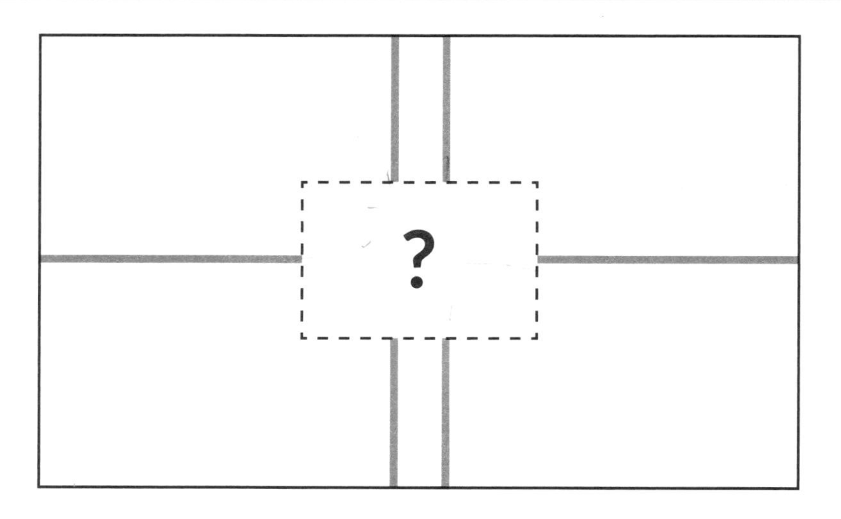

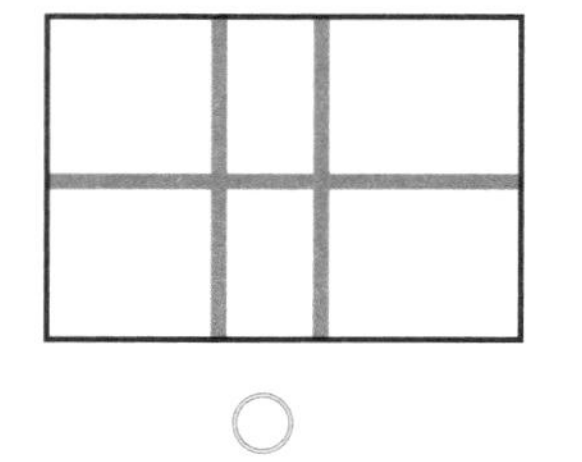
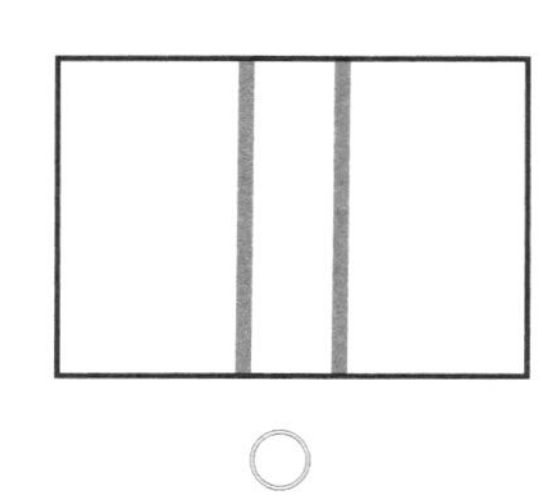
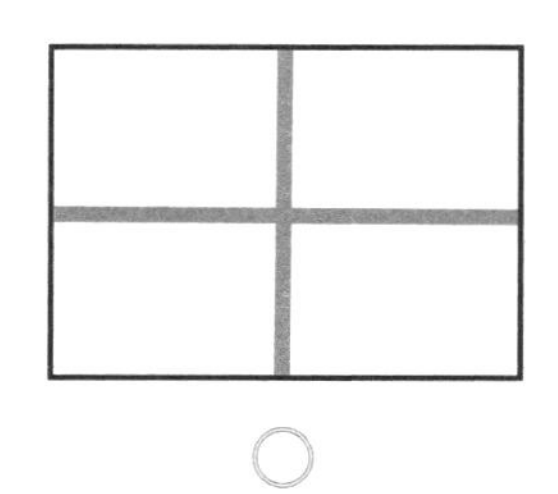
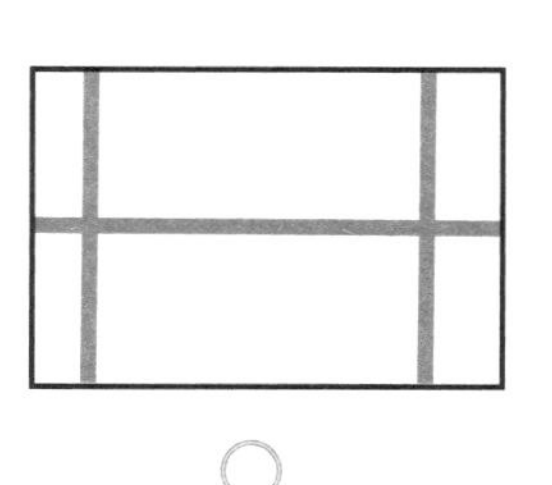
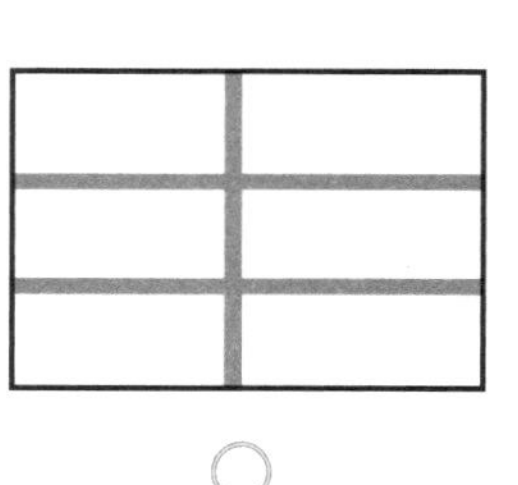

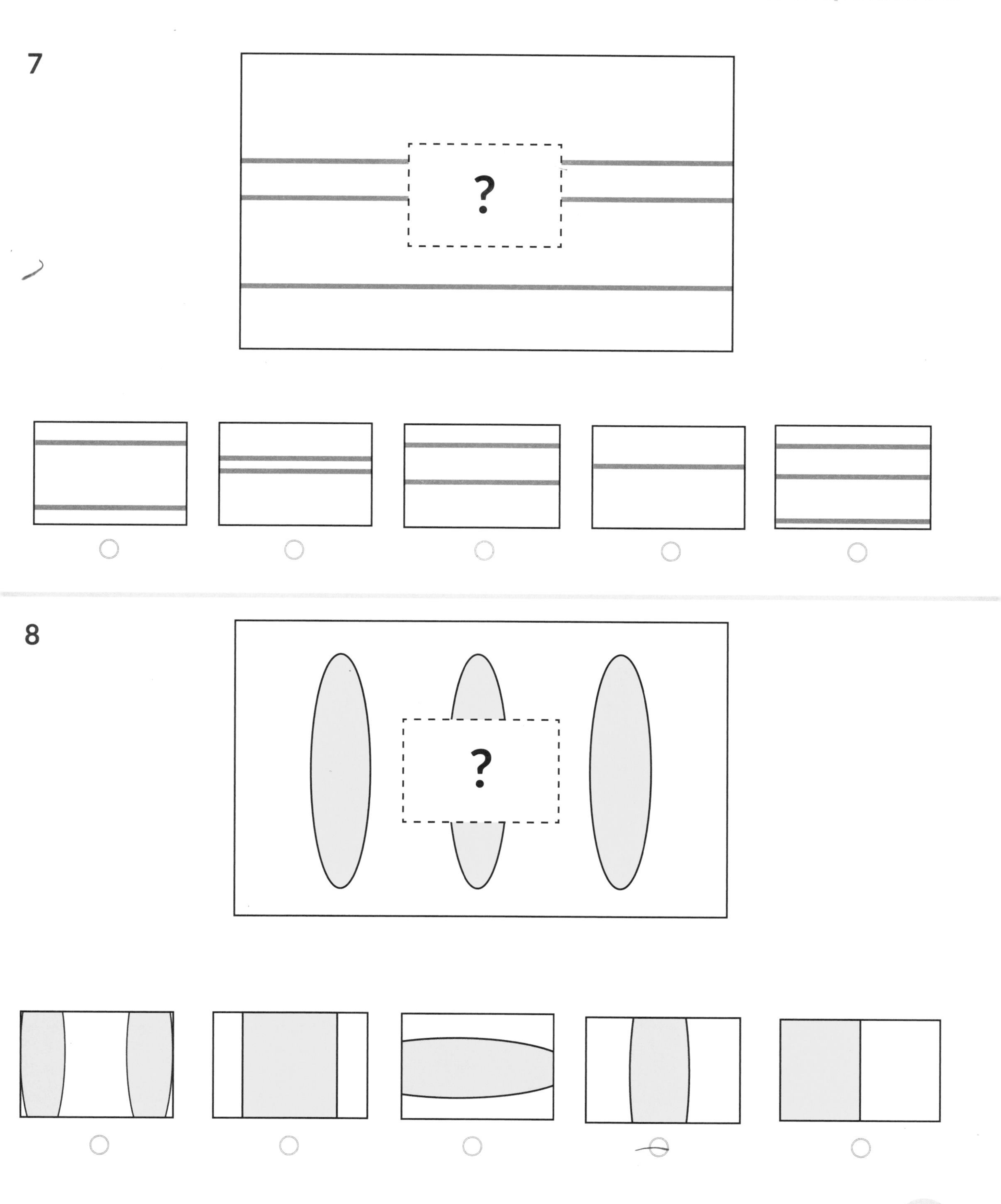
7
?
8
?

9

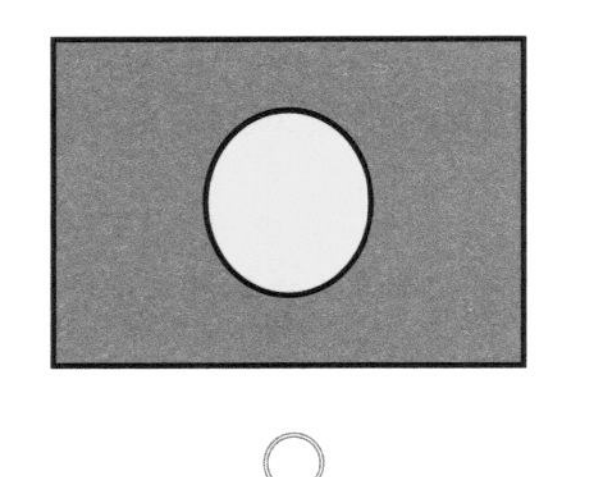 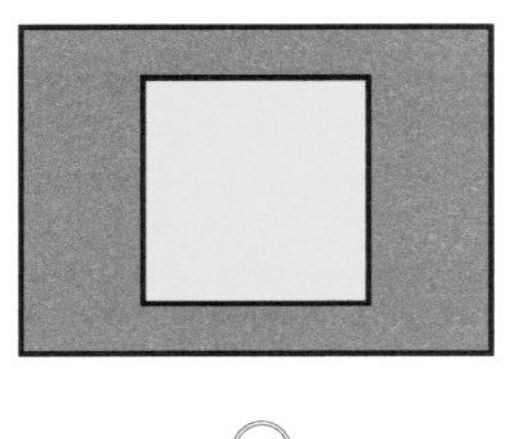 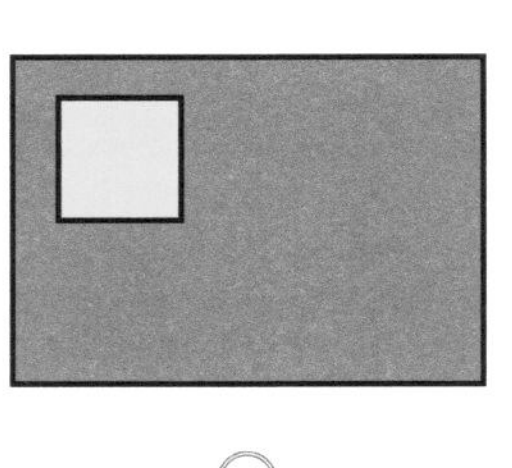 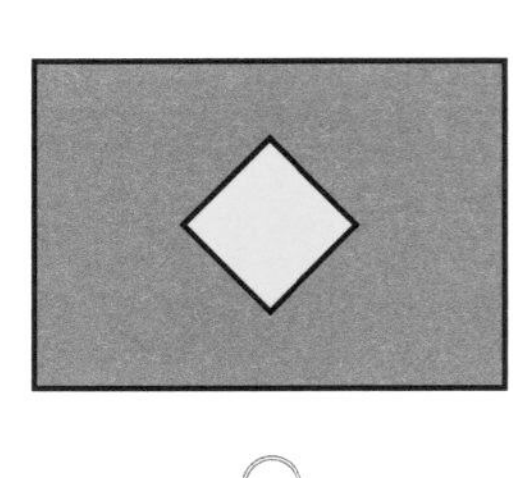 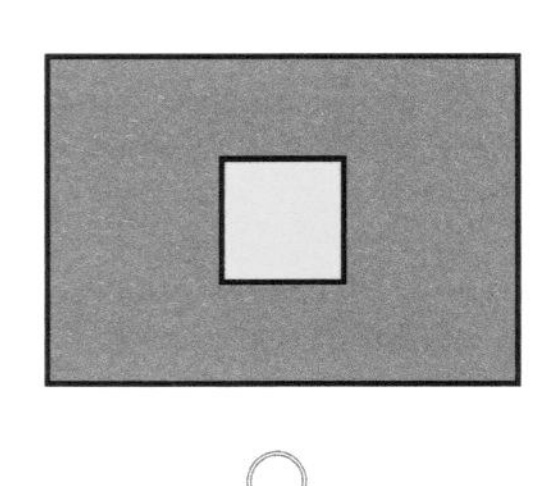

10

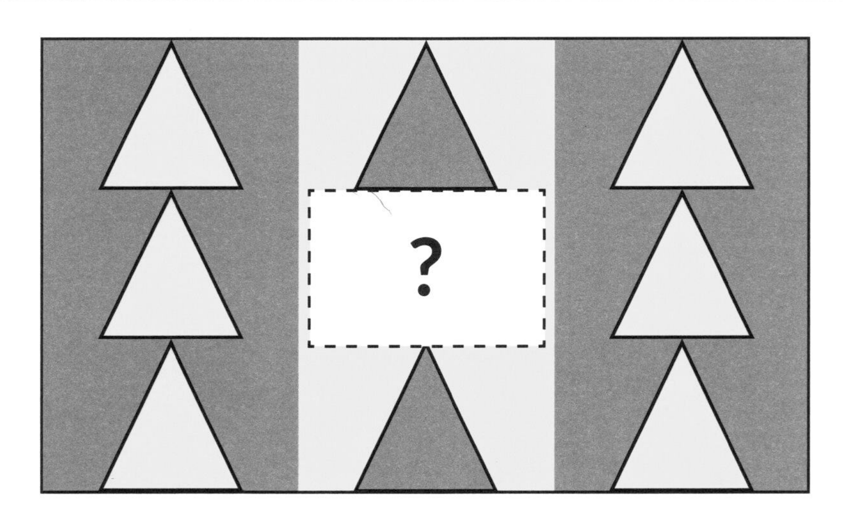

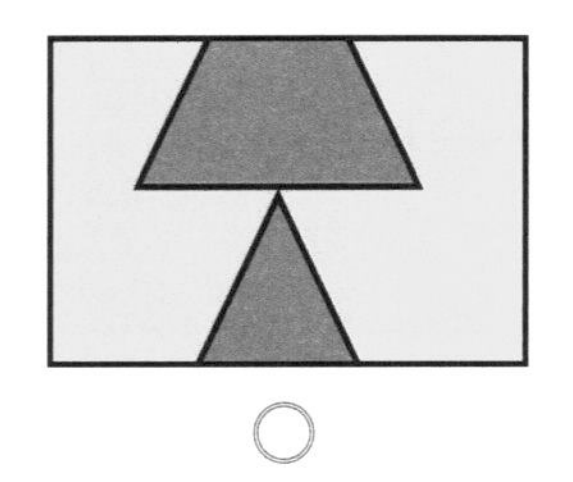 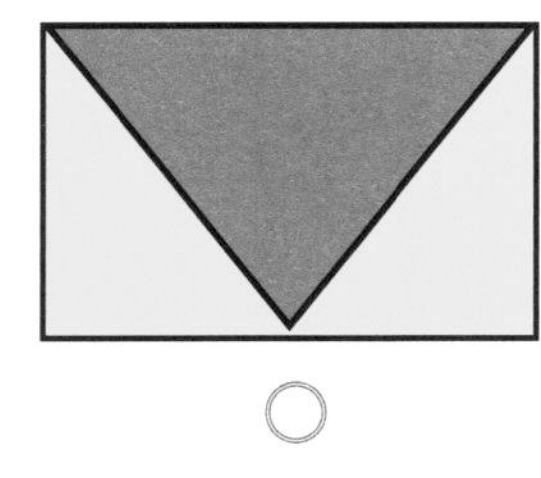 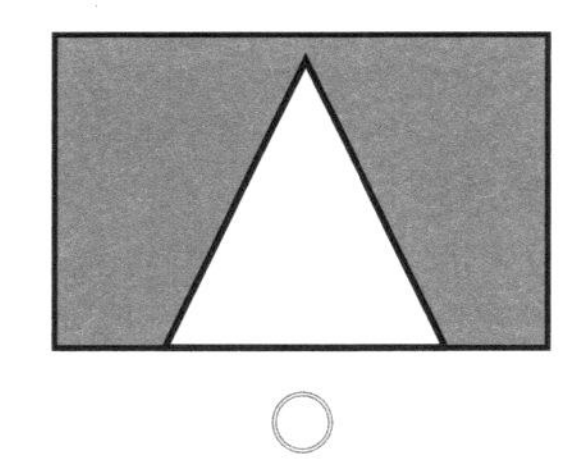 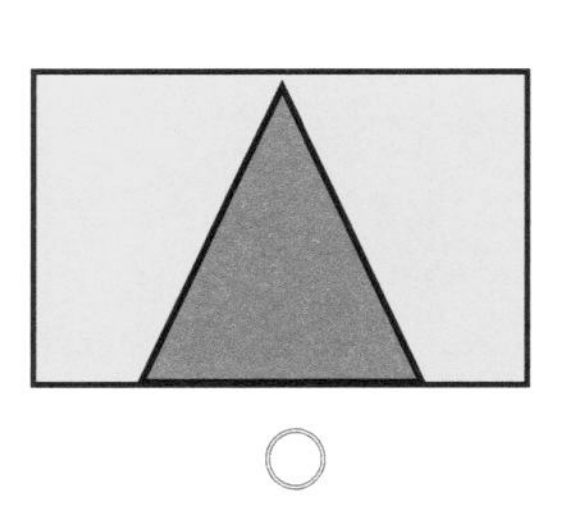 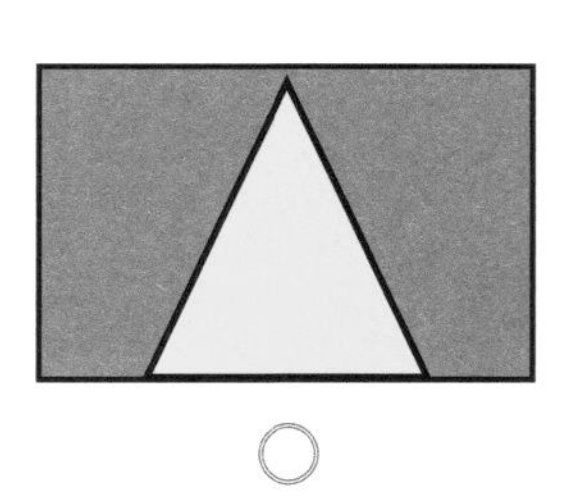

11

?

12

?

13

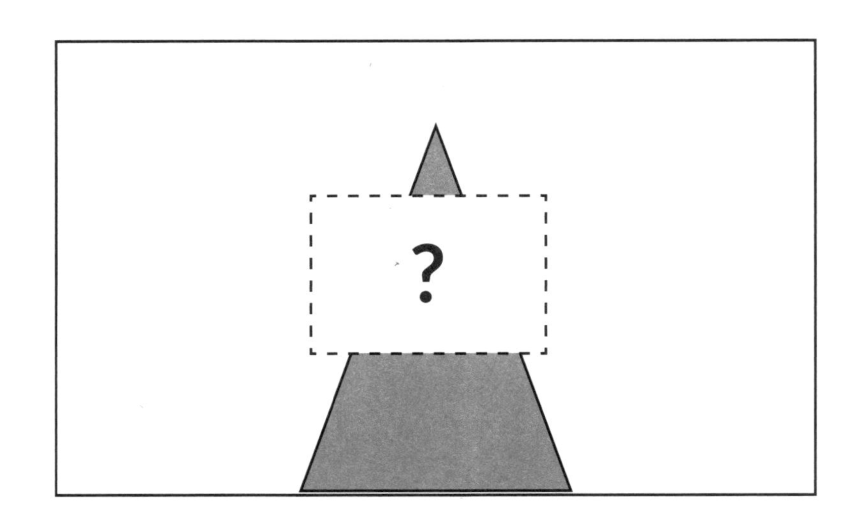

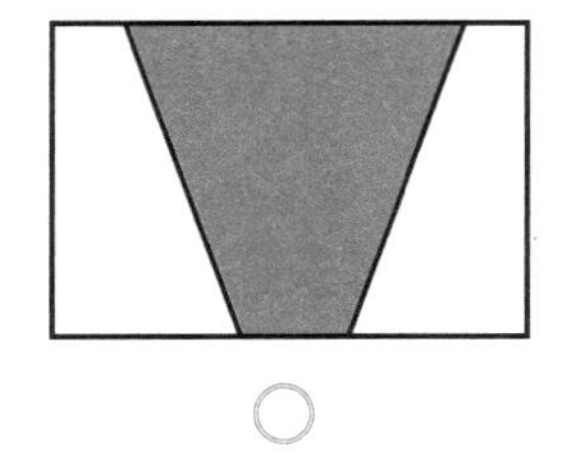
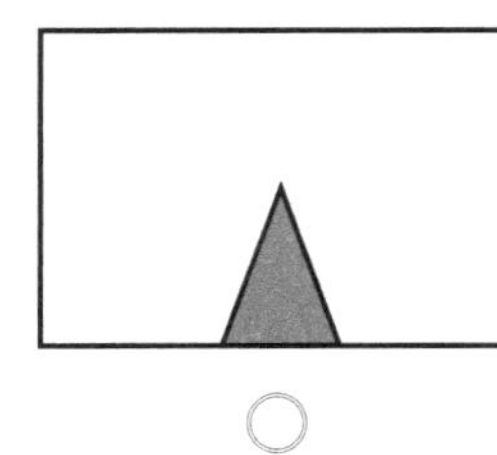
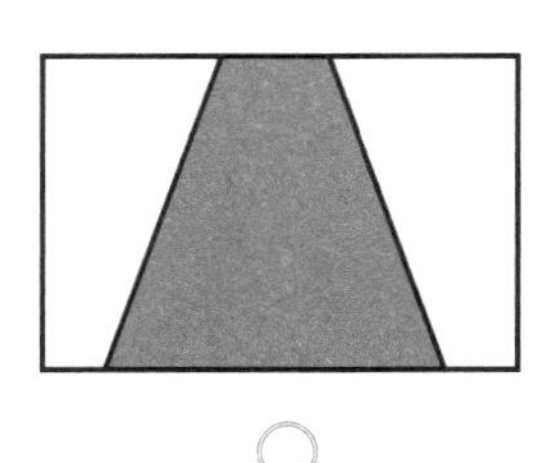
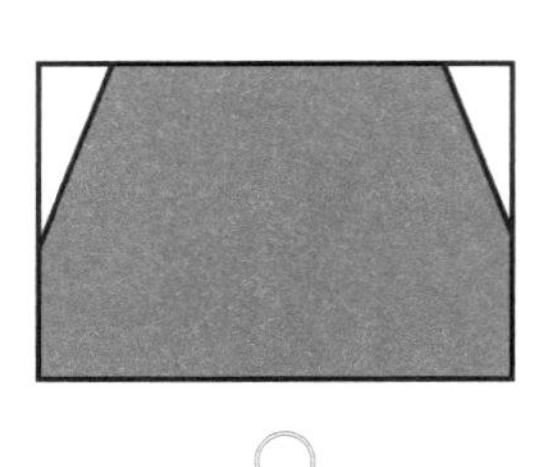
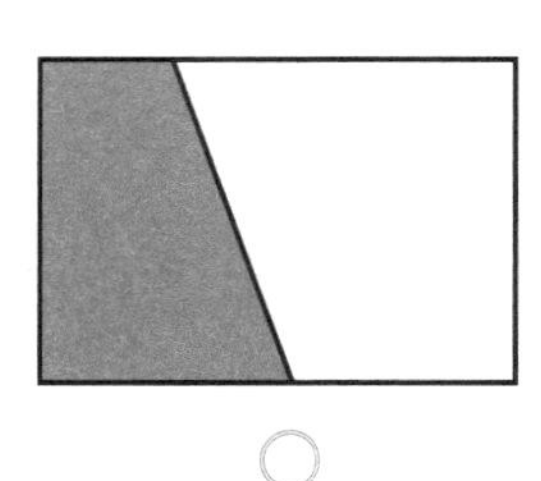

14

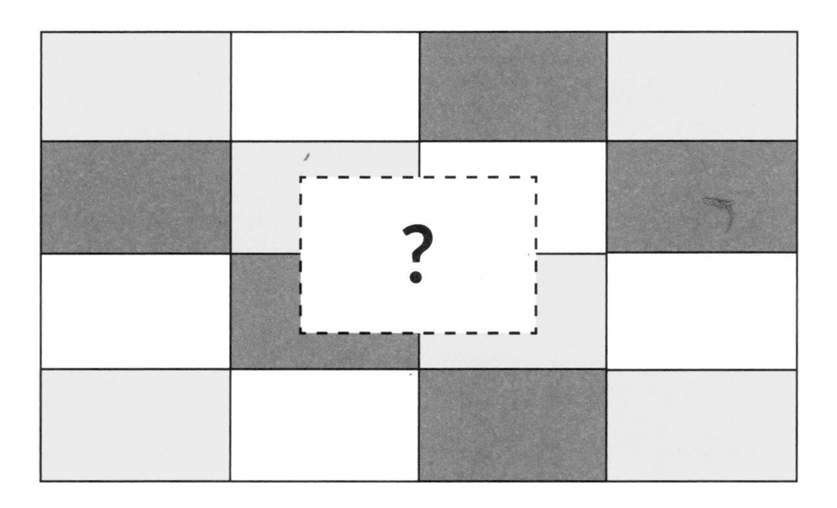

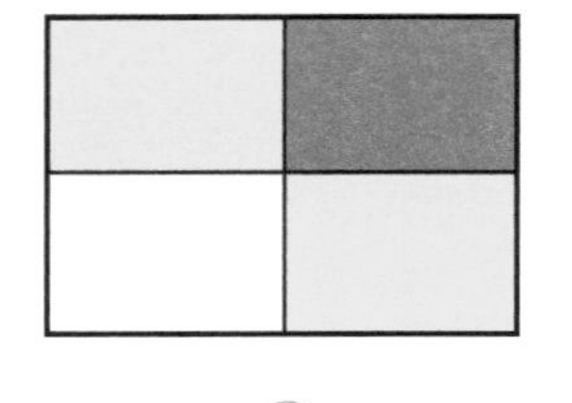
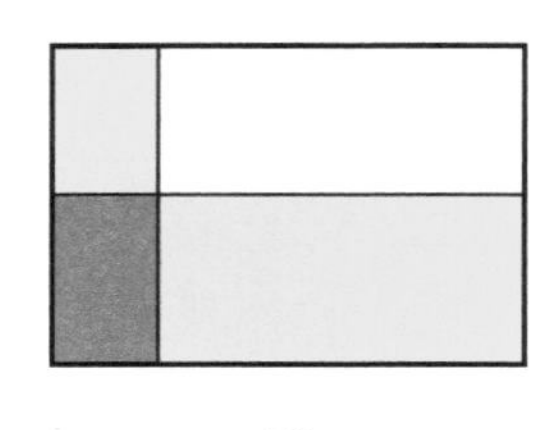
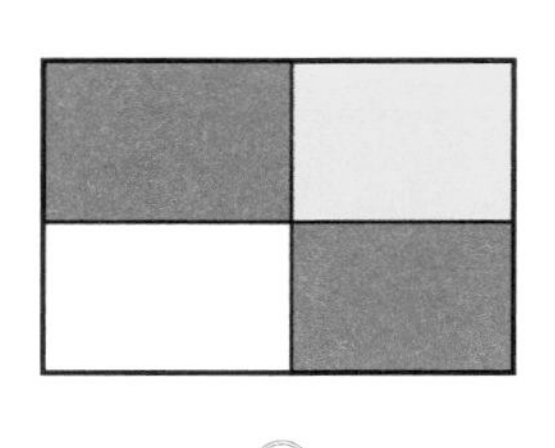
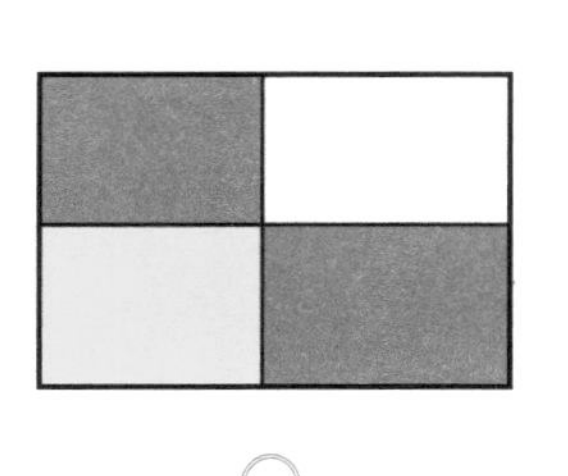

15

16

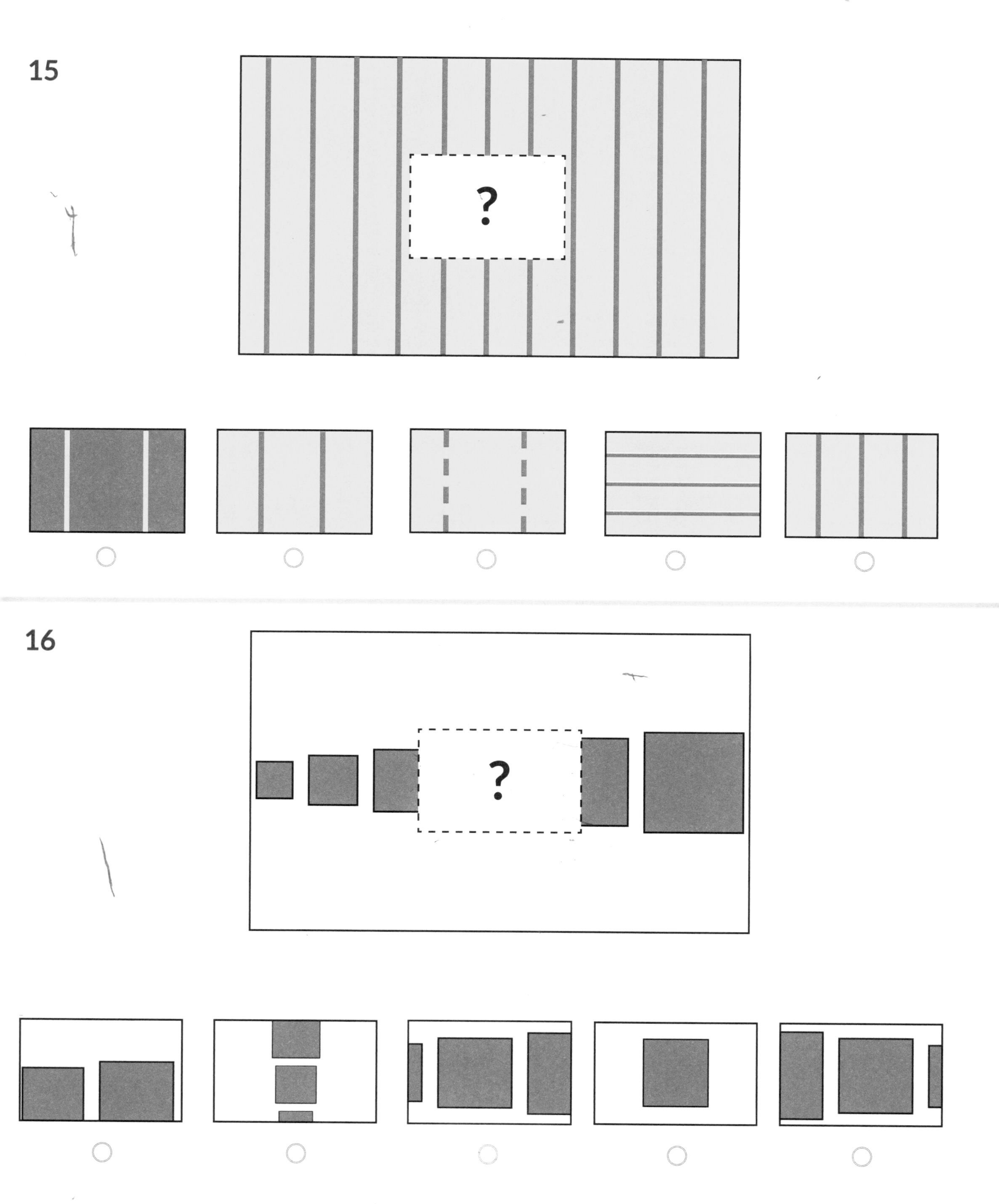

17

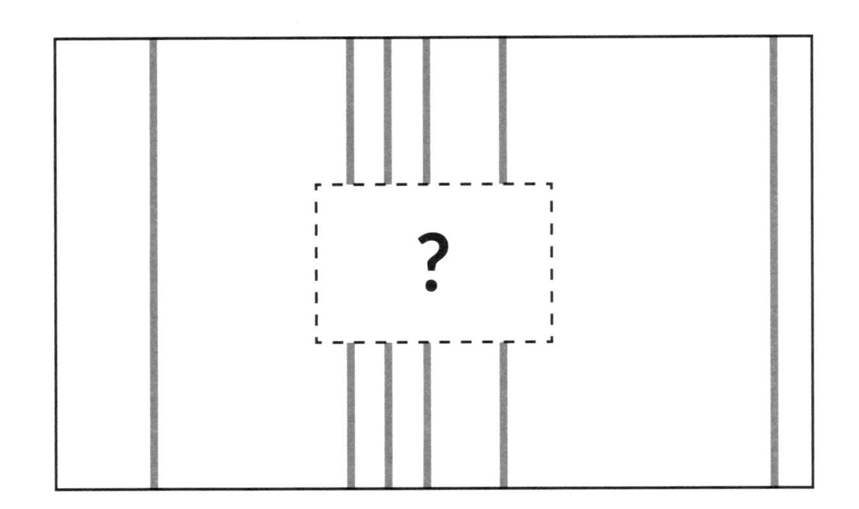

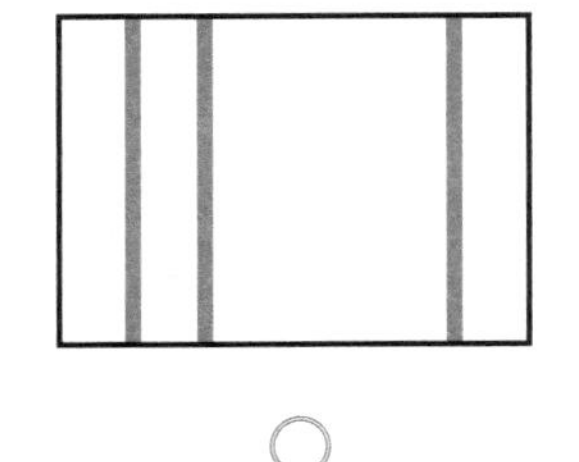
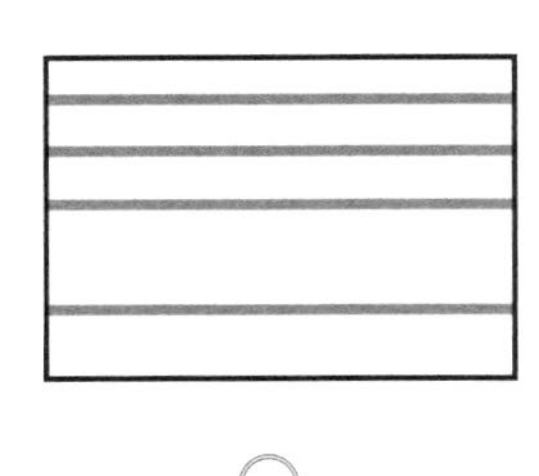
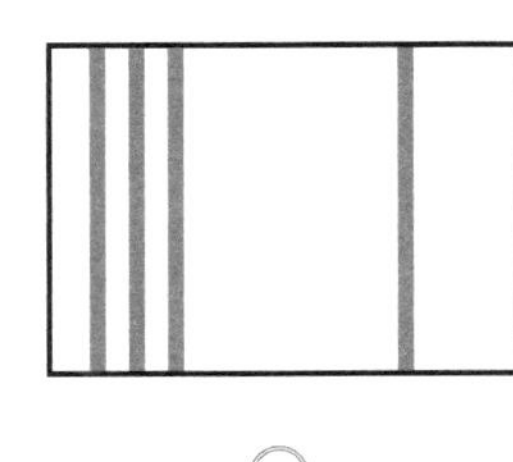
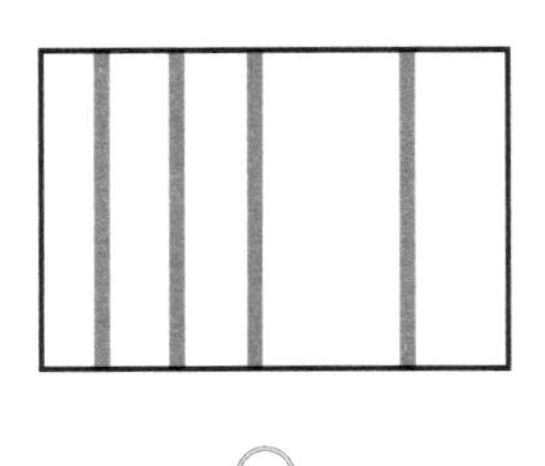
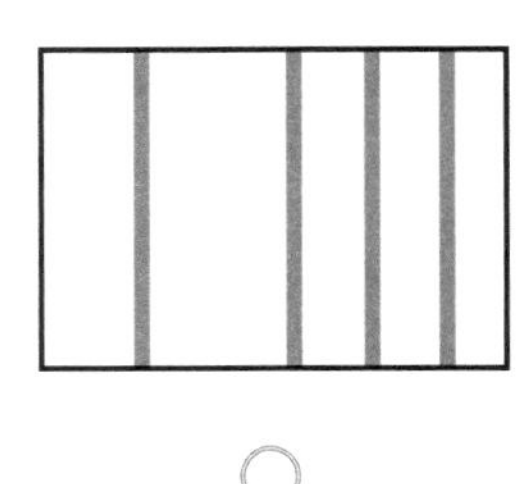

18

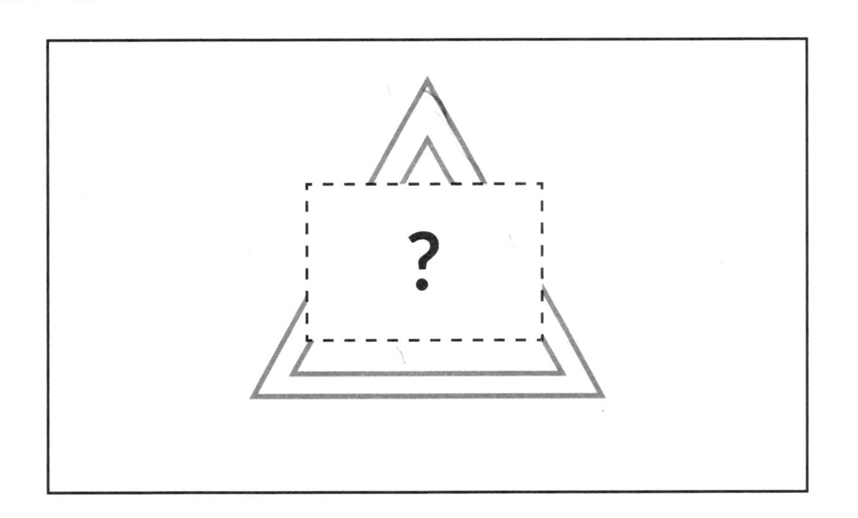

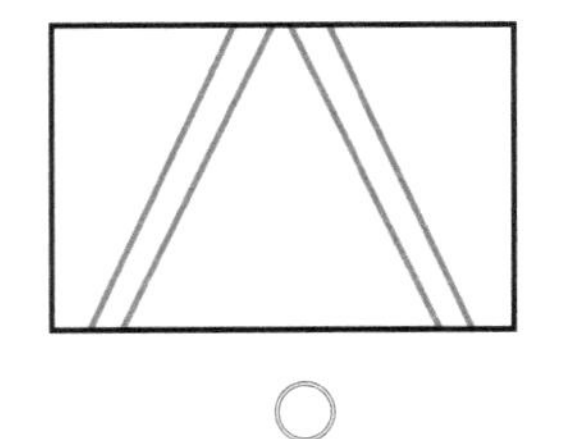
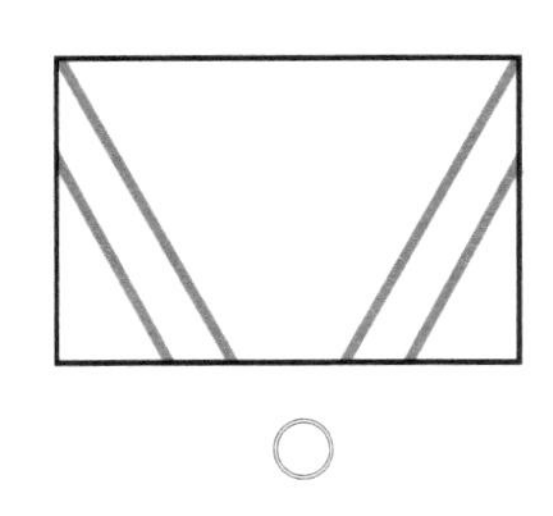
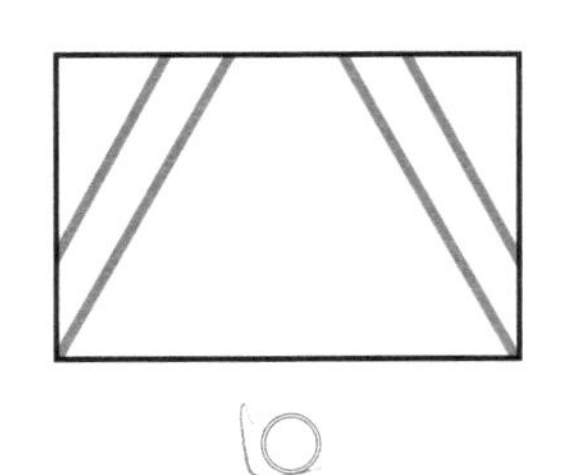
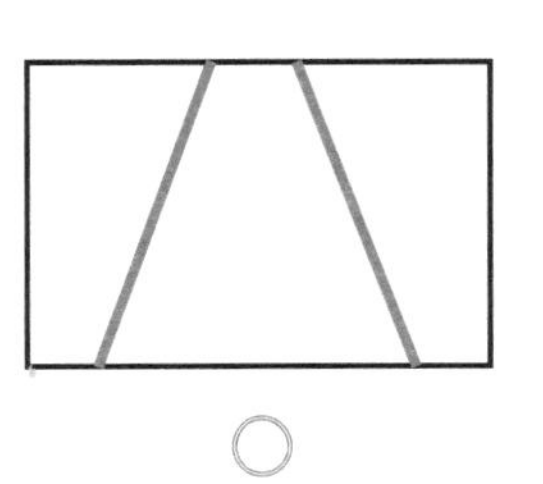
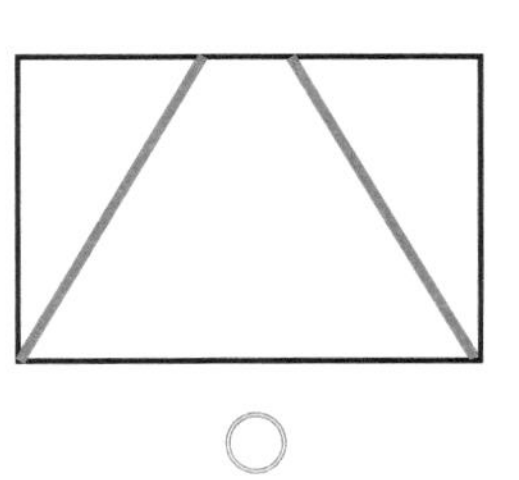

19

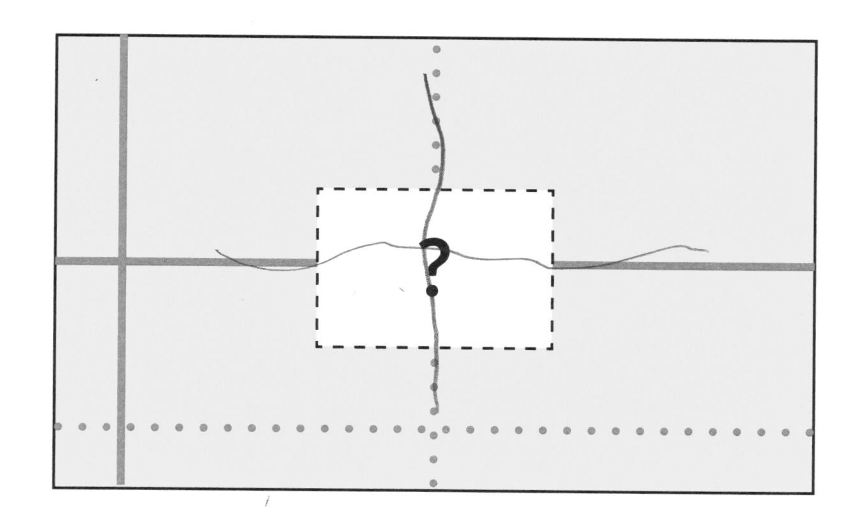

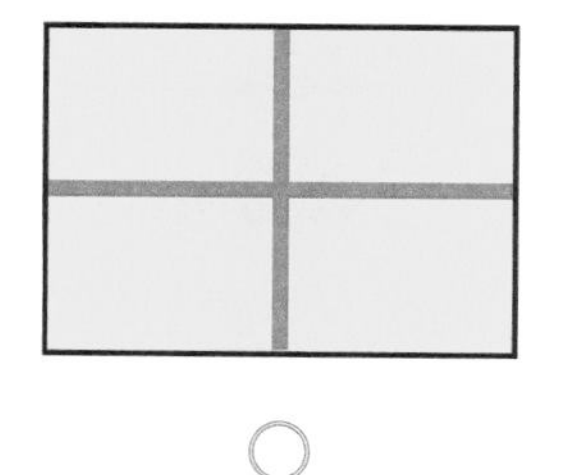
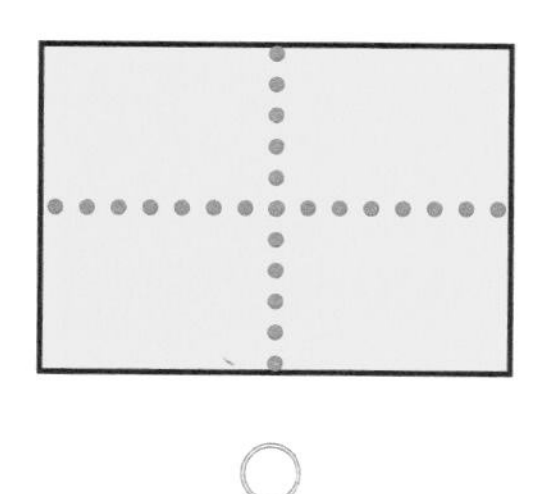
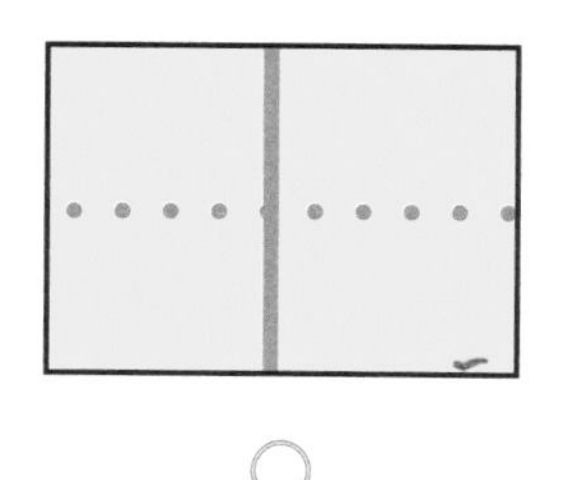
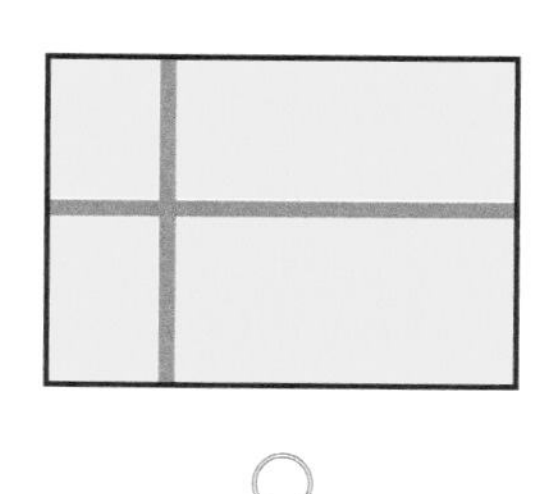
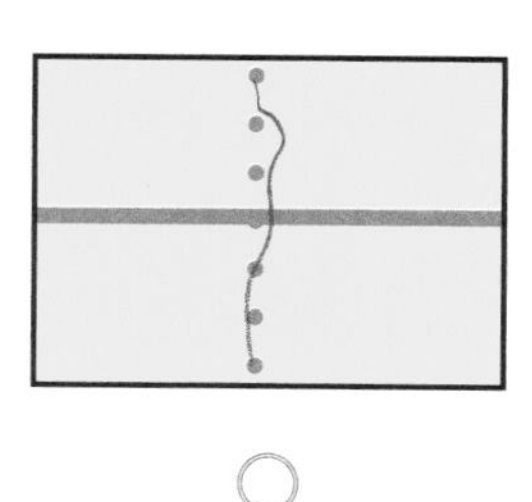

20

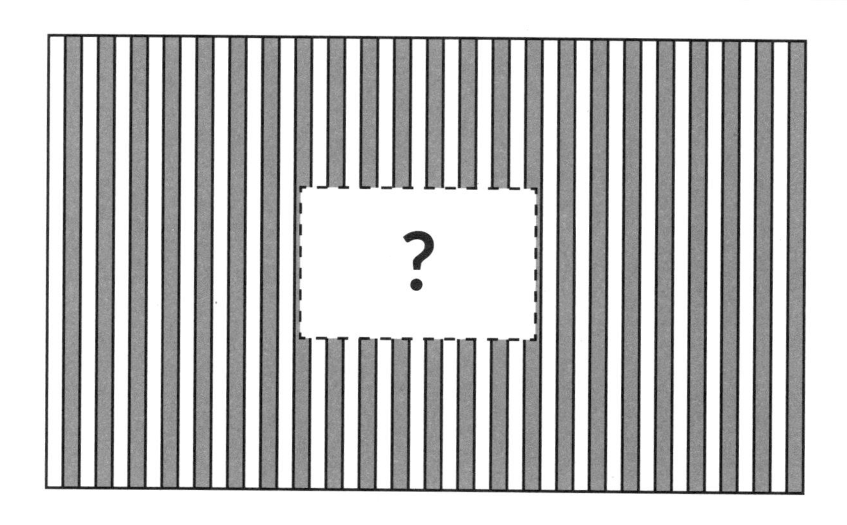

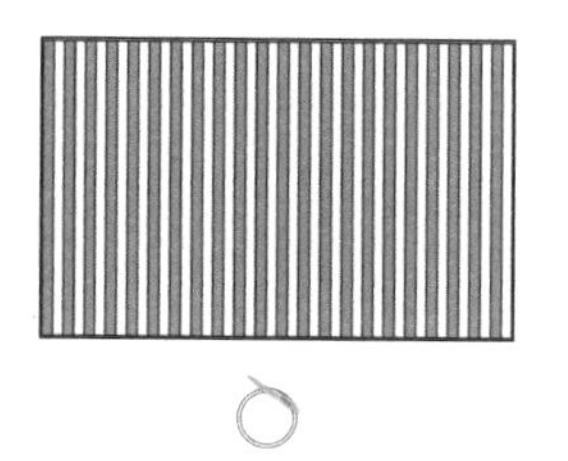
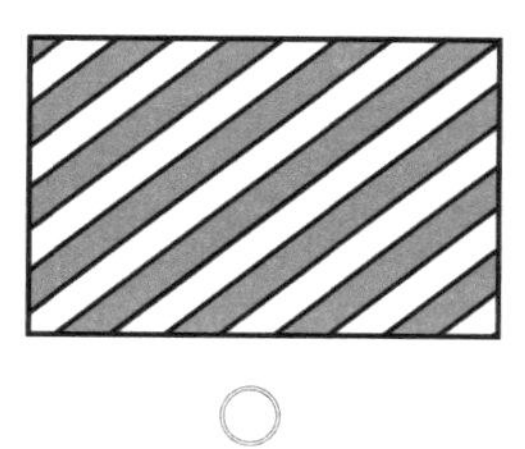
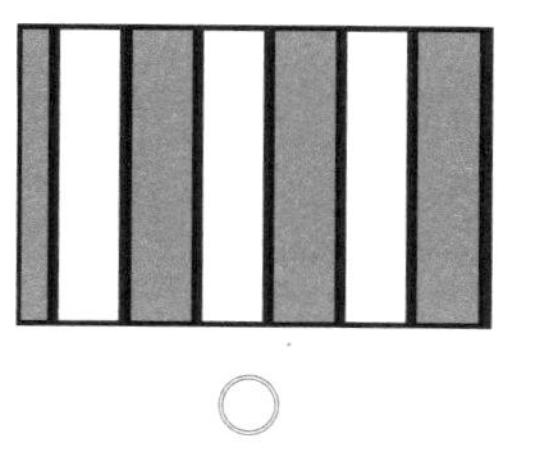
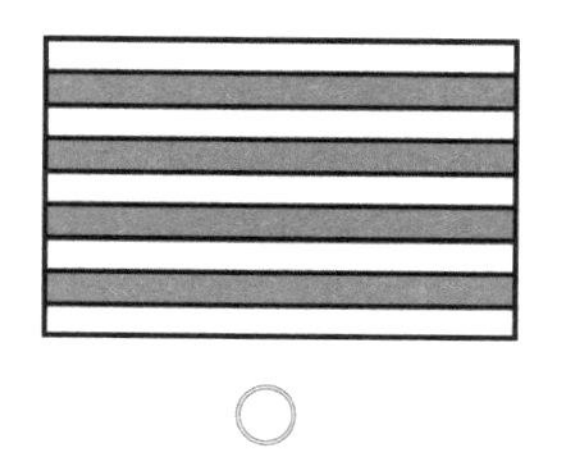
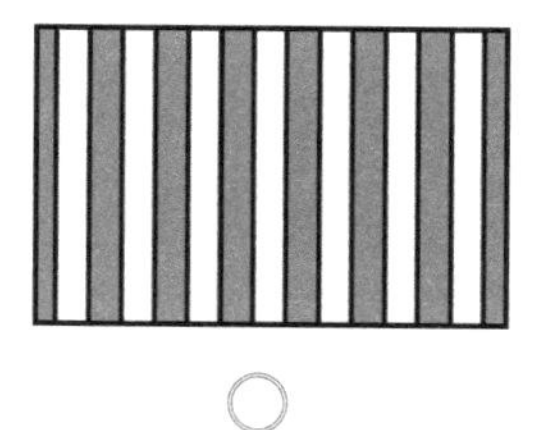

21

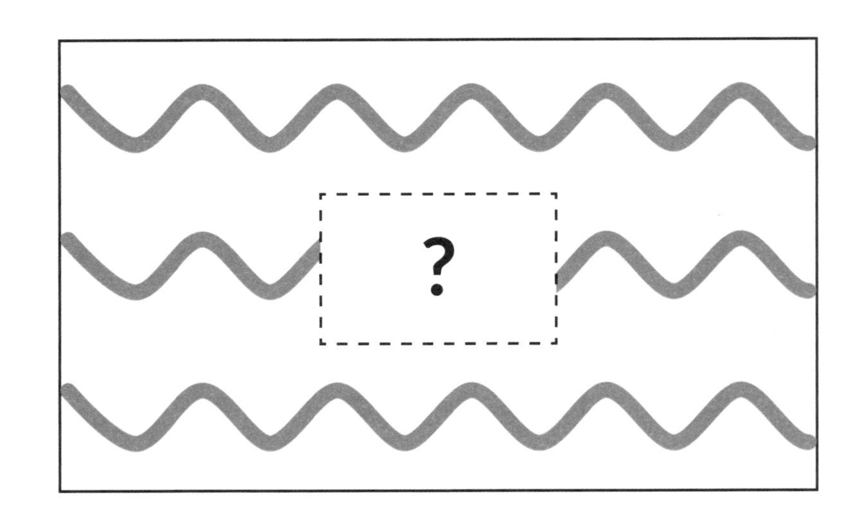

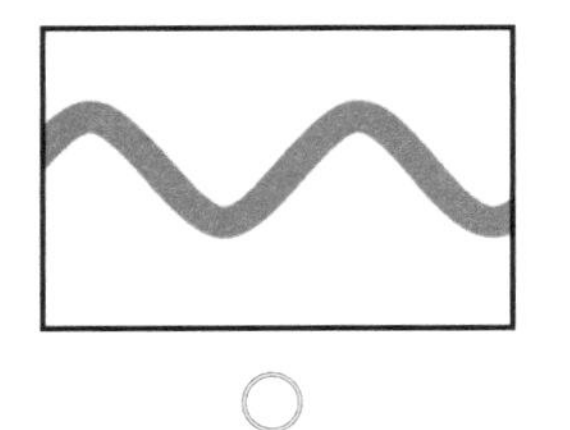

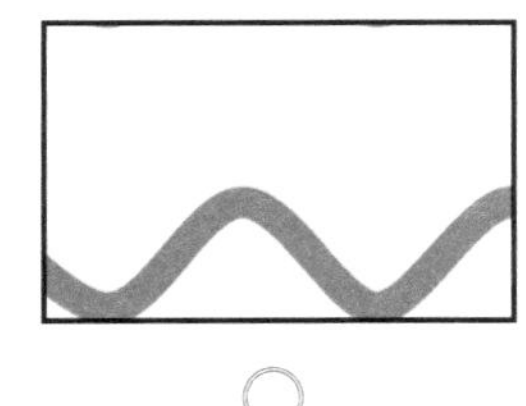

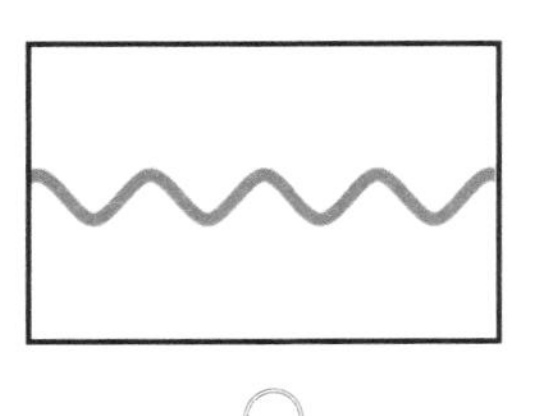

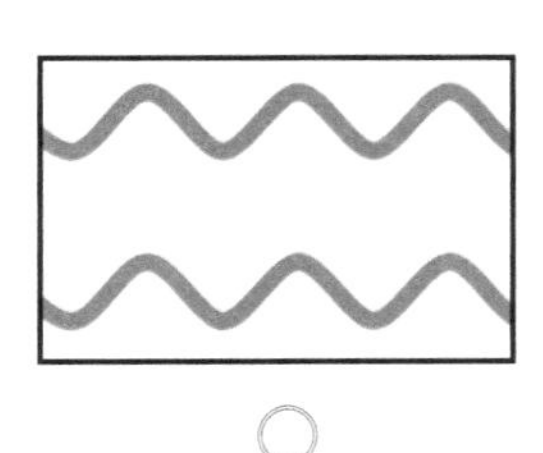

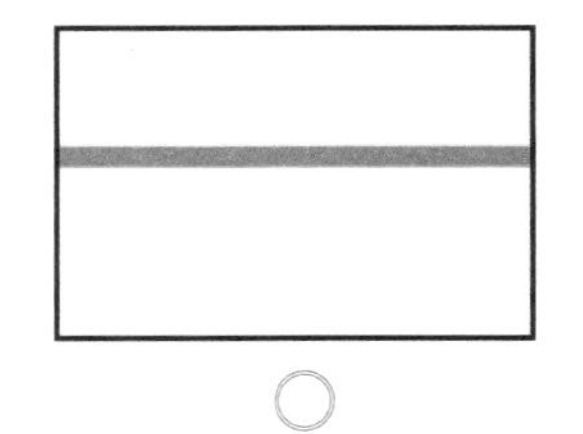

22

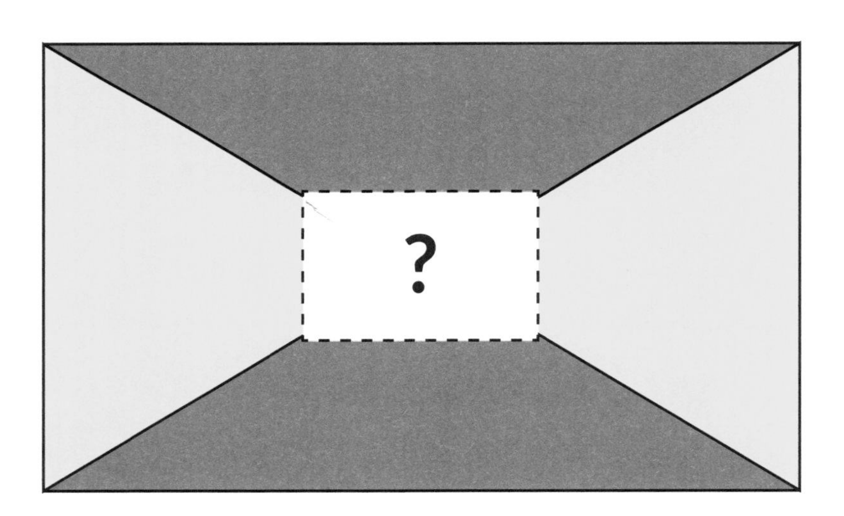

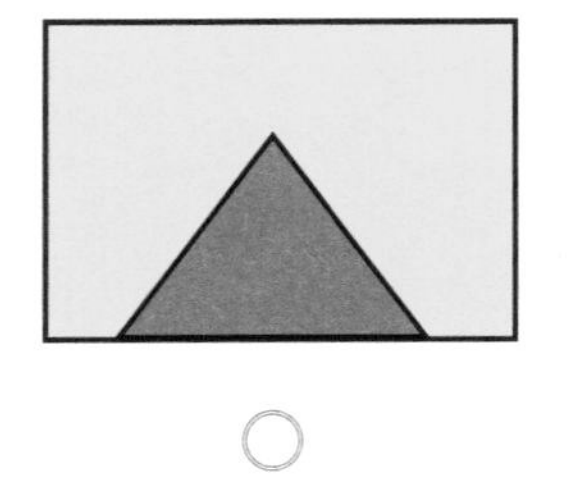

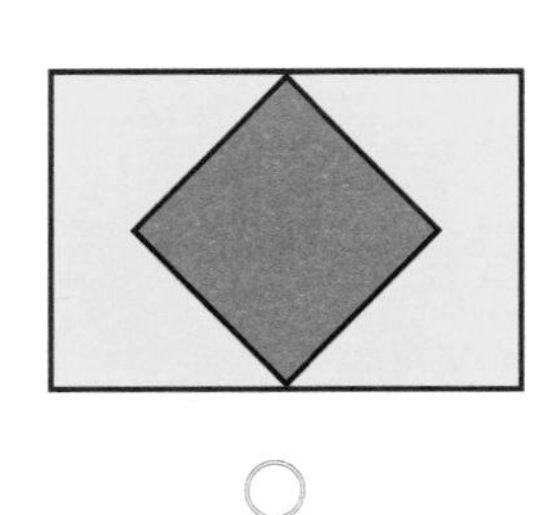

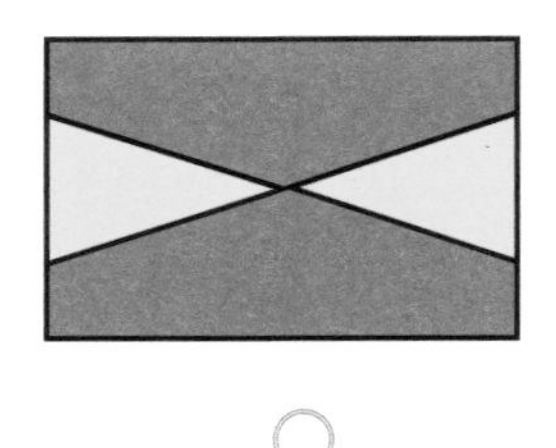

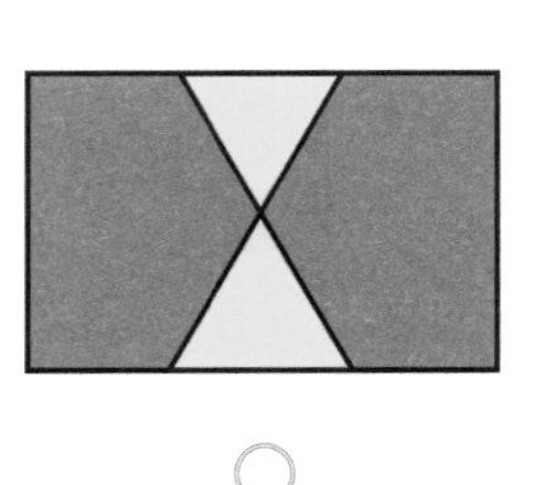

23

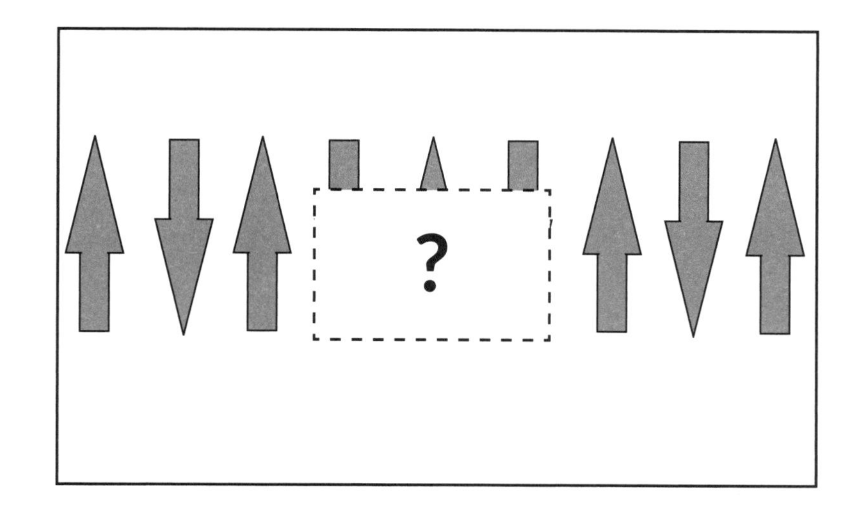

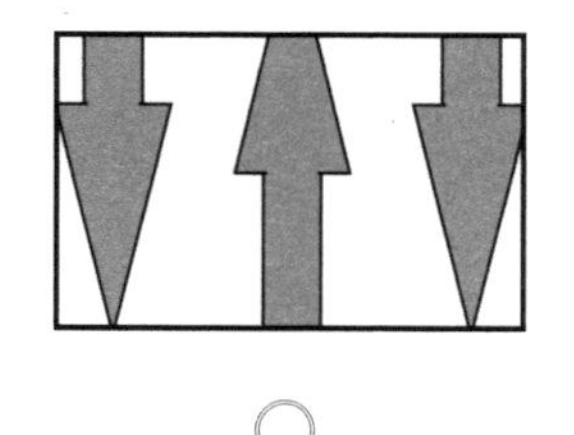
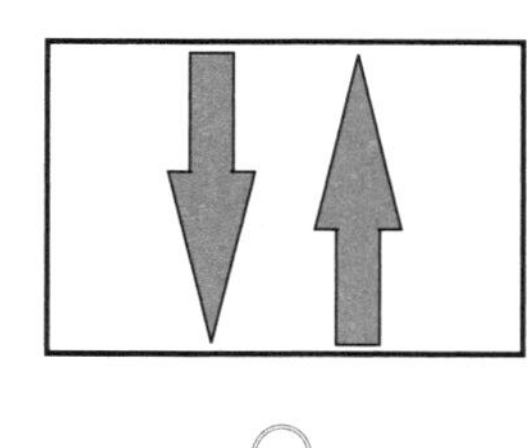
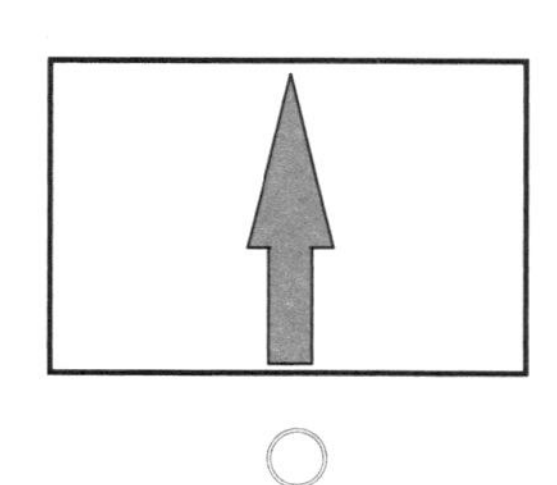
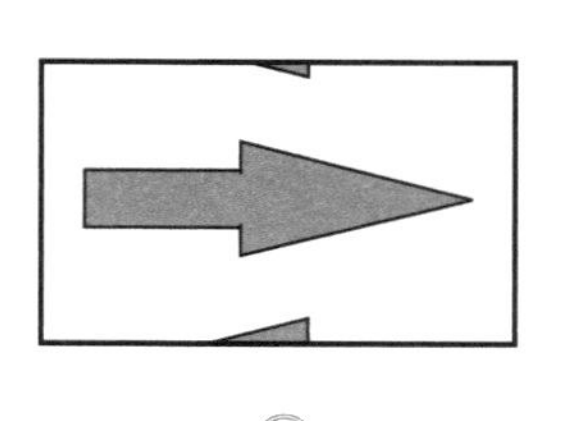
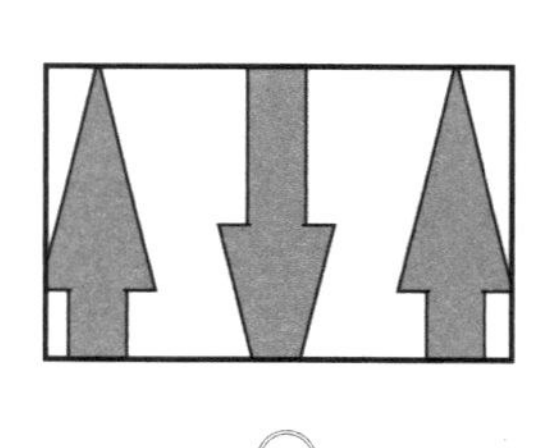

24

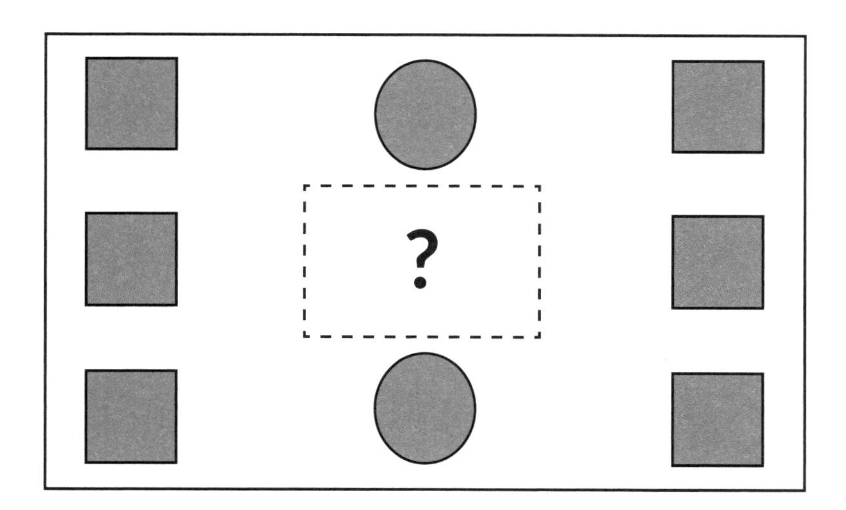

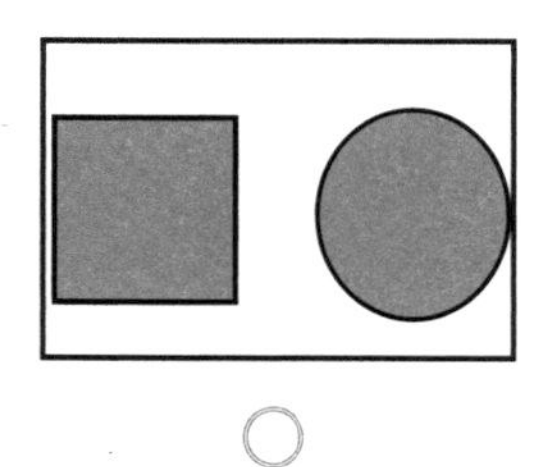
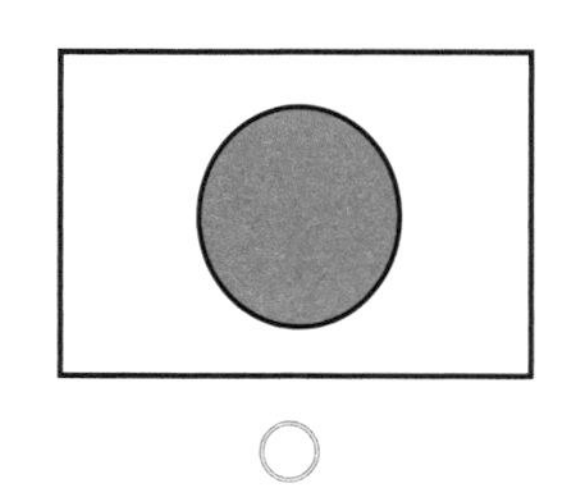
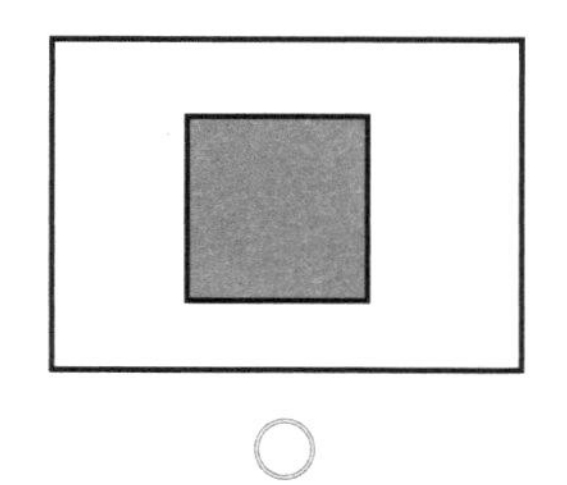
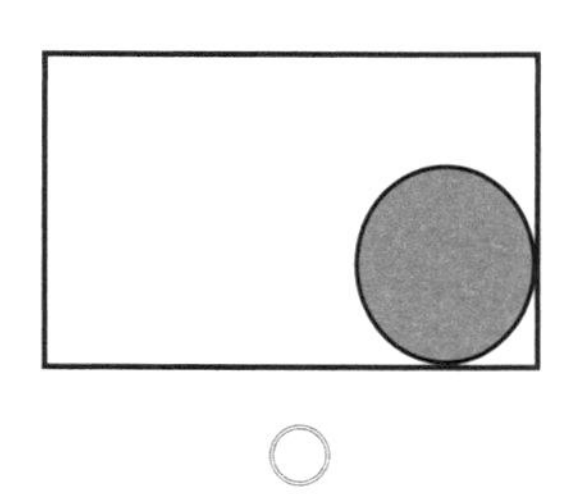
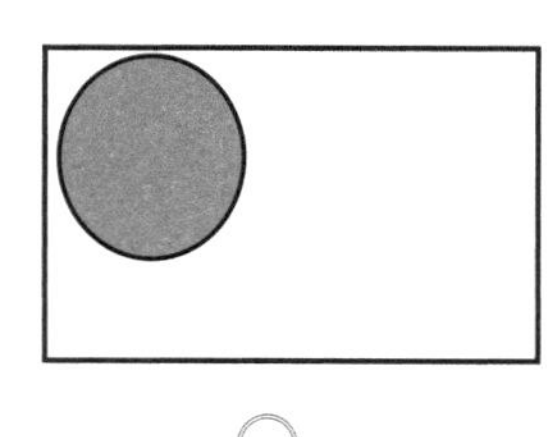

25

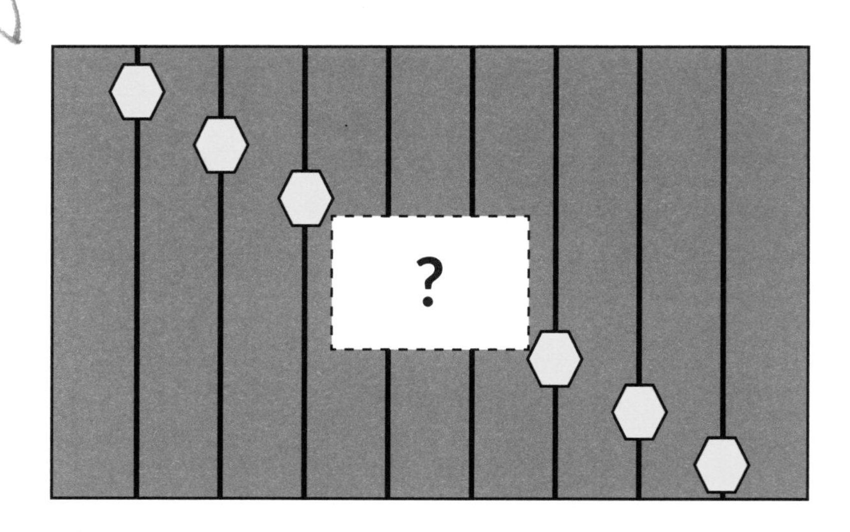

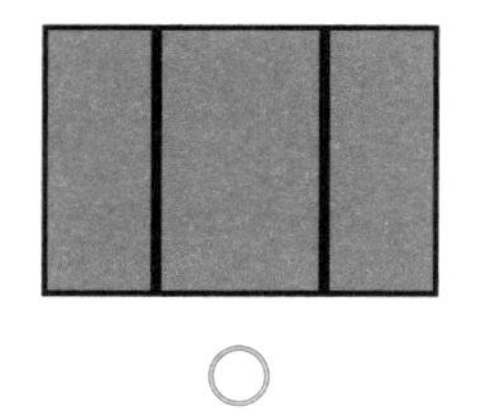

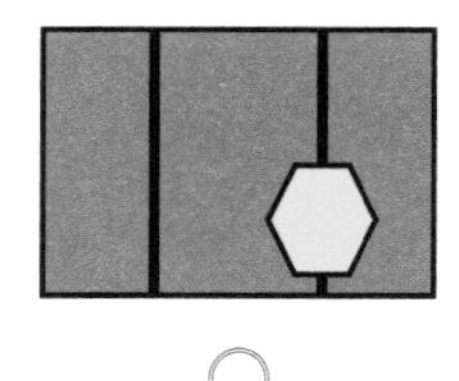

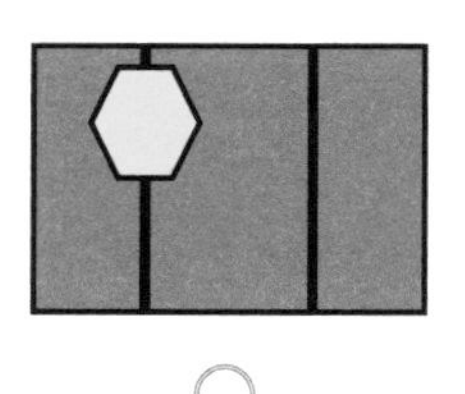

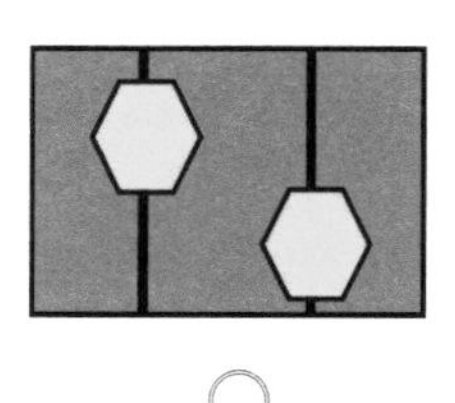

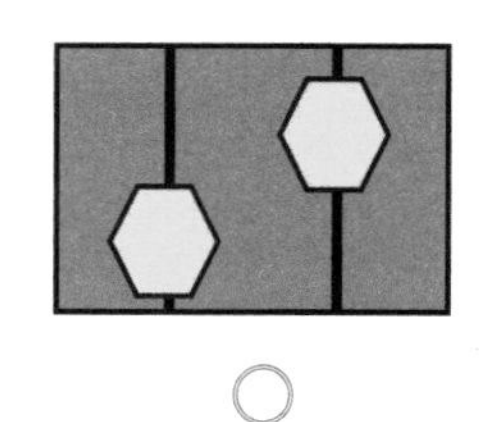

26

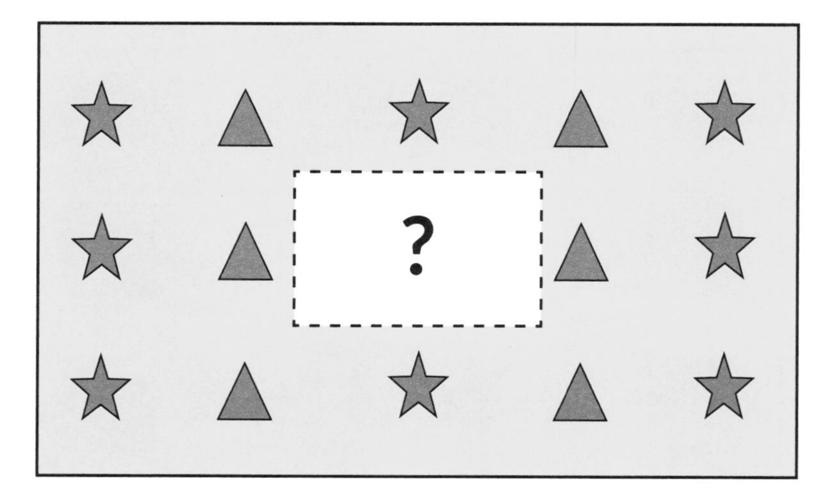

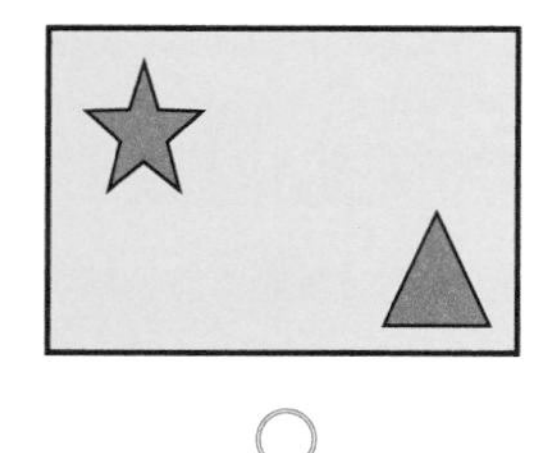

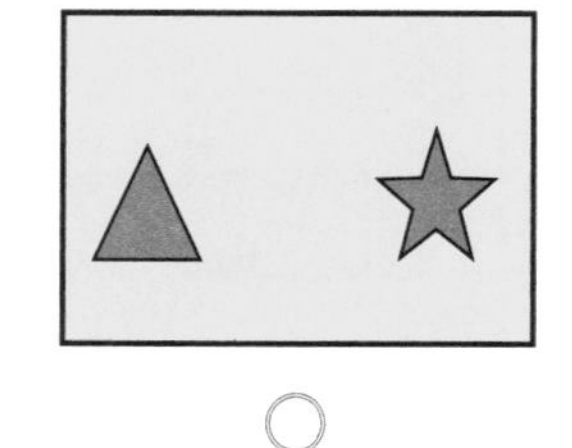

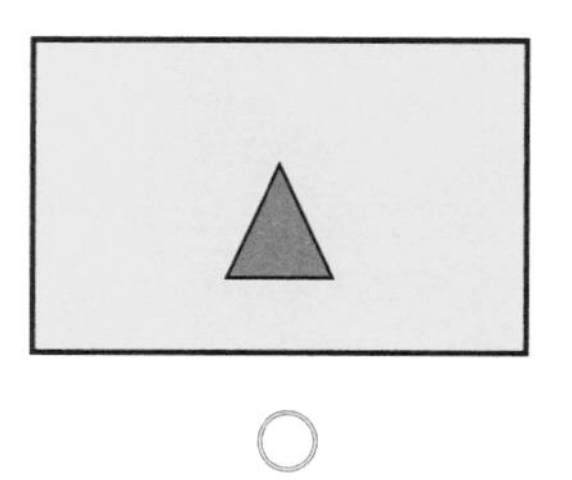

27

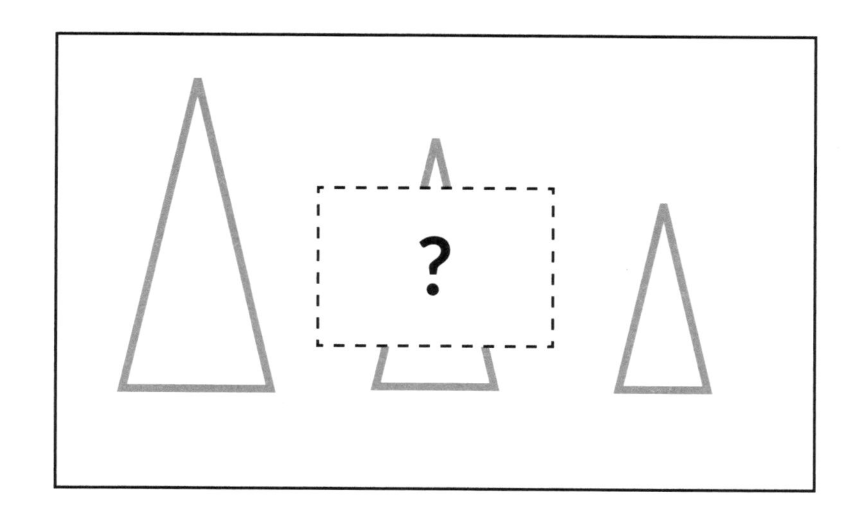

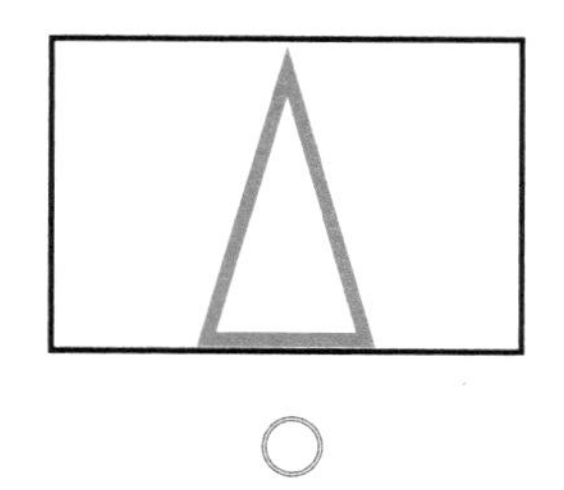
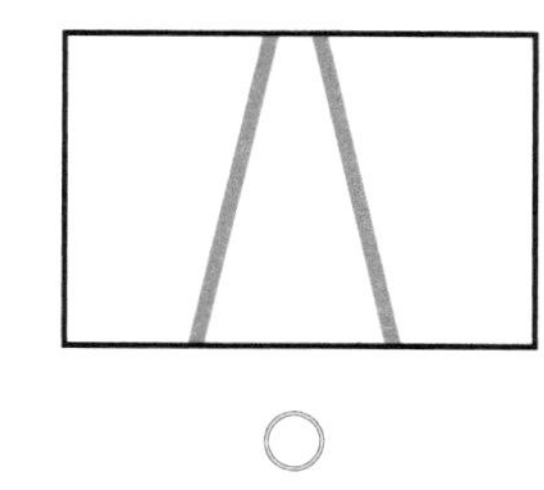
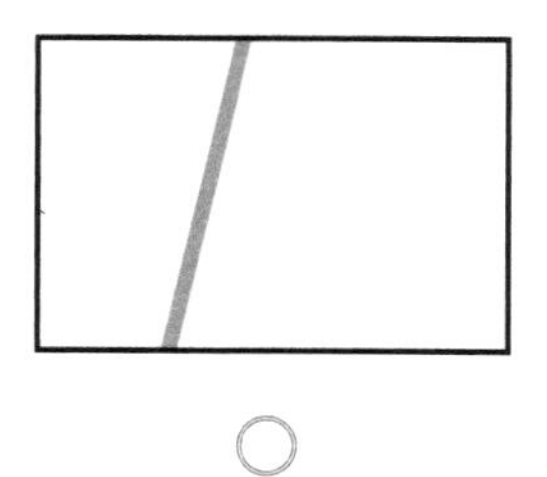
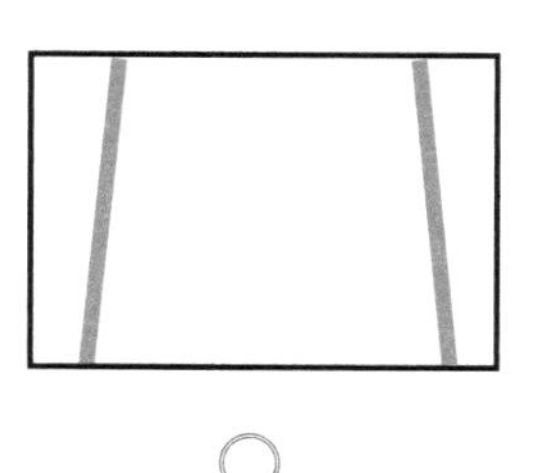
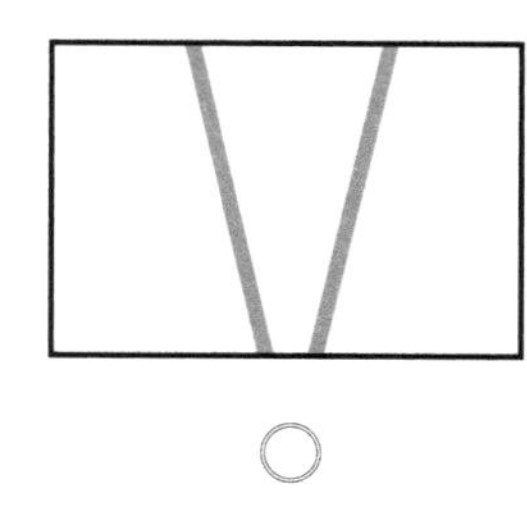

28

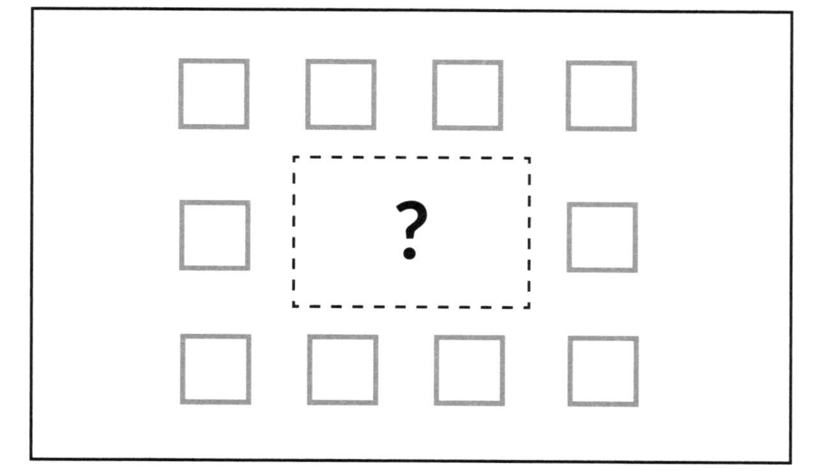

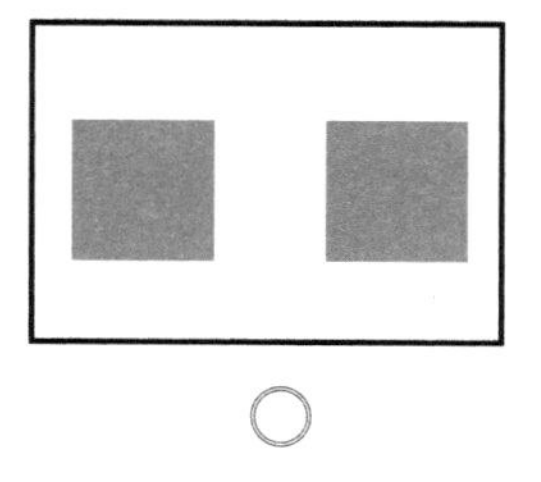
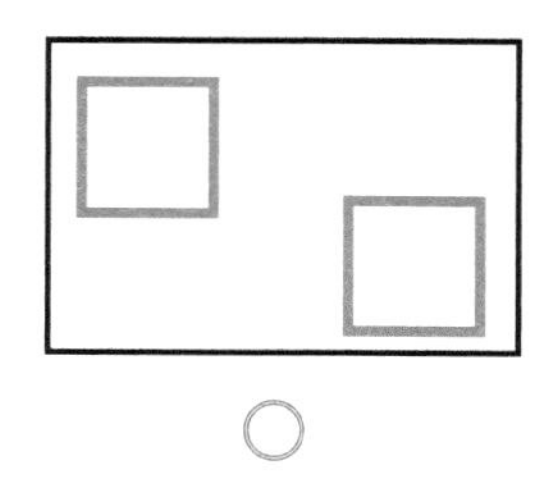
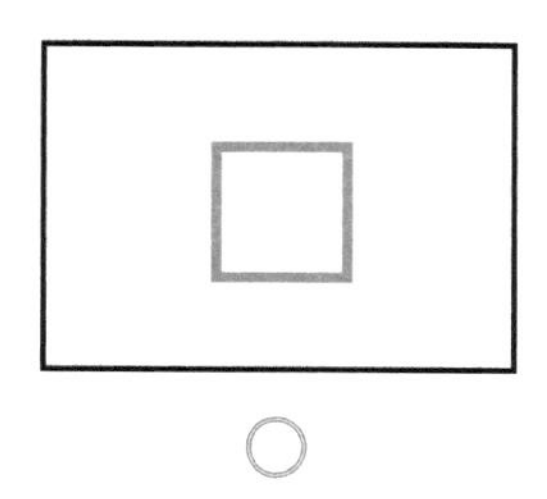
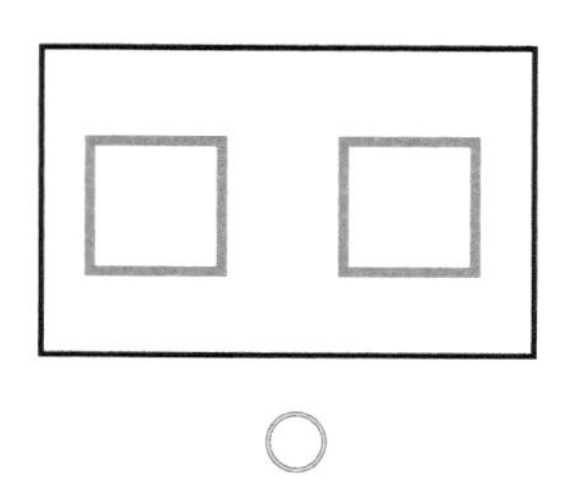
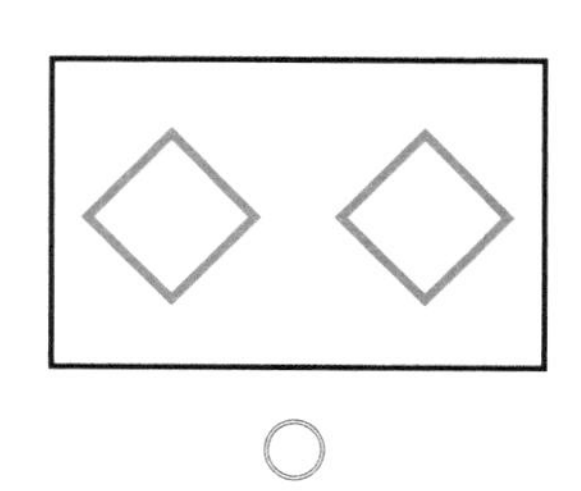

29

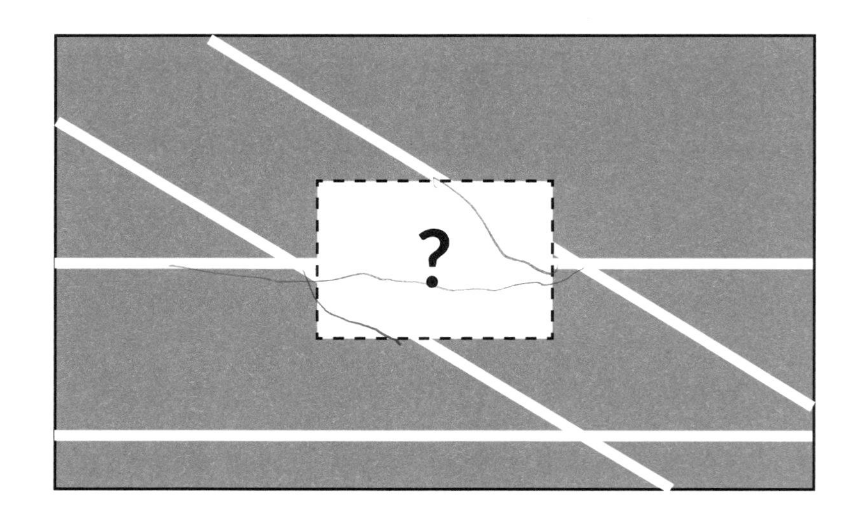

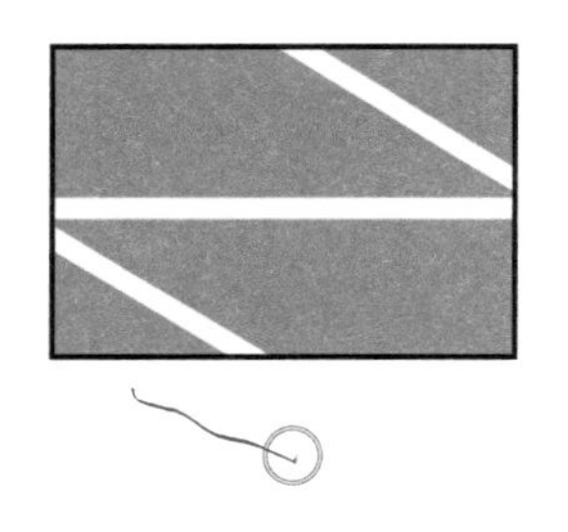
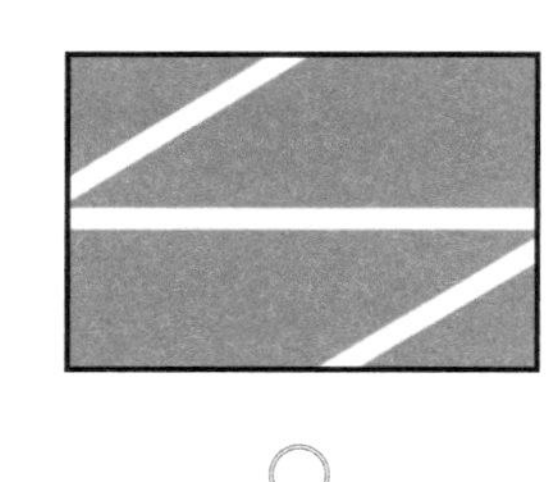

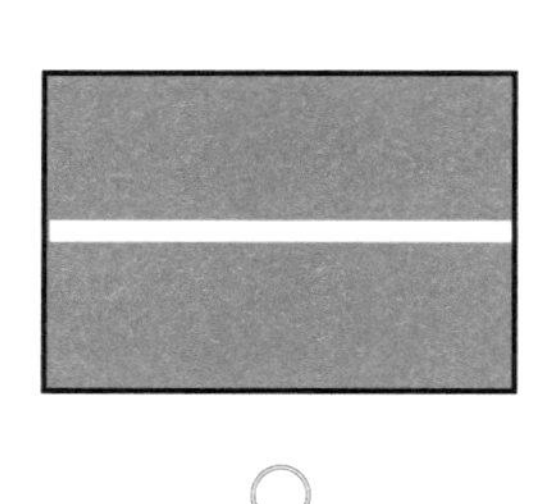
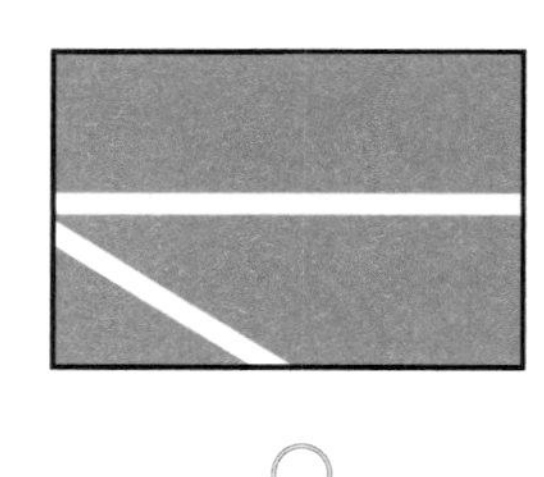

30

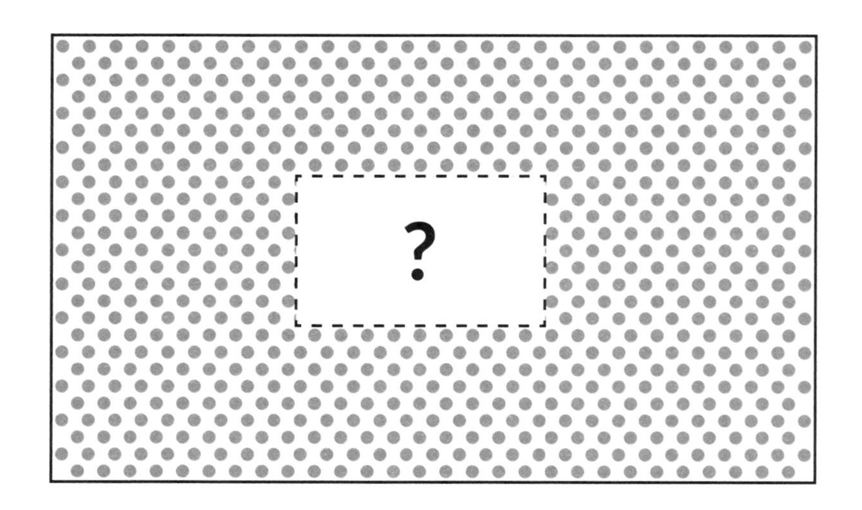

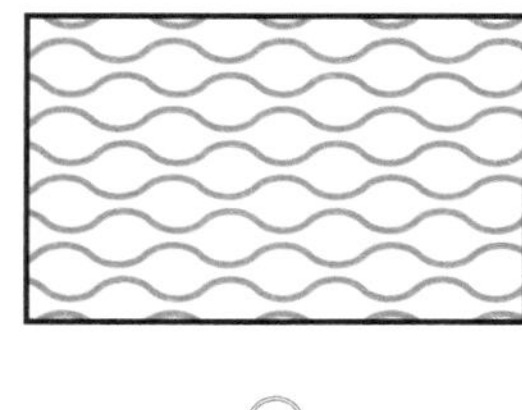
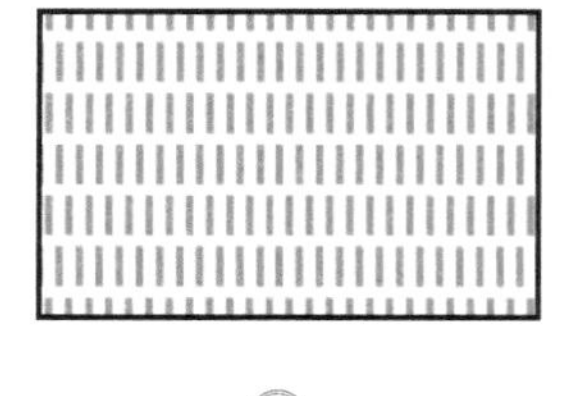
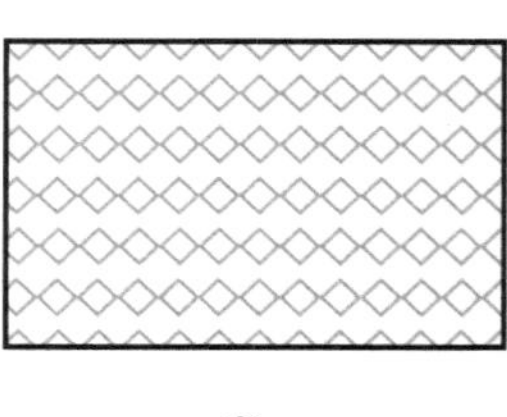

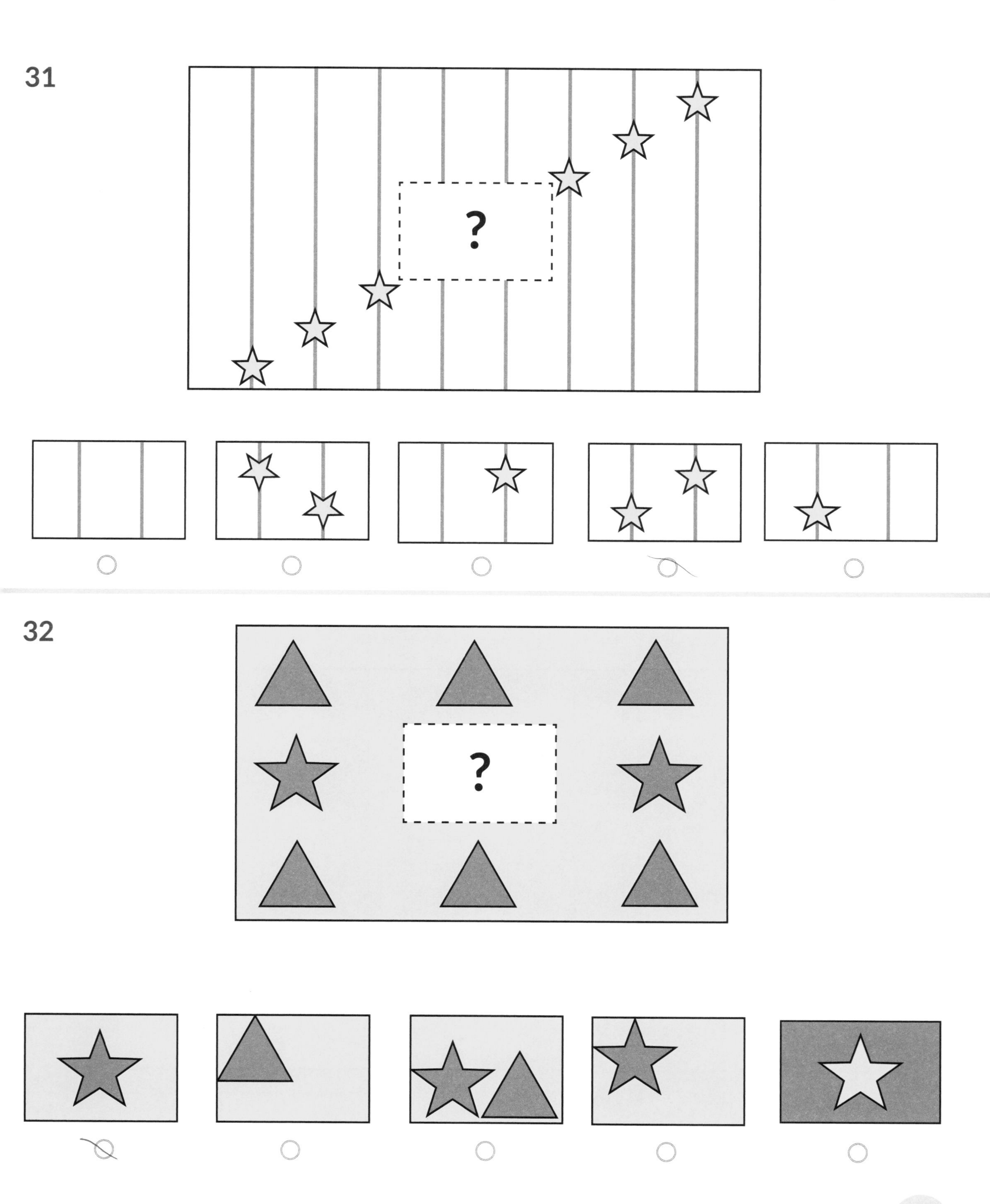

31
?
32
?

33

?

34

?

35

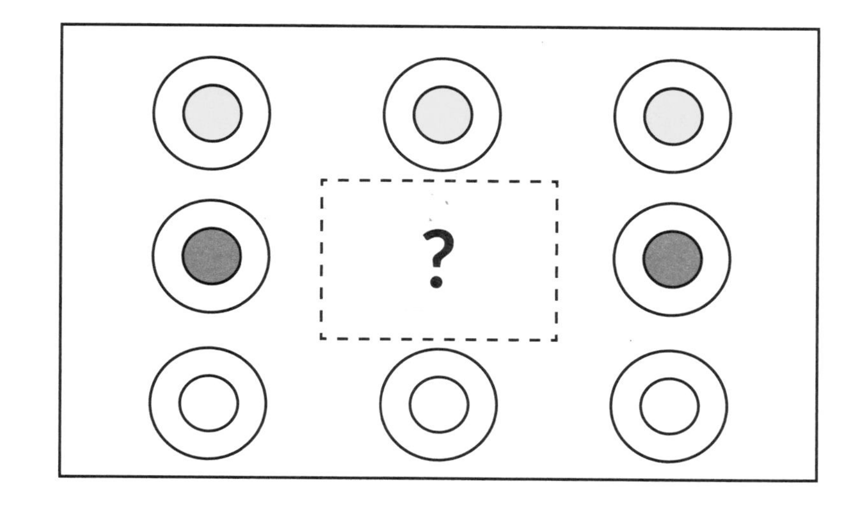

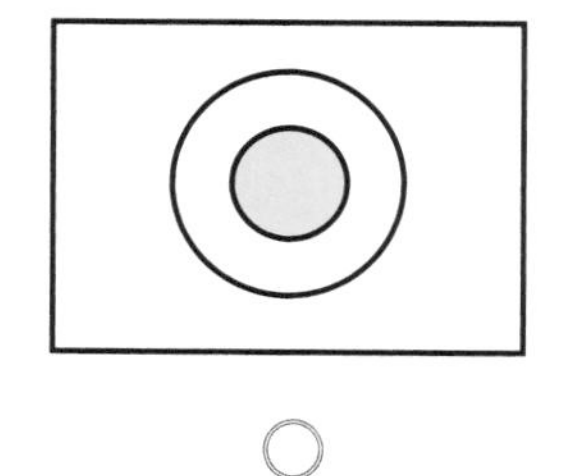
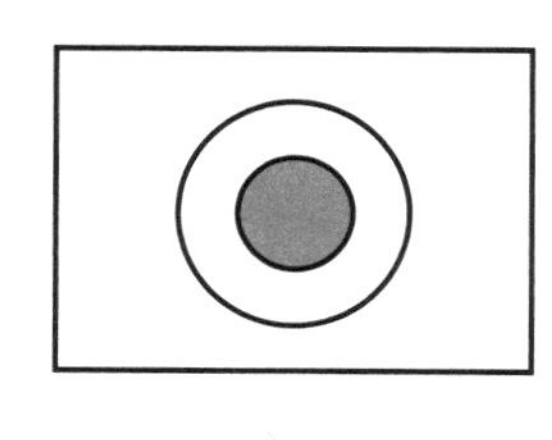
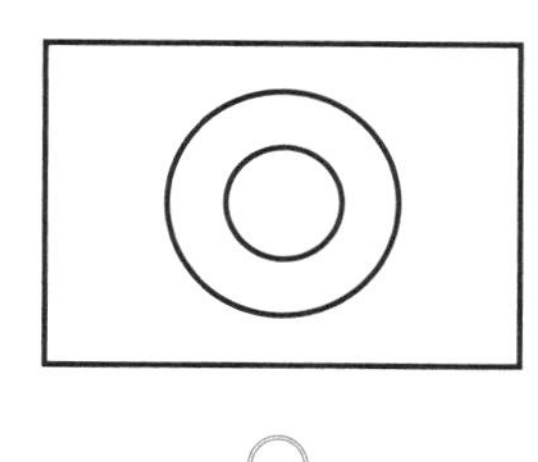
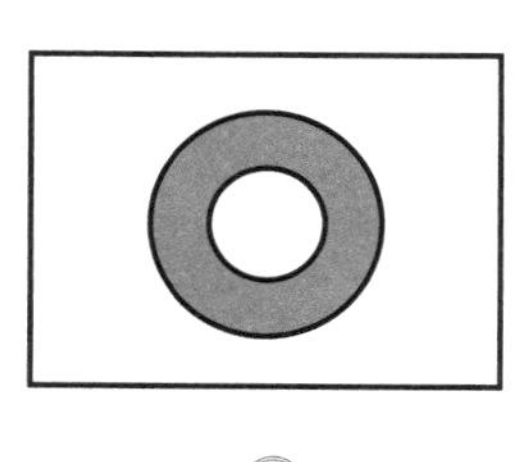
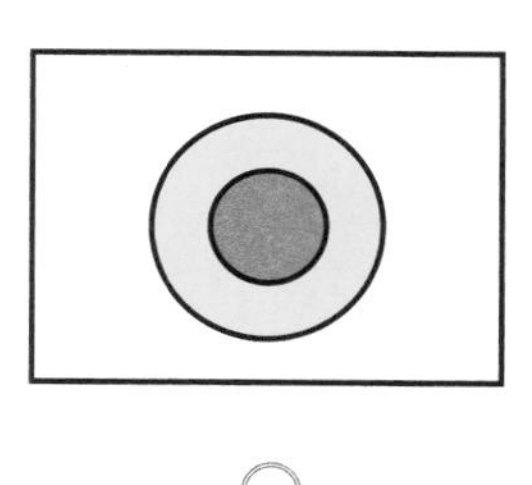

36

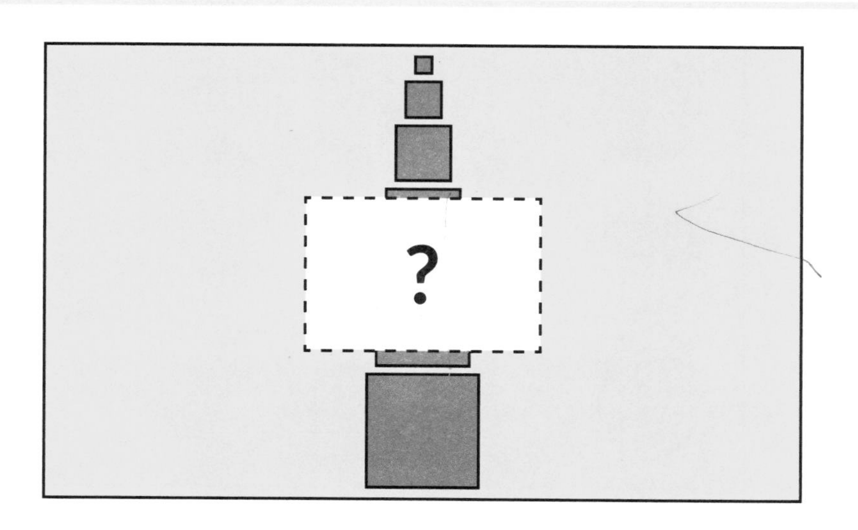

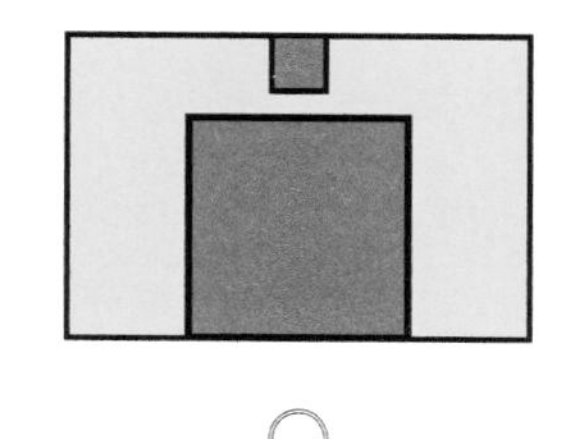
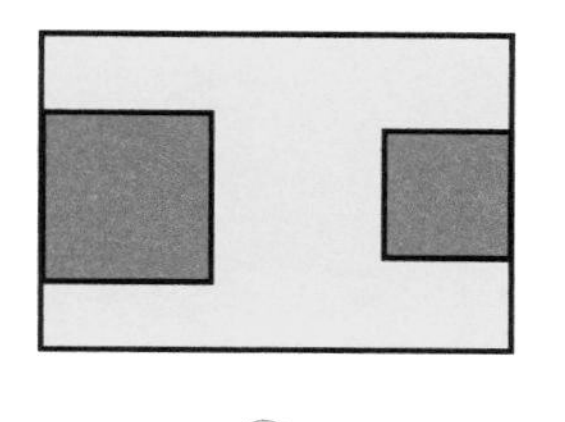
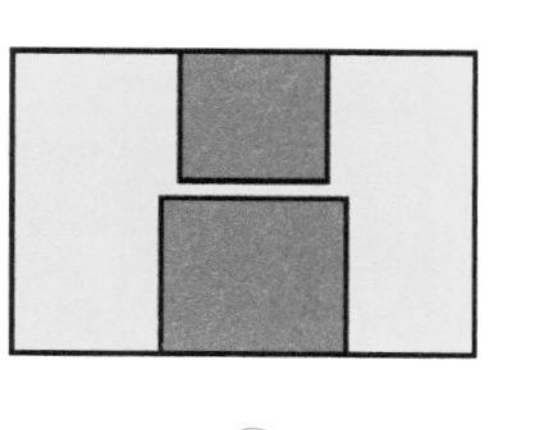
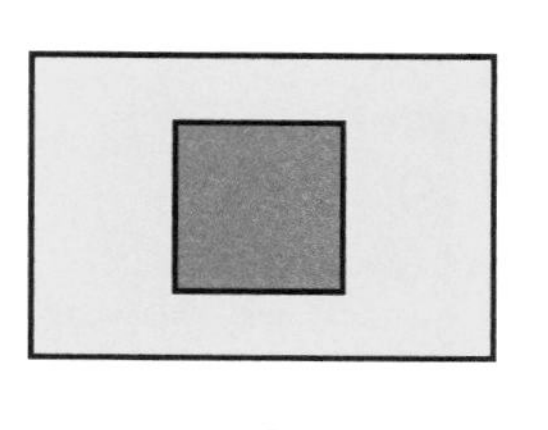
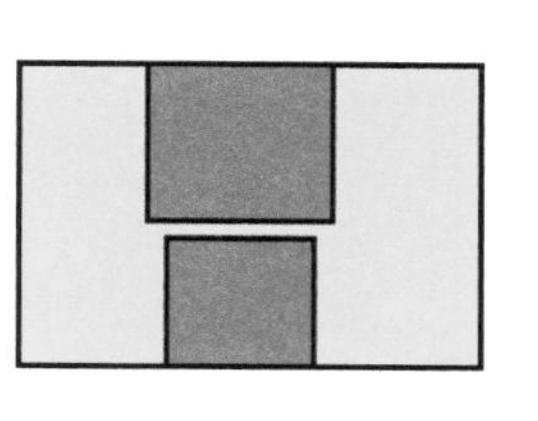

37

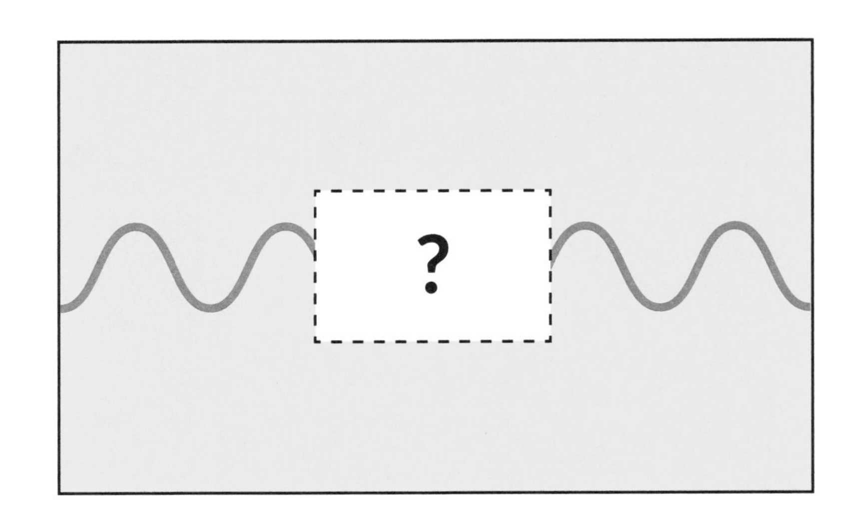

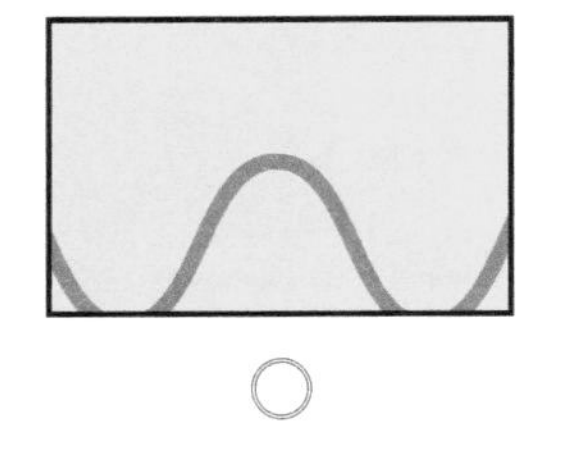

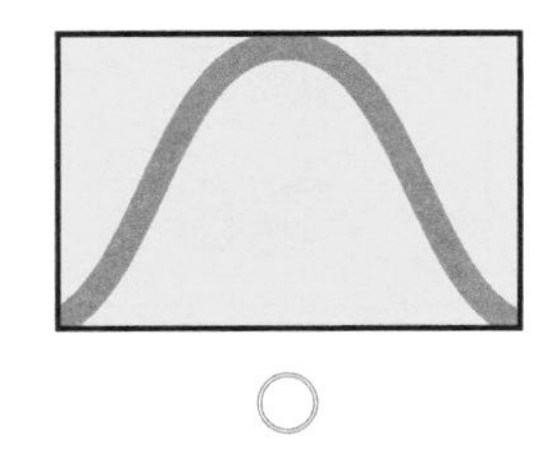

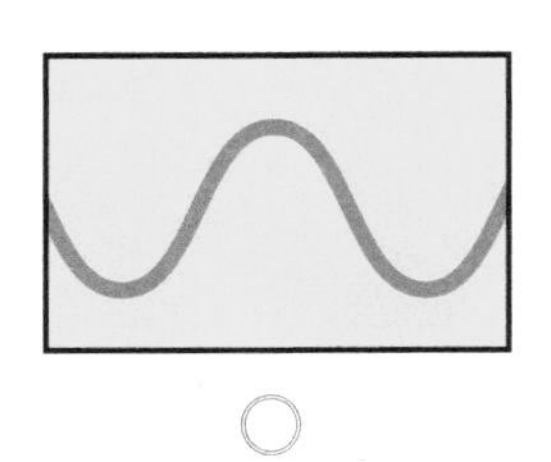

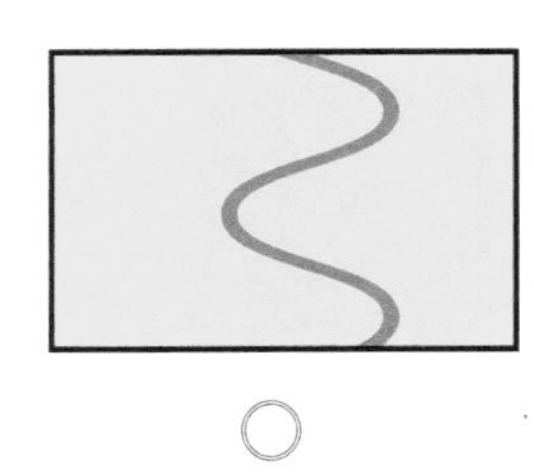

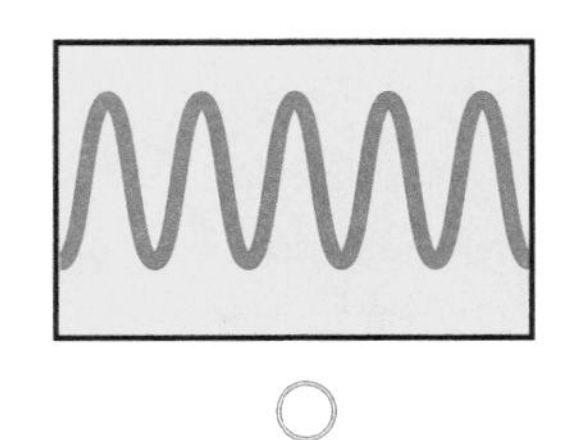

38

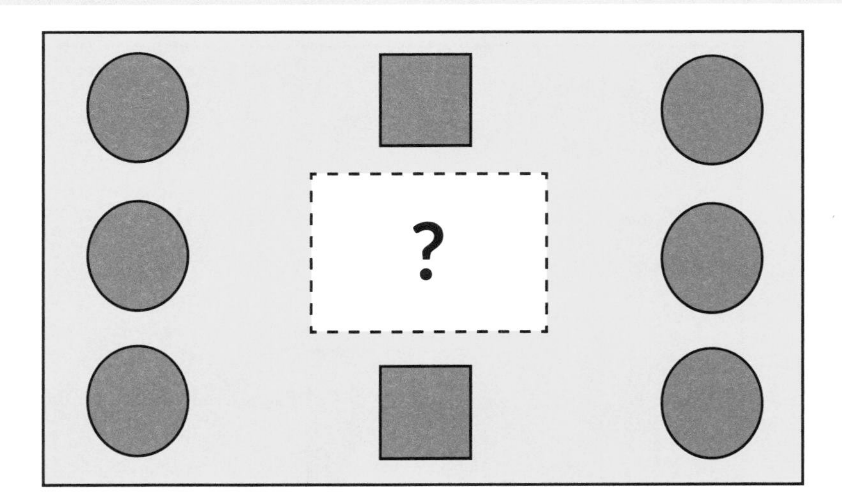

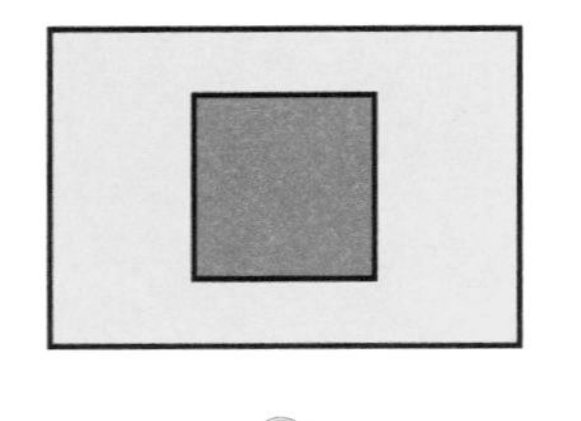

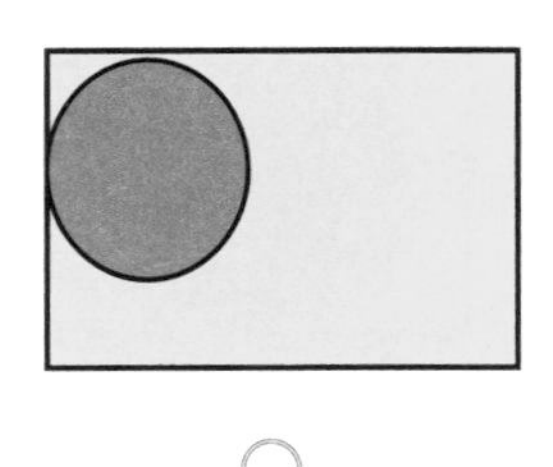

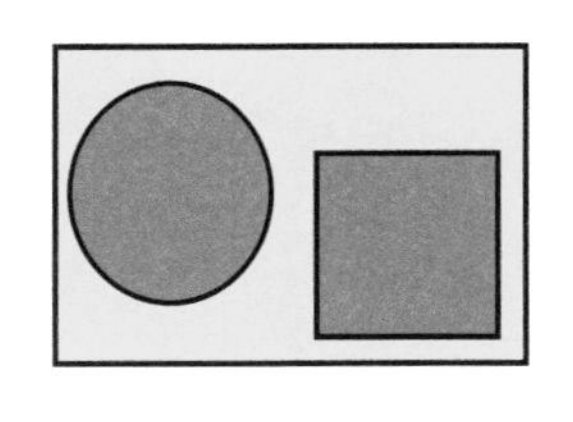

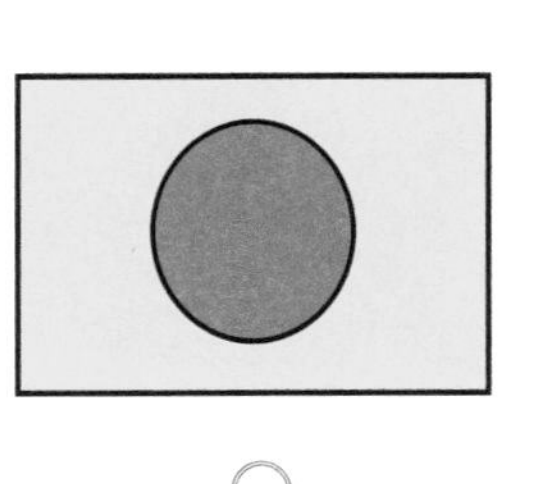

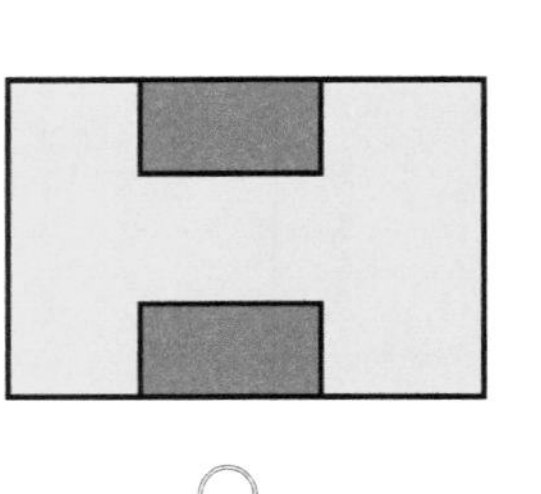

39

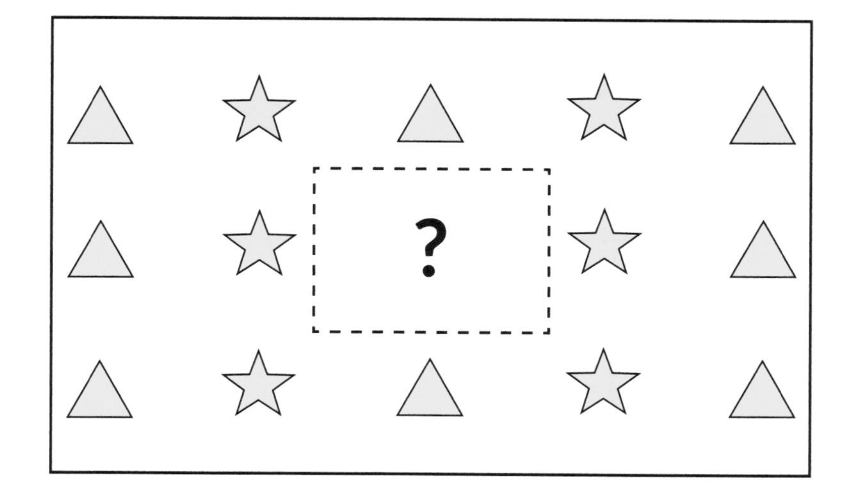

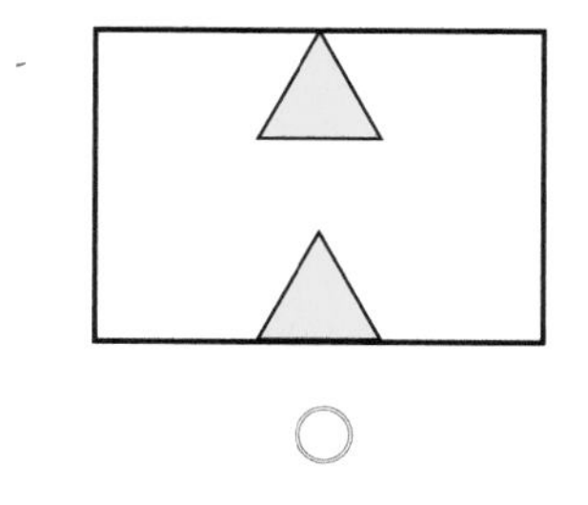 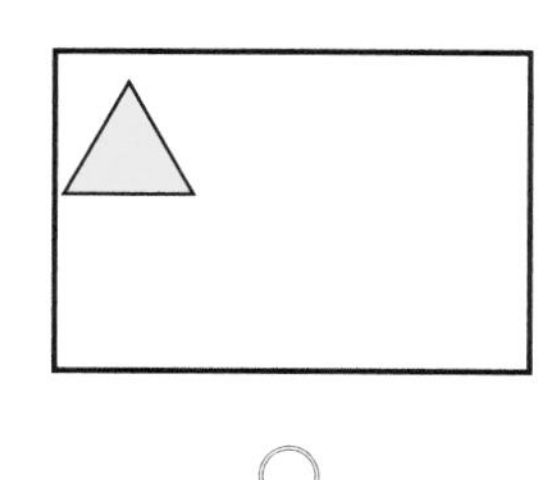 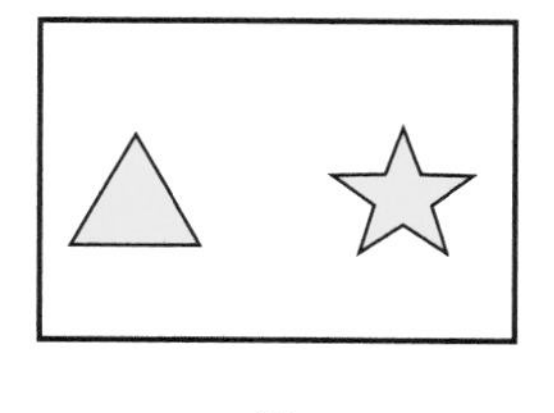 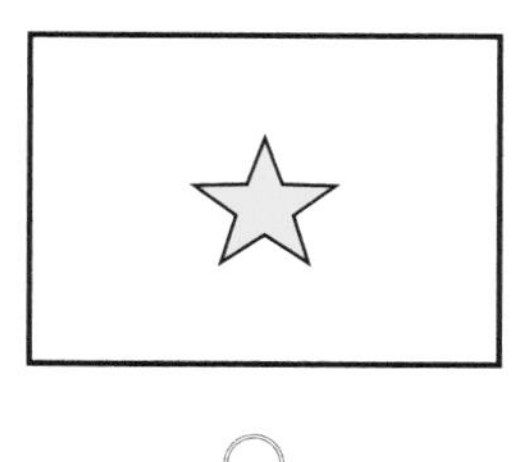 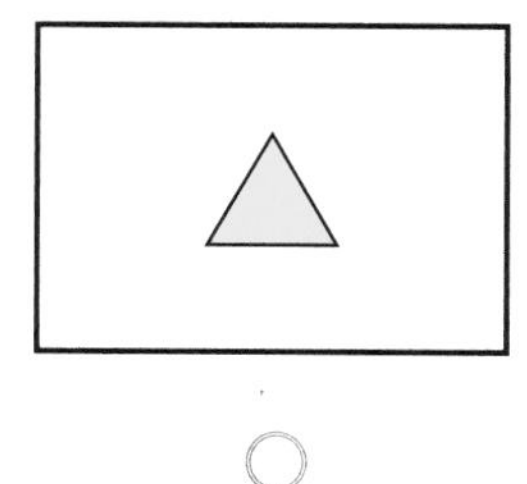

40

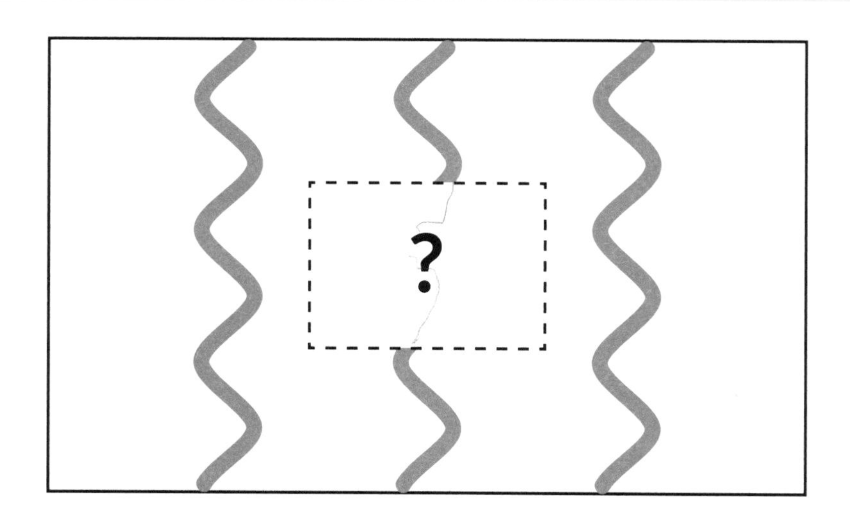

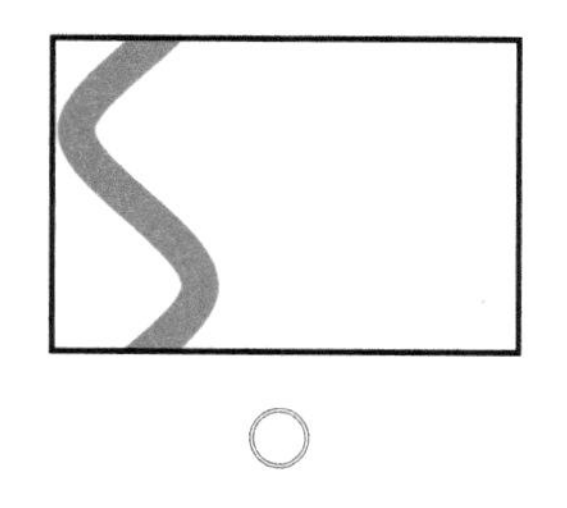 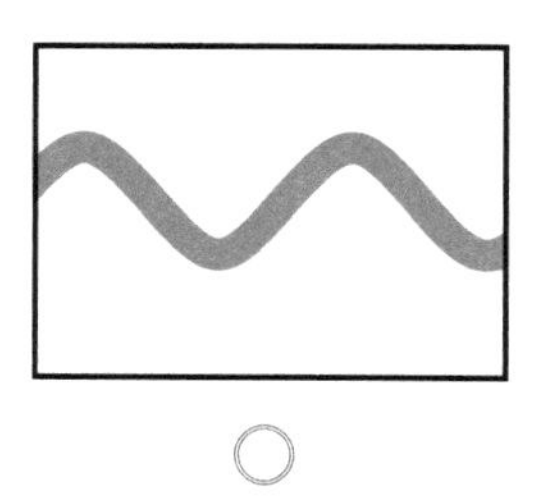 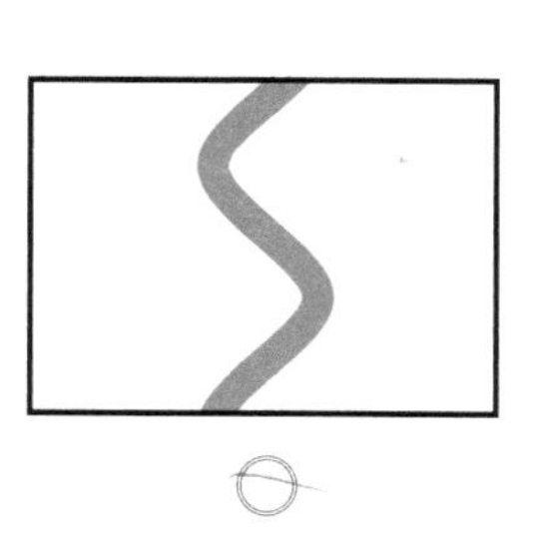 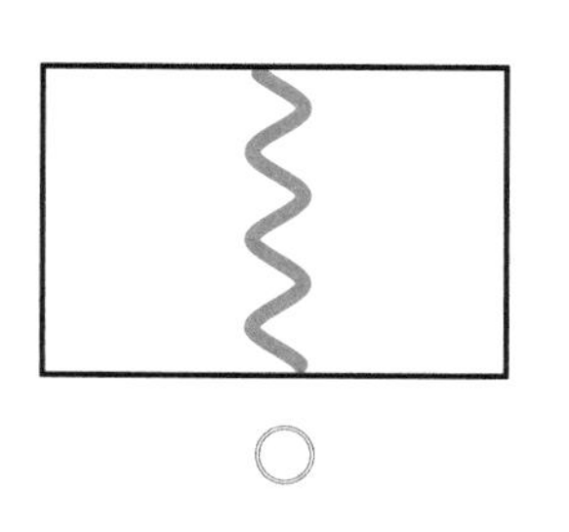 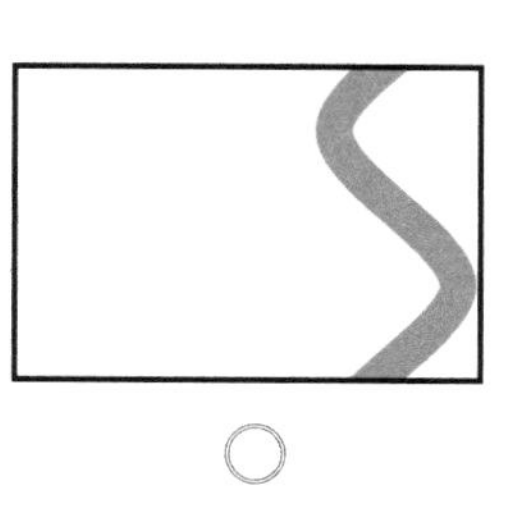

41

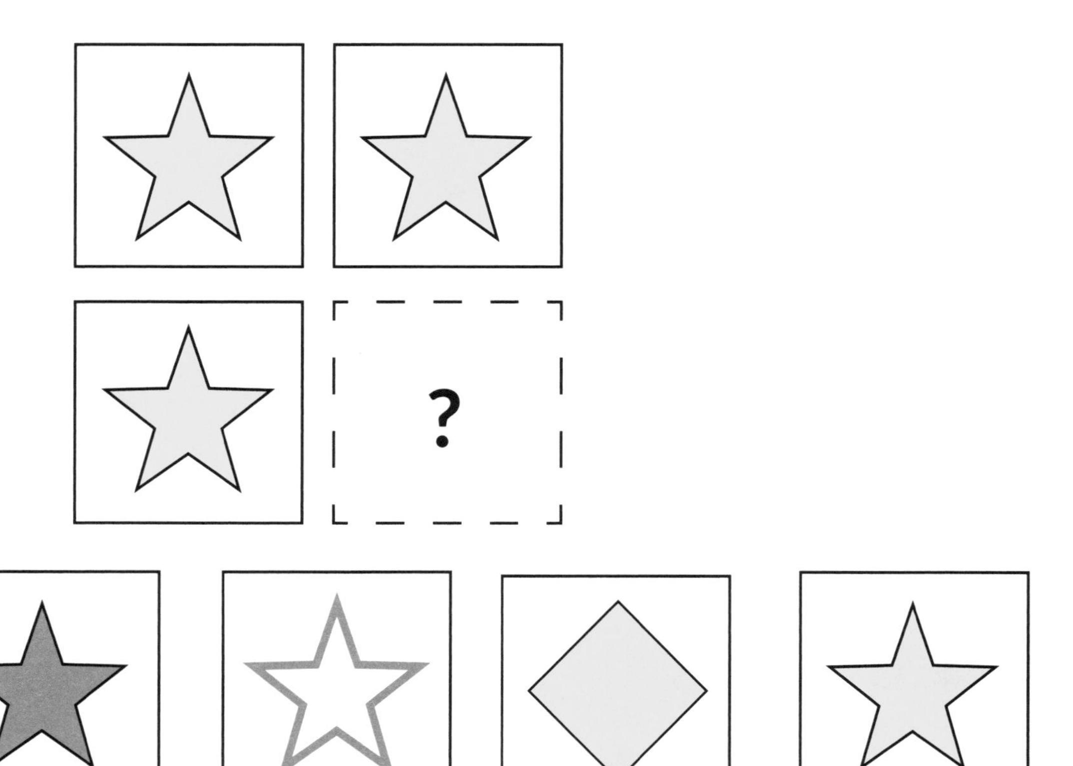

42

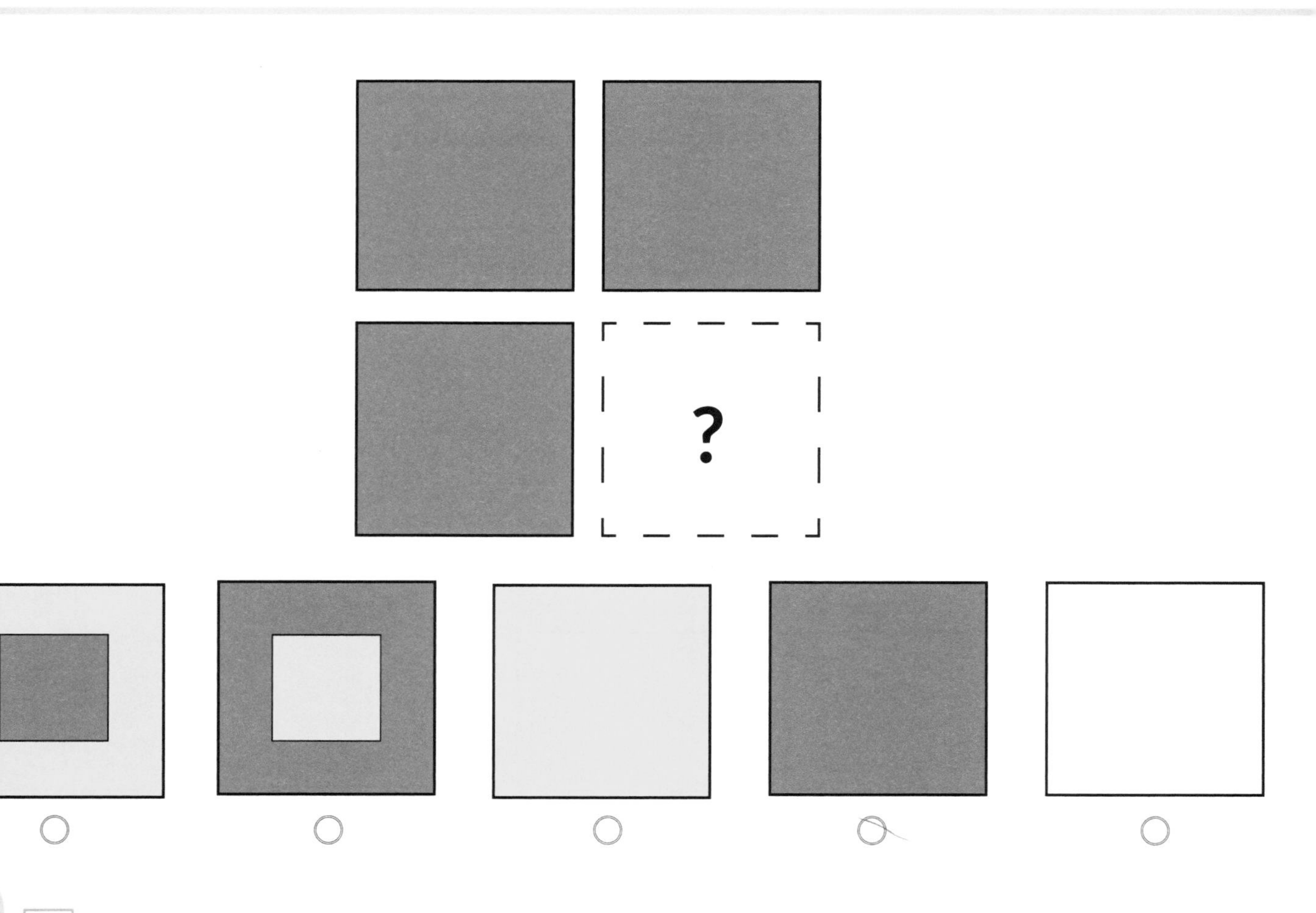

43

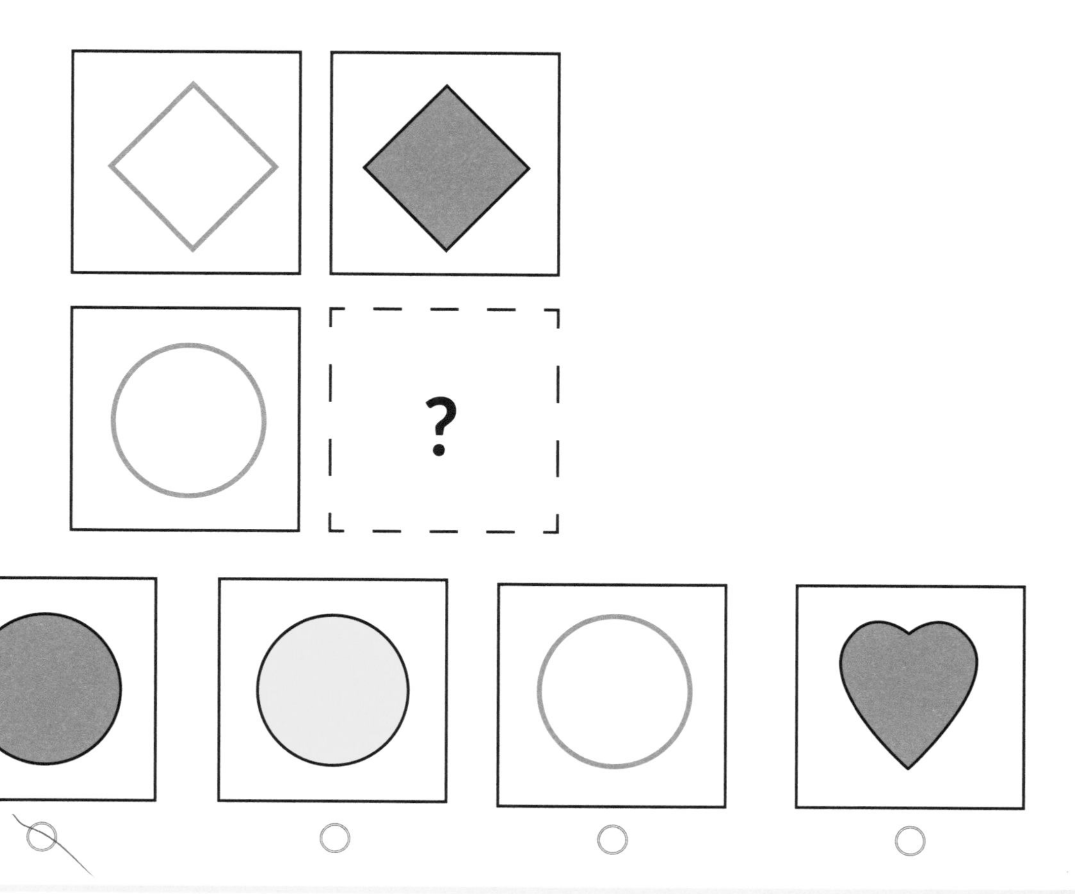

44

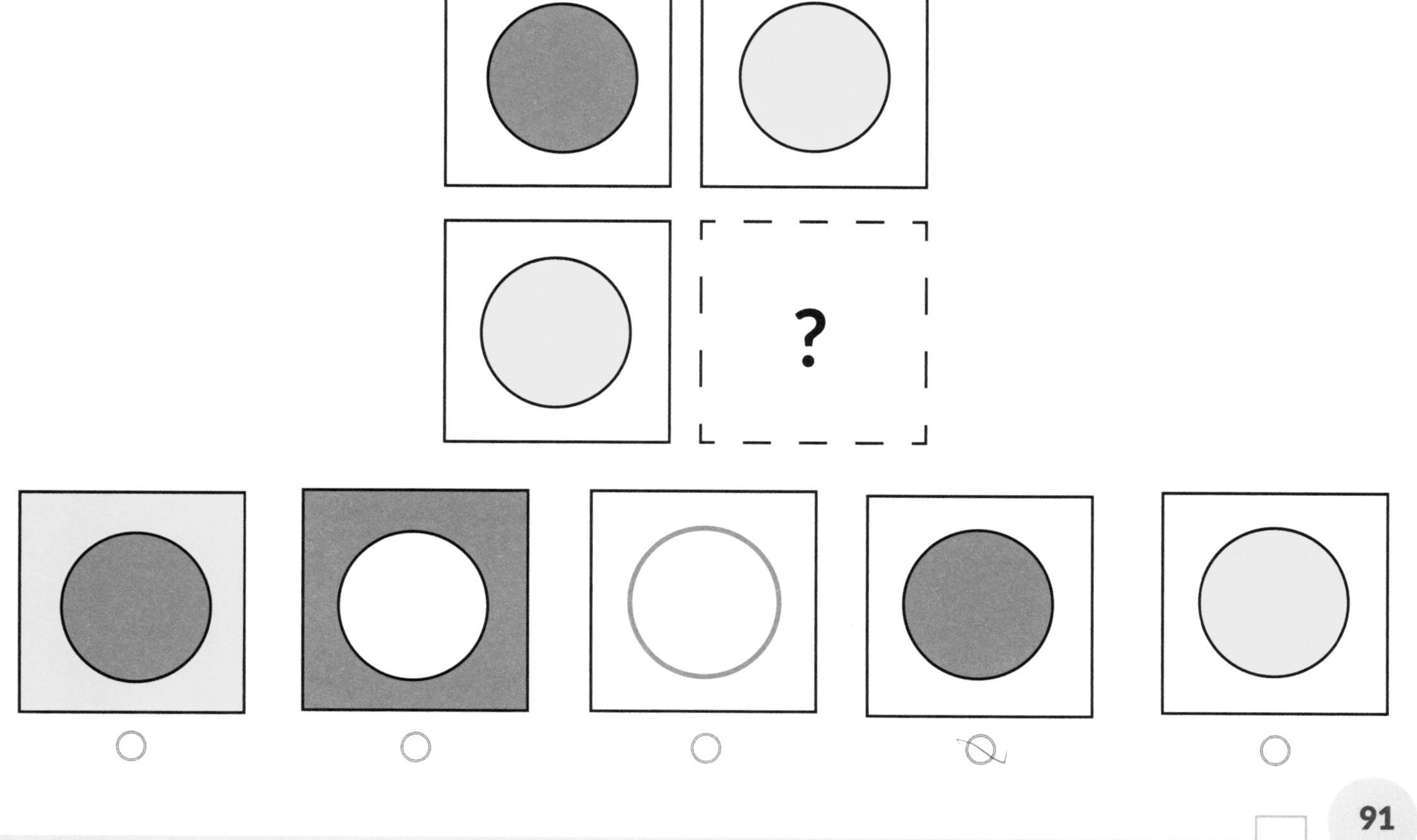

45

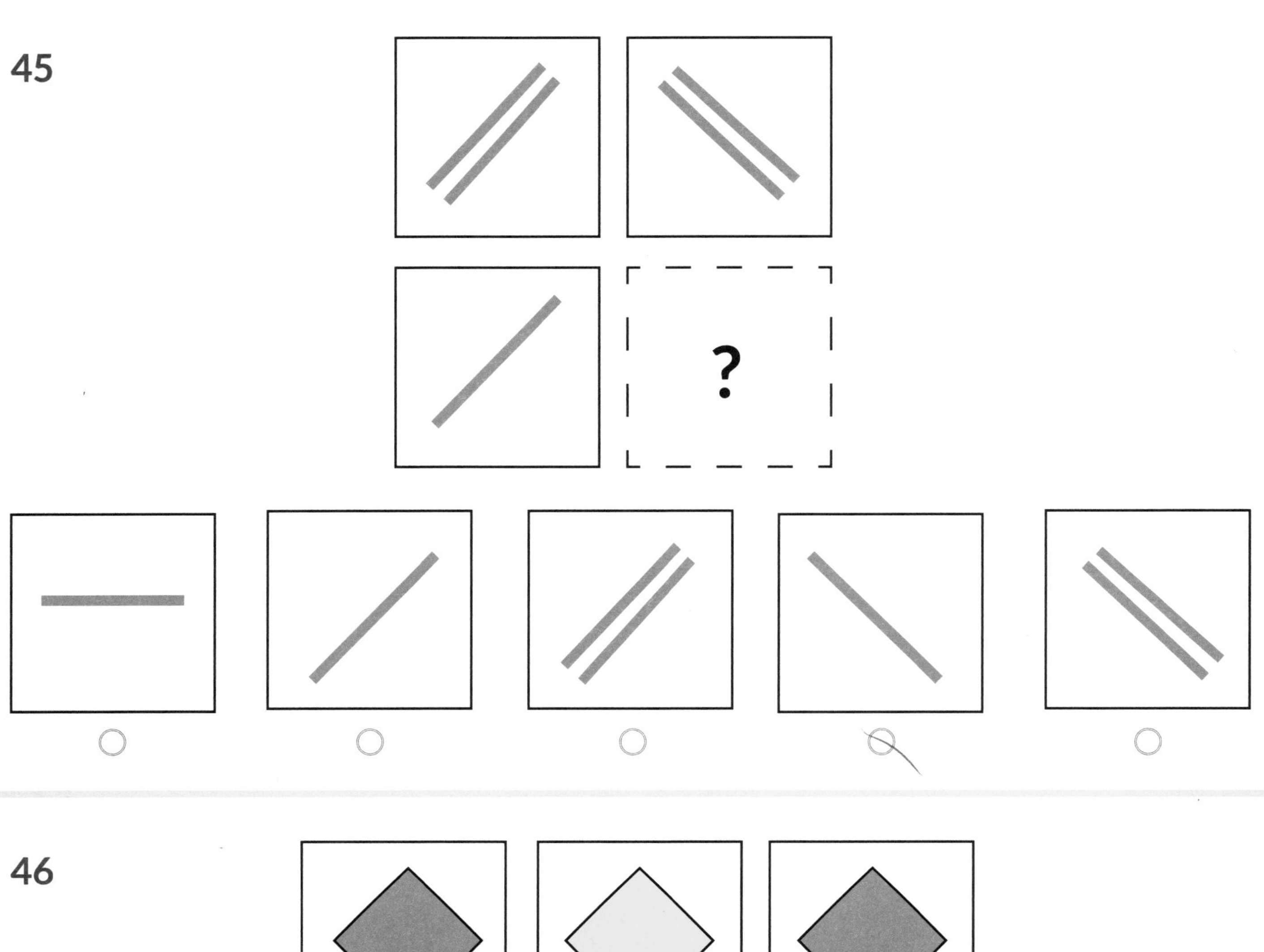

46

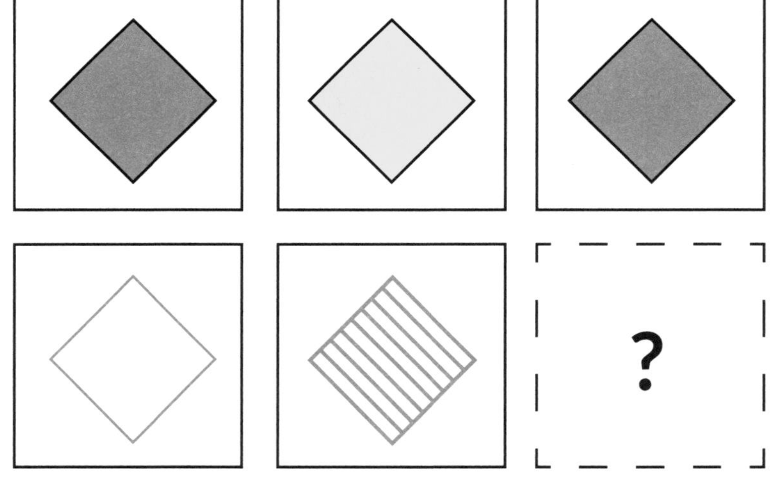

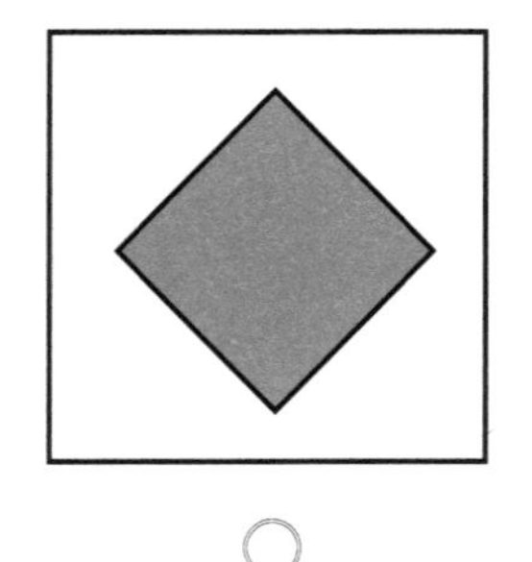

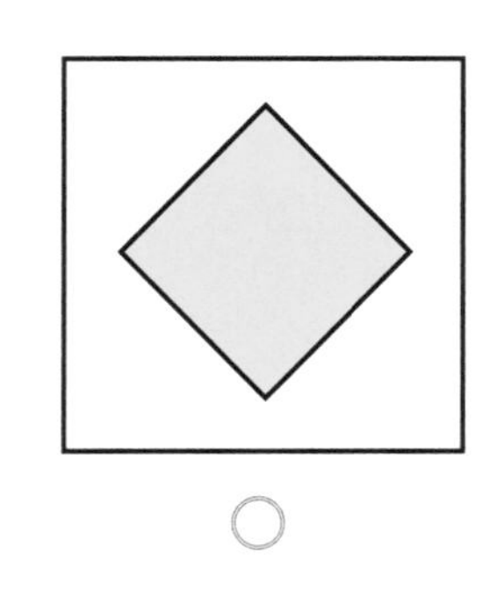

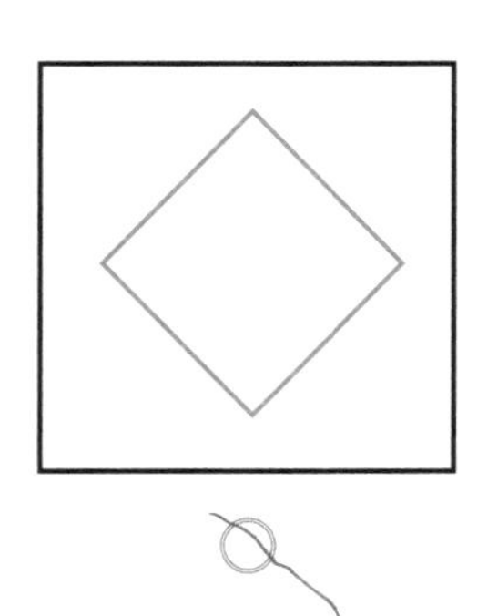

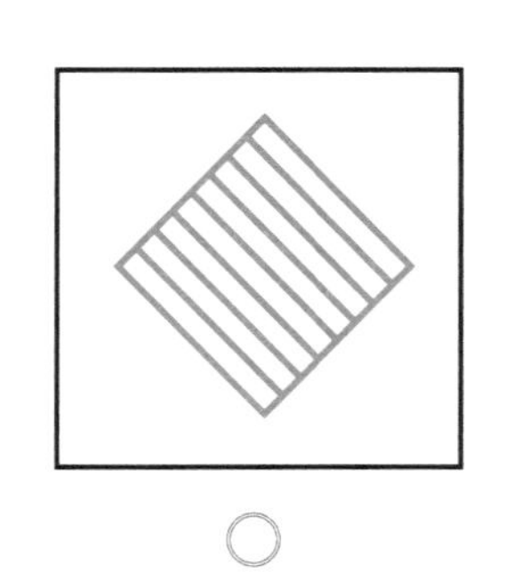

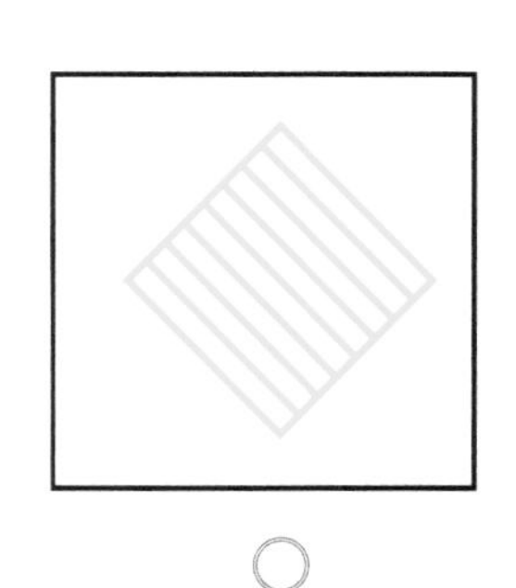

47

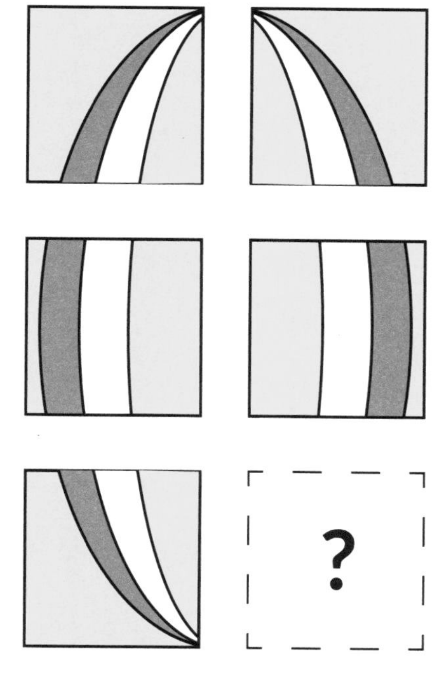

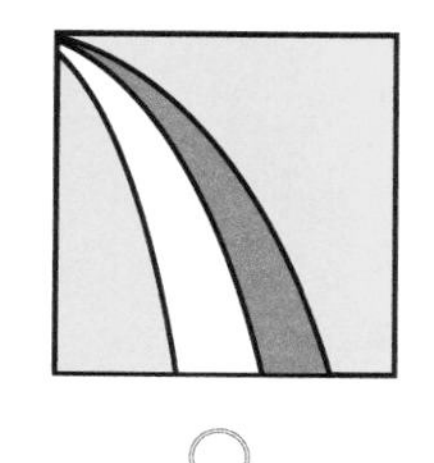

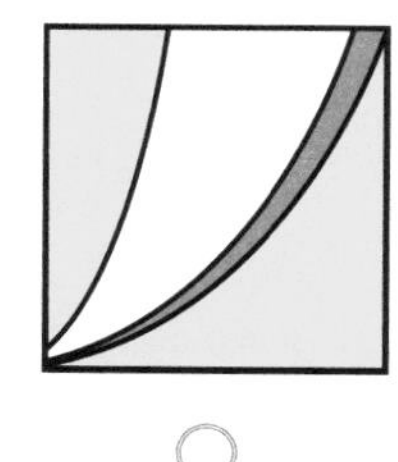

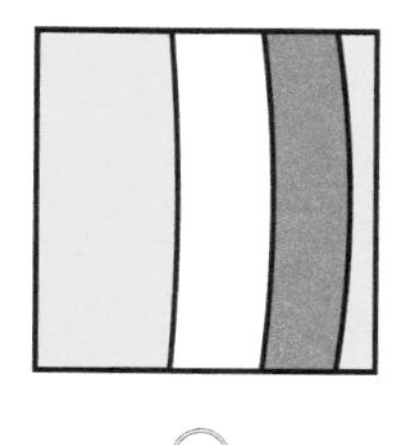

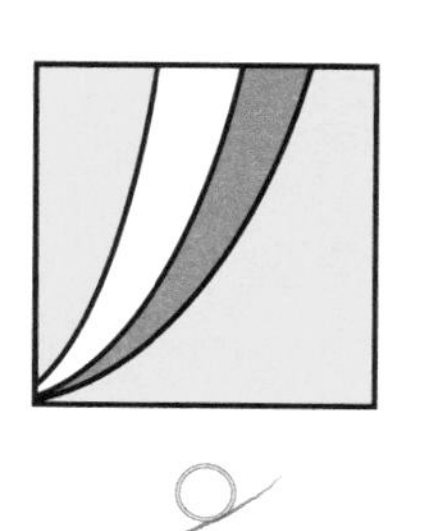

48

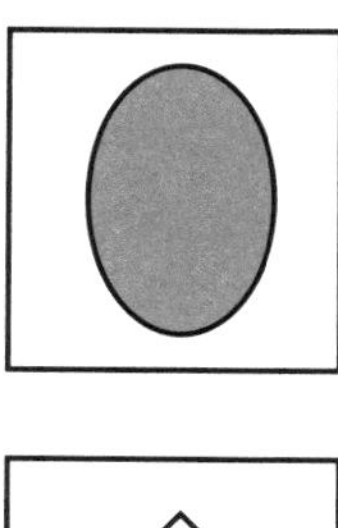

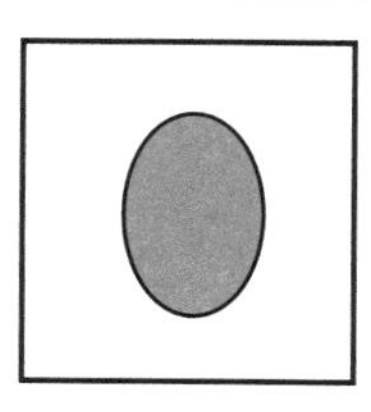

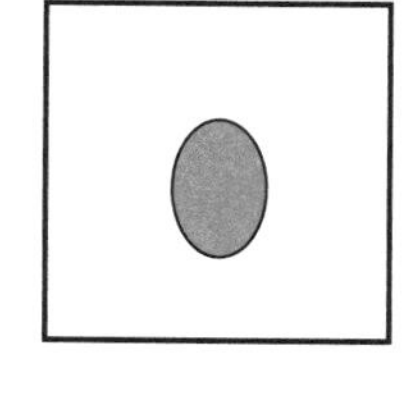

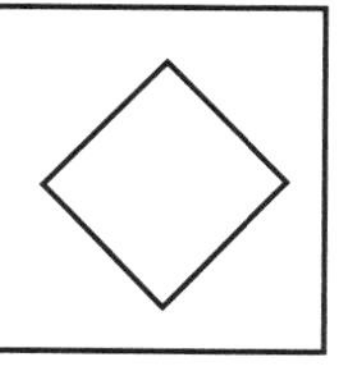

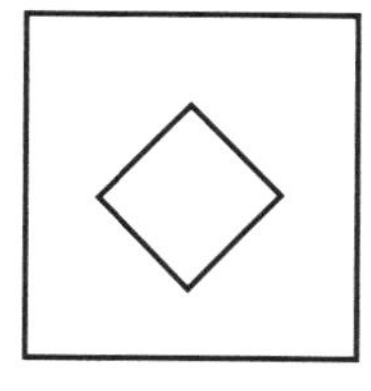

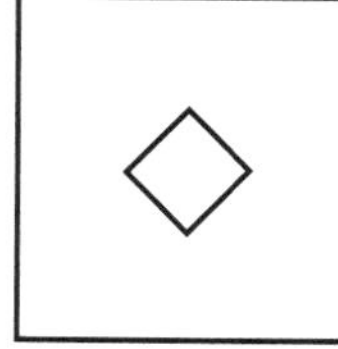

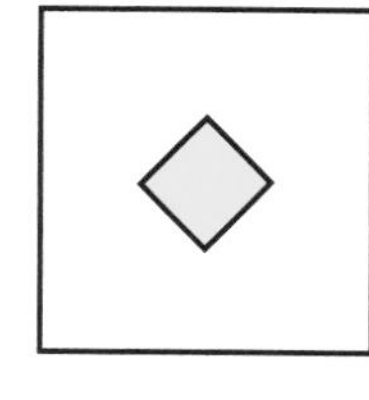

End of Practice Question Set and Exercises

Please cut out pages 95-99 along the dotted line. ✂
Use pages 95-98 to check answers for the Workbook. Use page 99 to read directions as well as check answers for the Practice Question Set.

Answer Key For Workbook

Identifying Identical Objects (Part I)

1. C
2. A
3. C
4. A, B
5. A, C
6. A, C
7. B, C
8. A
9. C
10. C
11. A, C
12. A
13. B
14. A, B
15. C

Identifying Identical Objects (Part II)

Note: In the pairs of letters below, the first letter is the object on the top row. The second letter is the object on the bottom row that it matches. For example "B-D" would mean that on the top row, the second object ("B") matches the fourth object ("D") on the bottom row.

1. A-B; B-C; C-D; D-A
2. A-C; B-D; C-A; D-B
3. A-C; B-D; C-A; D-B
4. A-D; B-C; C-A; D-B
5. A-C; B-D; C-B; D-A
6. A-D; B-A; C-C; D-B
7. A-A; B-D; C-B; D-C
8. A-D; B-C; C-B; D-A
9. A-C; B-A; C-B; D-D
10. A-D; B-A; C-B; D-C
11. A-B; B-A; C-D; D-C
12. A-D; B-A; C-B; D-C

Answer Key For Workbook

Finish The Puzzle

1. A
2. B
3. C
4. A
5. C
6. B
7. A
8. C
9. C
10. C
11. A
12. C
13. A
14. B
15. A
16. C
17. A

Shape Creation

1. A
2. B
3. B
4. A
5. B
6. A
7. C

Identifying Differences (Figure Classification)

1. C
2. A
3. D
4. A
5. B
6. A
7. D
8. B
9. C
10. B
11. C
12. A
13. C
14. A

Answer Key For Workbook

Identifying Differences, continued

15. B
16. B
17. C
18. B
19. A
20. C
21. D (this is not a triangle)
22. A (the part that is shaded is not equal to the other part)
23. B (the two shapes are not the same)
24. B (this has lines going a different direction)
25. C (this does not have horizontal lines)
26. A (this does not go from largest to smallest)

Patterns (Figure Series)

1. B
2. A
3. C
4. D
5. A

Pattern Completion

1. D
2. B
3. D
4. E
5. B
6. D
7. B
8. E
9. A
10. E

Answer Key For Workbook

Pattern Completion, continued

11. D
12. B
13. C
14. D
15. C
16. B
17. B
18. C
19. E
20. A
21. B
22. B
23. C
24. D
25. A
26. C
27. A
28. C
29. D
30. A
31. C
32. E
33. A

Reasoning by Analogy

1. E
2. D
3. E
4. B
5. B
6. D
7. D
8. A
9. C
10. A
11. C
12. D
13. A
14. B
15. B
16. E
17. B
18. C
19. C
20. C
21. A
22. D
23. C
24. A
25. B
26. C
27. A
28. A
29. B
30. E
31. A

PRACTICE QUESTION SET: DIRECTIONS & ANSWER KEY

If you wish to assign a time limit to the Practice Question Set to mimic the actual test, allow approximately 30 minutes. The directions for each question type are in the gray box. Each question type has the same directions for all the questions of that question type.

SECTION 1: PATTERN COMPLETION

Pattern Completion Directions (p. 70): Here is a puzzle where a piece is missing. (Point to the box that has the question mark.) Which one of the boxes in the bottom row (point to the bottom row of boxes) would go here? (Point to the box that has the question mark again.)

Answer / Child's Answer		Answer / Child's Answer	
1. D	______	21. A	______
2. A	______	22. E	______
3. C	______	23. A	______
4. A	______	24. B	______
5. C	______	25. D	______
6. A	______	26. E	______
7. C	______	27. B	______
8. D	______	28. D	______
9. E	______	29. A	______
10. D	______	30. B	______
11. A	______	31. D	______
12. D	______	32. A	______
13. C	______	33. E	______
14. E	______	34. D	______
15. E	______	35. B	______
16. C	______	36. C	______
17. D	______	37. C	______
18. C	______	38. A	______
19. E	______	39. E	______
20. E	______	40. C	______

Pattern Completion Questions Answered Correctly: ________ out of 40

SECTION 2: REASONING BY ANALOGY

Reasoning by Analogy Directions (p. 90): Look at these pictures that are inside the boxes. One box is missing. (Point to the bottom box that has a question mark.) Now, look below at the row of answer choices. (Point to the row of answer choices.) Which one would go here?

Answer / Child's Answer	
41. E	______
42. D	______
43. B	______
44. D	______
45. D	______
46. C	______
47. E	______
48. D	______

Reasoning by Analogy Questions Answered Correctly: _____ out of 8

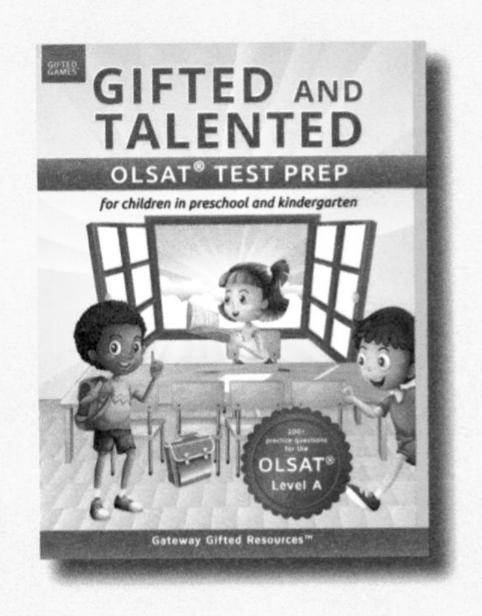

Check out our other books!

Plus, visit www.GatewayGifted.com today for a FREE eBook of 40+ questions!

We would be thrilled if you left us a quick review on the website where you purchased this book. We are a family-owned publishing company - a consortium of educators, book designers, kids' illustrators, parents, and kid-testers.

Did your child finish the exercises?
Here's a certificate for your new detective! (Please cut along the dotted lines.)

The Gifted Detective Agency

Congratulations to:

____

Our Newest Member!